Nothing Lowly in the Universe

An Integral Approach to the Ecological Crisis

Jennie M. Ratcliffe, Ph.D.

The Crundale Press

Hillsborough NC

Also by Jennie M. Ratcliffe:
Lead in Man and the Environment (1981)
Integrity, Ecology, and Community (2009)

The Crundale Press
Hillsborough, NC
TheCrundalePress@mindspring.com

ISBN: 978-1-7336600-0-6
Library of Congress Control Number: 2019904085

Book and cover design by Andrea Shapiro

The title "Nothing Lowly in the Universe" is from "Still," a poem by A.R. Ammons, in *The Complete Poems of A.R. Ammons*, Vol. I, 81, edited by Robert M. West (New York: Norton and Co., 2017). Used with permission of the publisher. The line reads, "…though I have looked everywhere I can find nothing lowly in the universe…"

Nothing Lowly in the Universe

An Integral Approach to the Ecological Crisis

It is not your responsibility to complete the work, but neither are you free to abandon it.

—Rabbi Tarfon

A saying of Rabbi Tarfon (c. 70 CE to 150 CE) from the *Pirke Avot* 2:16 (a classic treasury of wisdom of the Jewish sages).

ಬ Contents ೫

Introduction

Greta Thunberg is a child of the Anthropocene—the newly-defined age in which humanity, rather than natural forces, has radically impacted the wider natural world. When the then 15-year old Swedish teenager spoke at the 24th UN climate conference in December 2018, she summed up our predicament: "Our biosphere is being sacrificed so that rich people in countries like mine can live in luxury." She was not sure what future, if any, her generation and those to come would have, but was clear that the world's leaders had utterly failed them. It is perhaps a symptom of the ecological crisis itself that her message, and increasing evidence of global climate and ecological breakdown, still evoke only passing attention in the rush of mainstream news cycles and the instant world of online social media, and it is now children walking out of schools who must now try to grab the attention of the world's leaders. The almost incomprehensible reality is that, despite multiple warnings, humanity and the wider natural world are facing an existential crisis—the loss and suffering of much of human life and millions of other life-forms that have evolved over close to four billion years—in what may become the "sixth extinction" event in the history of life on Earth, this time by our own hand. According to a vast body of research by climate scientists, ecologists, and others, the world is rapidly reaching a tipping point. We may now have less than a decade in which to make radical changes in the way many of us currently live if we are to avoid runaway climate breakdown and ecological collapse.

How did we get to this point? It is clear from this evidence that we—by which I mean particularly those of us, mostly in richer countries, who already consume well beyond our essential needs, or who have the lion's share of global wealth and power—cannot continue with business-as-usual growth on a finite earth. We cannot continue to regard ecological impacts as "externalities" whose cost will come due elsewhere or maybe never, and to use the wider natural world as a commodity for short-term economic gain and deeply unequal consumption and development; and we cannot go on spending vast amounts on our military complexes in the name of security while largely ignoring the far greater threat to the survival of all life from ecological devastation, or the fact that ecological destruction disproportionately impacts the poorest, while "resource wars" amplify the threats from other conflicts and climate breakdown. Yet we continue to try to have our cake and eat it too, relying on end-of-pipeline technological, economic, social and political fixes that we hope will allow us to "decouple" economic growth and our current ways of living from their ecological impacts, or even using fixes for ecological destruction as yet another source of profit and growth. While urgent measures are now becoming necessary, they will only delay ecological collapse if we fail to address the interconnections between overconsumption, growth, conflict, and inequality, and their deeper causes. In other words, *we have been trying to address the ecological predicament using the same thinking and approaches that got us here in the first place*, despite abundant evidence that they are failing to prevent the looming crisis. Meanwhile, many of us, particularly in some of the richest countries, have lost a sense of what really sustains us in both the material and spiritual realms.

The roots of our predicament lie far deeper than most political, social or economic analyses suggest. What are these roots? And what are the principles and practices that will allow us to make the radical turning that is now called for, a turning that could lead us into what Thomas Berry has called the Ecozoic era and away from the ecological devastation of the Anthropocene?

The ecological crisis is, at its heart, a spiritual and moral crisis. It is a profound failure of moral imagination about what we are really risking, as if we can readily entertain the notion that ecocide and the mass destruction of human life were somehow justified or inevitable; and a spiritual failure of that part of us that knows and responds to the power of life, beauty, and love, and our kinship with all life. We are discovering that we cannot bend the inescapable laws of nature, yet we seem to be trapped between hubris and an inability to imagine a different future. At the root of this crisis is a fundamental belief in separation—between mind, body, heart and soul or spirit; between one human and another, and between ourselves, the wider natural world, and whatever we conceive of as the source of life and the truth of being, whether we call it God, Spirit, One, All That Is, the Infinite Source, Reality, or simply the great mystery. In the West, in particular, we have emphasized an anthropocentric way of thinking (partly from traditional Christian and scientific worldviews) that is predominantly mechanistic, dualistic, and hierarchical, with humans at the apex of life. This way of thinking also fosters violence to each other and the earth, with its emphasis on domination, opposition, competition, win-lose or either-or thinking, and individualism, rather than cooperation, interdependence, and co-responsibility. And by reducing much of nature to insentient object, machine, or even adversary, and regarding ourselves as superior, or uniquely made in God's image, we have typically thought of nature as a resource to be used, exploited or destroyed at will, even as we are exhorted to be "stewards" or keepers of the earth in our scriptures.

Yet from out of these worldviews, and as part of the process of integrating Eastern and Western philosophies, science and religion, the lost voices of indigenous peoples and women, we are evolving new understandings of the earth's systems, the cosmos, and our capacity for spiritual awe and wonder. The more we realize how indivisible the whole of life is, the more the apparent separation between ourselves and the wider natural world, or the parts of nature we consider useful to humans and those that we (mistakenly) think are not, begins to dissolve. We are also now seeing a creative synthesis of science and spirituality and of our fundamental ideas about the nature of mind, consciousness, matter, and spirit, and envisaging—or restoring—a new, yet ancient, understanding that speaks to the reality of nonduality, interconnection, mutuality, and co-arising. Within ourselves, we are beginning to understand the inner landscape of our violence by integrating the masculine and feminine aspects of ourselves, our projections, and the suppressed parts of our psyches. Further, I believe, we are seeing a greater alignment of the inner realm of spiritual contemplation with outer action in the world.

If separation and distancing are at the heart of our predicament, the restoration of a sense of integrity as the wholeness, interdependence, and reciprocity of all life, is at the heart of its healing. It also reminds us that we are not only sustained by material things but by the wonder and numinosity of life. The nature of integrity, in fact, can be said to constitute life, the truth of our unity with all that is, and nonviolent love. Ultimately, *we cannot so easily destroy that which we come to love, to see as kin, as an integral part of us and the commonwealth of life.*

Far from being esoteric or simply "new age" ways of thinking that are largely irrelevant or naive in the face of the ecological crisis, understanding how to integrate each of these inward and outward levels or spheres—from the psychospiritual to the technological, scientific and economic— is a vital part of realizing and articulating the principles we will need as the foundation of practical action to restore a livable and peaceable earth. A central key to these principles and practices, in this holistic vision, lies in the integration of some of the oldest wisdoms and traditional ways of living with the newest insights in ecology, ecotheology, quantum physics, systems thinking, econom-

ic theories, psychological and consciousness studies, experiments in nonviolence, and political analysis.

The purpose of this book is to explore the roots of the ecological crisis
and show how a radical transformation of our ways of living, grounded in
spiritual and moral principles common to many of our wisdom traditions, is
both vital to the survival and thriving of our world and the commonwealth of
life and eminently possible, as demonstrated by many examples of ways these
principles are being put into practice around the world. The chapters that
follow are organized into three interconnected parts, which trace the causes
of the ecological crisis down from the interconnected branches of economic,
technological, social, political, and religious and psychological driving forces
to their roots in our dominant paradigms, beliefs, and ways of thinking, and
explore how these can be reframed or re-rooted in deeper psychospiritual
understandings and principles. These, in turn, can transform each of these
economic, technological, religious and sociopolitical spheres in new, life-
enhancing, and practical ways.

Part I first gives an overview of the ecological crisis, describes the symptoms of our predicament, and analyzes why current and proposed population-
based, economic, scientific and technological fixes are failing to ameliorate
the ecological crisis. Subsequent chapters analyze the deeper religious, scientific, cultural and psychospiritual causes and drivers of the crisis and how they
interact. Based on this analysis, and drawing primarily on a Quaker perspective but also on Buddhist, Abrahamic, Gandhian and other wisdom traditions,
Part II explores how we can reframe our habitual paradigms and ways of
thinking, and (re)discover the spiritual and moral principles that can ground
us in life-sustaining ways of living on an earth restored. The Quaker testimony of integrity, in its deeper meaning of the truth of the unity, reciprocity and
sacredness of all things, and the love that springs from that realization, is at
the heart of these principles, and gives rise to the interconnected testimonies
of peace, simplicity, equality, community and sustainability as branches
emerge from a common root. These testimonies bear a striking similarity to
the principles articulated by Gandhi and other spiritual visionaries from many
other traditions. In turn, they undergird the principles of what I describe as
an integrated deep ecology, deep economy, and deep peace, and articulated,
for example, in Arne Naess's ecosophy, Thomas Berry's Great Work, and
E.F. Schumacher's nonviolent economics. This means a fundamental regard
for *all* life as having inherent worth and sacredness, and a search for ways to
live in "right relationship" with the whole earth community—nonviolently,

equitably and simply—by satisfying our essential human needs while minimizing our violence to each other and all life-forms. A comparable search can also be discerned in the responses of a number of other faith traditions to the current ecological crisis, and these are also discussed.

Part III re-examines each of the social, economic, scientific and technological spheres critiqued in Part I in the light of the principles explored in Part II, to explore how they can be transformed to bring about the radical changes in the way we live that are now called for. I describe numerous examples of ways that the principles of a deep ecology, economy, and peace can and are being put into workable practice around the world, from agroecology, conservation, and appropriate science and technologies to new "steady-state" economics, self-reliant "transition towns," clean energy programs, poor people's campaigns or alternatives to militarism and violence. Each chapter also explores their strengths and limitations in the light of the challenges we face. For example, how can individuals or small local, self-reliant communities address climate breakdown while recognizing that we also need collective action at the state, national and global governance level? And how can the conservation of wilderness or indigenous ways of life and traditional economies, agriculture and technologies be conserved or integrated with modern technologies? Critically, the examples in these combined chapters show that addressing the destruction of other life-forms is an integral part of addressing violence, injustice, inequality, poverty and conflict in human communities and vice versa. Working to prevent war and conflict fosters nonviolence to each other and to the earth; practicing a nonviolent ecology that yields local long-term food security or greater simplicity in our ways of living reduces conflict and provides for human needs and an earth restored. Each depends on the other, if we are to sustain a whole earth community. Rather than simply requiring a sacrifice of our current ways of living among those of us who live in richer countries, which has often been the overriding focus, these principles and practices point the way not only to the future survival of all life but also to a more peaceable, equitable, and sustainable world now.

More than half a century ago, Teilhard de Chardin wrote that humankind was approaching the point where we must choose between "suicide and adoration." As the ecological crisis deepens, the very urgency of our predicament can produce a transformative realization of our condition and accelerate creative pressure for radical change. Despite formidable challenges, we are already seeing signs of some positive shifts as we approach the middle third of the 21st century. We have something deep within and around us to help us, if we can pay attention and stay close to the roots—roots from which the power to act wisely on behalf of all life arises. As the Quaker John Woolman wrote in the 18th century, these roots constitute the "pure principle" that belongs to all religions and none, and is woven throughout this book: the realization of the wholeness and unity of all things and the unifying power of nonviolent love, not as an esoteric ideal but as rock-bottom reality. Holding to these roots, it seems to me, means having the humility, patience, and wisdom to remain teachable, to ground our lives in love and the utmost compassion for our condition, and to not give up on the world.

❧ ❧

I owe much of my thinking to several interconnected strands that weave throughout the book. First, I draw on my experience of being a long-term member of the Religious Society of Friends and on the wisdom of the testimonies as ways of living. Being among Quakers has also taught me much about how to align the inward guidance and leadings of one's spirit, soul, conscience, or Inner Light, with outward, practical action in the world. Spiritual realization does not precede but *proceeds* interactively with lived experience and practical work in the world. As we live up to the Light we are given, more will be given, as Quakers put it.

I also draw on a life of participation in peace, justice and ecological concerns at the community level and beyond. This has led me to the work of many Quaker and other visionaries from Gandhi, A.T. Ariyaratne, Arne Naess, E.F. Schumacher, Ivan Illich and Thomas Berry, to Rachel Carson and other conservationists, activists, and pioneers of local community movements. Growing up in a low-income working class family in semi-rural postwar England has been a critical influence, too—from learning how to live simply and thriftily, growing our own food, buying little, and valuing solidarity and sharing with others, to walking in nature. I was also the beneficiary of a larger collective society that provided a basic level of material security in healthcare, education, and welfare, and made educational opportunities possible without deep poverty. I also owe my thinking to over four decades of research work in public health as a biologist and environmental epidemiologist. My principal research work (on environmental carcinogens and reproductive toxins) has illuminated not only ways in which we, sometimes unwittingly, cause violence to life, even down to the molecular level, but also the amazing resilience and healing power of life itself.

Lastly, I continue to be taught and nourished by a lifelong love of the wider natural world. I have found that we don't have to become mystics, or spend decades in solitary contemplation in a desert or mountain hut in order to discover the inherent numinosity, awe and wonder and interdependence of the earth community. We can become aware of the "I-Thou" relationship of which Martin Buber spoke, in multiple ways, gradually or suddenly, through science, art, music, poetry, through meditation, prayer and contemplation, or simply spending time in nature in stillness and silence, noticing a wren building its nest, or sun sparkling on water, or a tiny beetle crawling patiently up a blade of grass in a city park. These various paths have led me to search for ways to integrate these threads, through science, spiritual contemplation, and social action, and to a growing realization of how the poetic and spiritual experience of the natural world and the study of chromosomes, organisms, pathologies and ecologies can be all of a piece, and where "spirit" and "matter," human and other than human, dissolve into one unified whole.

I, like many others, have also been engaged in a very personal search to reconcile times of confusion, doubt, and grief at the violence we are committing to each other and the earth through war or ecological breakdown with a deep inward conviction that transforming the way we live is possible. To me this means rejecting a false, if comforting, optimism, and also recognizing that grief, sorrow, and doubt are an integral part of our human condition—an indivisible part of what enables us to love and cherish each other and the natural world and to seek to live nonviolently, grounded in a growing sense of unity with all life.

I—we—who have any degree of knowledge, choice and power in the world owe it to Greta Thunberg and future generations of children to do everything we can to ensure that theirs is a livable, sustainable and peaceable world. I—we—also owe it to every living creature on this precious earth to do the same, not only because our human lives completely depend on them, and on the air, rocks, rivers, and oceans, but because every living being is a sacred and integral part of the whole commonwealth of life. There is, indeed, nothing lowly in the universe. We don't know what the outcome of our efforts will be, but if we keep faith with life, listening within to conscience, our inner Guide or spirit, and putting love into action together, I believe we will have done what we are called to do.

PART I

PREDICAMENT

[Everything has changed] save our modes of thinking, and we thus drift toward unparalleled catastrophe.

—Albert Einstein

What good is it to save the earth if humanity suffers?

—Oil executive, speaking to Al Gore

Albert Einstein, referring to the newly unleashed power of the atom bomb, from a letter reported in "Atomic Education Urged by Einstein," *New York Times*, May 25, 1946.

Unnamed oil executive, at the 2015 World Economic Forum, quoted by Al Gore, in Jo Confino, "Al Gore: Oil Companies 'Use Our Atmosphere as an Open Sewer,'" *The Guardian*, January 21, 2015, http://www.theguardian.com/sustainable-business/2015/jan/21/al-gore-lord-stern-oil-companies-fossil-fuels-climate-change.

Chapter 1

The State of the Earth

We do not have another 30 years to dither. Much will have to change if the ongoing [ecological] overshoot is not to be followed by collapse during the twenty-first century.

—Dennis Meadows and Jorgen Randers[1]

Fifty years of exponential growth has accumulated to such an extent that we have reached Planetary Boundaries—and crashed through them. ... The conclusion is stark: the planetary stability that our species has enjoyed for 11,700 years...can no longer be relied on.

—Johan Rockström[2]

In 1972, I stood with a group of fellow students in a laboratory at Manchester University in England, watching a plot unfold on a primitive black-and-white computer screen. We were among the earliest students to play with the system dynamics "World Model,"[3] which was developed first by Jay Forrester and later Donella Meadows and others at the Massachusetts Institute of Technology. It was the first interactive systems model of the causes and consequences of global economic and population growth. The subsequent report, called *The Limits to Growth*, became one of the most famous environmental books of the era.[4] The output of the model comprised various scenarios of the interactions between five composite variables: population, agricultural output, industrial output, resources, and pollution. The computer ran various scenarios in the model over a specified time period, mostly out to the year

---

[1] Donella Meadows, Jorgen Randers and Dennis Meadows, *Limits to Growth: The 30-Year Update* (White River Junction, VT: Chelsea Green Publishing Company, 2004), xvi.

[2] Johan Rockström, Foreword, World Wildlife Fund, *Living Planet Report 2016: Risk and Resilience in a New Era* (Gland, Switzerland, 2016), 5-6, https://www.worldwildlife.org/pages/living-planet-report-2016.

[3] System dynamics uses computer models to allow us to see how multiple *interactions* and *feedbacks* work in highly complex systems and to understand what can happen to all parts of the system when one or another component is changed. The World Model comprised hundreds of data inputs, each with multiple interactive connections and feedback loops.

[4] Donella H. Meadows et al., *The Limits to Growth* (New York: Universe Books, 1972).

2000,[5] a date that seemed almost infinitely distant to a young Master's student on the cusp of a career in environmental research and with a new world ahead of me. The unmistakable message was that business-as-usual economic growth would eventually end abruptly in a crash.

Back in the early 1970s, it seemed that we'd have plenty of time to turn the giant tanker of growth around and avoid ecological collapse. Progress was being made—pollution controls were being beefed up; a plethora of creative "alternative technologies" was being tested, published and experimented with, albeit by small groups of environmentalists and others[6]; small companies were beginning to build solar panels and water heaters; public transportation and cycling were growing rather than shrinking; and terms like "self-sufficiency" and "clean energy" were beginning to appear in the media.

On a national and international level, the US Environmental Protection Agency was founded (1970); the European Economic Community began its Environmental Action Program (1972); commissions were set up; and international conferences held,[7] some of which we budding environmental researchers attended and gave our first papers at. Reports of the effects of chlorofluorocarbons on the ozone layer in 1974 gave the first indications that humans could influence the environment on a planetary scale, and data on global warming were beginning to appear, albeit still the province of a select group of climate scientists, who met for the first time in Geneva in 1979 at the World Climate Conference, organized by the World Meteorological Organization.[8]

---

[5] The year 2000 was chosen for the first models not because the authors claimed that it marked an abrupt end to growth or that we only had until 2000 to avoid ecological collapse, but in part because variability and uncertainty in the model's inputs and outputs increase over time, and 2000 also bookended an informative 30-year span for the first research models. As the authors stressed, their system dynamics modeling was an effort "to identify different possible futures," not *predict* the future, a distinction often lost by many on both sides of the environmental debate.

[6] For example, the Centre for Alternative Technology (http://www.cat.org.uk/), located in Machynlleth, Wales, was founded in 1973. When I visited in 1974, composting, windmills, solar ovens, and solar water heaters were already in use. Today, CAT offers practical trainings and courses, a graduate program, and a wide range of resources and technical advice on alternative technologies and many aspects of sustainable living.

[7] United Nations, *Report of the United Nations Conference in the Human Environment*, Stockholm, June 2-16, 1972, A/CONF.48/14/Rev.1, http://www.un-documents.net/aconf48-14r1.pdf.

[8] For a history of the emergence of climate change as a scientific and policy issue and the establishment of the World Climate Programme and related agencies, see John W. Zillman, "A History of Climate Activities," *World Meteorological Organization Bulletin* 58 (2009): 141-50, https://public.wmo.int/en/bulletin/history-climate-activities.

By the 20-year update of Meadows' *Limits to Growth* in 1992, using data on population growth, pollution, resource use, and production up to the 1990s,[9] the world had grown further into measurable overshoot or unsustainability. However, using different model scenarios, the authors suggested that this overshoot could still be mitigated by a combination of technological, policy, and economic shifts. The update coincided with a major United Nations summit on the environment and development, the "Earth Summit,"[10] that established principles and an action agenda to guide sustainable development (the Rio Principles and Agenda 21; see Chapter 2). The summit also formed a backdrop for the setting up of the Earth Charter in 2000, the first international declaration of ethical principles for a "just, sustainable and peaceful" world into the future, now endorsed by thousands of governments, nongovernmental organizations, and other bodies.[11]

By their 30-year update in 2004,[12] human ecological overshoot was clearly continuing apace, despite undoubted progress in areas such as legislative agreements, pollution control, efficiency, food production, and technological innovations. The authors noted that the overall challenge is how to reach sustainability—a concept that was still vague and subject to misinterpretation, as was the very idea of limits to growth itself. The interpretation of their work as calling for "zero economic growth" implied to many a static or stagnating state, rather than a dynamic equilibrium composed of qualitative development and a mix of judicious material growth in certain areas, and negative growth in others (decreased use of energy from fossil fuels, for example) depending on natural limits, who benefits, and for how long. The critical dilemma was how "to increase consumption [on the part] of the world's poor while reducing humanity's total ecological footprint."[13] Note that the authors also modeled the effects of implementing the highly controversial policy of attempting to actively reduce population growth, based on the then world population, and the results of their models, and the ethical complexities of such policies, are dealt with in detail in Chapter 2 (The Population Fix). (Briefly, Meadows'

[9] Donella Meadows, Dennis L. Meadows, and Jorgen Randers, *Beyond the Limits* (Post Mills, VT: Chelsea Green Publishing Company, 1992).

[10] United Nations Conference on Environment and Development (UNCED), Chair Maurice Strong, Rio de Janeiro, June 3-14, 1992, http://www.un.org/geninfo/bp/enviro.html.

[11] Earth Charter Initiative, "The Earth Charter," http://Earthcharter.org/discover/the-Earth-charter/. See further discussion of the Earth Charter in Chapter 8.

[12] Meadows, Randers, and Meadows, *Limits to Growth: The 30-Year Update*.

[13] Meadows, Randers, and Meadows, *Limits to Growth: The 30-Year Update*, xv.

model shows that only a minor reduction in population can be achieved, even if drastic one- or two-child policies were introduced worldwide, in the time we have left to avoid ecological collapse and the resulting loss of life through death and disease.)

Finite Earth: The Reality of Limits

The Meadows' 30-year experiment sets the stage for how we might think about the ecological predicament from the point of view of the structure of our global economies and technologies. The three basic lessons of their system models are clear. First, there are absolute limits to growth on a finite planet. Second, our current "business as usual" policies are leading to an eventual dramatic collapse in population and our material economies, unless we significantly change course. The third lesson is the most important but perhaps the easiest to overlook: If we reduce economic growth early enough, we can avoid the crash landing of ecological, economic, and population collapse. In sum, *economic growth as we have pursued it* **must** *end, but stabilizing growth can occur in an orderly way if we incrementally adapt our ecological footprint to the biological capacity of the earth, and thereby avoid the extremes of mass suffering and ecological devastation that will be unavoidable if we maintain our current trajectory.*

A further critical lesson can be gleaned from their work. While we are beginning to grasp how complex systems behave in the presence of multiple interacting factors that feed back on each other—in sometimes unexpected ways that we cannot understand simply by trying to think about them—the models can only allow us to see what happens when *numerical* changes in the variables are introduced into the systems the models represent[14] (e.g., the actual populations of the world, observed industrial outputs and energy inputs, etc.). But, as the authors emphasize, they cannot model *structural* changes to the systems themselves, and what we might call paradigm shifts—changes in our thinking and, critically, in our moral, spiritual, or ethical priorities. They conclude that *none of the measures to alter the current system*, e.g., economic or technical fixes, while urgently needed, *will do more than buy us time if we fail to address the underlying causes driving the system.*[15] These include both the multiple factors that have resulted in population growth and "the norms, expectations, goals, pressures and incentives that cause natural resources to be used more wastefully than money, that distribute income and wealth inequitably, that

---

[14] Meadows, Randers, and Meadows, *Limits to Growth: The 30-Year Update*, 237.

[15] Meadows, Randers, and Meadows, *Limits to Growth: The 30-Year Update*, 236.

make people see themselves primarily as consumers and producers, that associate social status with material or financial accumulation, and that define goals in terms of getting more rather than giving more or having enough."[16]

Faced with the three patterns that they identified in 30 years of analysis— the incessant and continuing pursuit of growth, the reality of physical limits to growth, and delays in society's responses to approaching those limits—by the early 2000s, Donella and Dennis Meadows and Randers were much less optimistic about the future than in 1972.[17] In their business-as-usual model, even with generous assumptions about resource availability and advanced technologies, when the physical limits of the planet are reached, material and food resources become increasingly scarce, pollution soars, industrial and food output crashes, and human populations decline rapidly due to rising death rates (Figure 1-1). Growth is stopped not by wisdom but by tragedy.

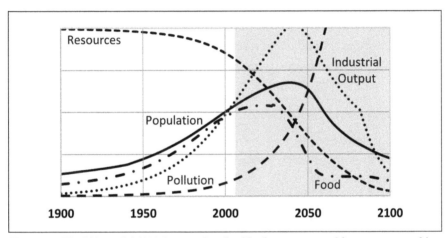

Figure 1-1. World3 model (2004) assuming double the nonrenewable resources and improved technological capacity compared with 20th-century business-as usual scenarios so that industrial output grows for 20 years longer. Reproduction of Scenario 2 in Meadows et al.[18] using the Vensim simulation of World3.[19]

Despite this grim prognosis, Dennis Meadows and Randers decided to keep a chapter (renamed "Tools for the Transition to Sustainability" in their book) previously written by Donella Meadows (who died in 2001), describing

---

[16] Meadows, Randers, and Meadows, *Limits to Growth: The 30-Year Update*, 238.

[17] Meadows, Randers, and Meadows, *Limits to Growth: The 30-Year Update*, xviii, xvi.

[18] Meadows, Randers, and Meadows, *Limits to Growth: The 30-Year Update*, 173.

[19] The data for the plot were generated using the Vensim version of the World3 model, and run on the Vensim Model Reader x 32. Used with permission. Both are available at http://www.vensim.com.

tools for the transition to a sustainable future, in the hope that "if we persist in our pedagogic effort, the world's people will increasingly choose the right way ahead, out of love and respect for their planetary companions, current and future, human and nonhuman."[20]

Donella Meadows acknowledged that while they had identified concrete technological, economic, and policy steps to move us toward sustainability, they had hesitated to mention several tools for transformation because they were considered too "unscientific to be taken seriously in the cynical public arena."[21] These tools were *visioning, networking, truth-telling, learning,* and *loving.* (In an almost amusing and apologetic tone, Meadows pointed out how much easier it is to talk about emission controls or recycling.) She concluded, "Individualism and short-sightedness are the greatest problem of the current social system.... Love and compassion institutionalized in collective solutions is the better alternative.... The sustainability revolution will have to be, above all, a collective transformation that permits the best of human nature, rather than the worst, to be expressed and nurtured."[22] Her vision is a plea for the future of all life on Earth and consistent with the spiritual perspective that I will explore in the following chapters.

New Names for a New Reality

Over the nearly 50 years of my involvement in ecological concerns, certain words stand out as markers of a path of progressive ecological degradation, loss, and crisis. The word "ecocide" first appeared in the media around 1990. It is now commonly found on internet searches, as are the terms "ecological refugees," or "climate refugees," meaning people who are displaced from their land, means of survival, or livelihoods as a result of climate disruption and ecological destruction. In 2000, the atmospheric chemist Paul Crutzen proposed the name "Anthropocene" for the geological epoch we are experiencing, in recognition of the profound global impact humans are having on the wider natural world.[23] For geologists (among whom our current epoch, as part of the Cenozoic era, is named the Holocene, dating from the last major Ice Age of almost 12,000 years ago), the rapid adoption of the term

[20] Meadows, Randers, and Meadows, *Limits to Growth: The 30-Year Update,* xvii.

[21] Meadows, Randers, and Meadows, *Limits to Growth: The 30-Year Update,* 271.

[22] Meadows, Randers, and Meadows, *Limits to Growth: The 30-Year Update,* 281.

[23] Christian Schwaegel, "Living in the Anthropocene: Toward a New Global Ethos," *Yale Environment 360,* January 24, 2011, http://e360.yale.edu/features/living_in_the_anthropocene_toward_a_new_global_ethos.

in the media sparked a major academic debate—including a journal of the same name—about whether to adopt the term formally and when to date the start of such an era. (The Agricultural or Industrial Revolution? The atomic or plastic age? The age of climate breakdown?) In 2009, a team of prominent geological scientists formed the Working Group on the Anthropocene, convened to study the question, and in 2016, they officially recommended adopting the term with a starting date of 1950, when human impacts on the climate, numbers of species, and global levels of plastic and other forms of pollution began to accelerate significantly.[24]

The phrase "the sixth extinction" began to appear in journal articles and the media around 2014, prompted by the publication of the Pulitzer Prize-winning book of the same name by Elizabeth Kolbert.[25] (The first five mass extinctions occurred about 444, 375, 251, 200, and 66 million years ago, thought to be due variously to ice ages, sea level falls, volcanoes, asteroid collisions or methane eruptions.) Starting about 100,000 to 200,000 years ago with the emergence of modern humans, and increasing with the advent of agriculture about 10,000 years ago, extinctions of species are now occurring at a significantly higher rate than that seen for millions of years, Kolbert writes.

The most significant human impacts on other life-forms have occurred over a remarkably short period. In addition to the actual or near-total extinction of an increasing number of species, including 300 species of mammals, about 60% of vertebrate populations—including fish, birds, and land animals—have been lost over the past 40 years, according to a comprehensive 2018 World Wildlife Fund report,[26] and the world is on track to lose close to 70% of vertebrates by 2020. Half of all land mammals have lost more than 80% of their distribution range over a similar period, leading one researcher to speak of "biological annihilation" on an unprecedented scale.[27]

---

[24] See, for example, Damian Carrington, "The Anthropocene Epoch: Scientists Declare Dawn of Human-Influenced Age," *The Guardian*, August 29, 2016, https://www.theguardian.com/environment/2016/aug/29/declare-anthropocene-epoch-experts-urge-geological-congress-human-impact-Earth; or Joseph Stromberg, "What Is the Anthropocene and Are We in It?," *Smithsonian Magazine*, January 2013, http://www.smithsonianmag.com/science-nature/what-is-the-anthropocene-and-are-we-in-it-164801414. .

[25] Elizabeth Kolbert, *The Sixth Extinction: An Unnatural History* (New York, NY: Henry Holt and Company, 2014).

[26] World Wildlife Fund, *Living Planet Report 2018: Aiming Higher* (Gland, Switzerland, 2018), https://www.worldwildlife.org/pages/living-planet-report-2018.

[27] Geraldo Ceballos, Paul Ehrlich, and Rodolfo Dirzo, "Biological Annihilation Via the Ongoing Sixth Mass Extinction Signaled by Vertebrate Population Losses and Declines,"

The mass collapse of wildlife populations is a combined result of direct exploitation and killing, together with habitat and food-source loss, arising from increasing human impacts on a global scale. Multiple studies from the 1960s on have documented accelerating global deforestation; soil loss and desertification; loss of sources of freshwater (glaciers, ice sheets, lakes, and rivers); increasing conversion of land for mining, food production, and building; high levels of water extraction; and the pollution of freshwater, oceans, air and land together with the accelerating global impacts of human-caused climate disruption. Some of the more iconic threatened species of wildlife, such as the savannah elephant, polar bear, panda, whale or mountain gorilla, get a measure of public attention and thus conservation efforts, but the vast majority of lost species and the scale of their destruction go largely unnoticed and unmourned.[28]

Overshoot: Ecological Footprints

The majority of available reports documenting ecological destruction do so from the human point of view. They use terms such as "resource scarcity,"—shortages of crops, drinking water, fishing stocks, materials for consumer products, or recreational amenities—or impacts on "biocapacity," rather than impacts on wildlife. Nevertheless, measures of human impacts on air, land, water and economically important life-forms, such as livestock, fish stocks and food crops, are signals that we are putting pressure on the wider natural world and thus threatening both our own survival and that of untold numbers of other life-forms.

The idea of an ecological "footprint," as a way to express human impacts on the wider natural world through a single, composite measure, was developed by Wackernagel and Rees in the mid-1990s.[29] It is based on comparing estimates of the "biologically productive" area of land that is or can be used to provide everything we use (from food and water to all the materials and energy we use for our cars, buildings, consumer goods etc.), versus the amount of available biologically productive land, and taking into account the *rate* at which such productive land is used versus the rate at which it can re-

Proceedings of the National Academy of Sciences of the United States of America 114 (2017): E6089-96, https://doi: 10.1073/pnas.1704949114.

[28] George Monbiot, "Disposable Planet," *The Guardian*, September 14, 2016, http://www.monbiot.com/2016/09/15/disposable-planet/.

[29] Mathis Wackernagel and William Rees, *Our Ecological Footprint* (Gabriola Island, BC: New Society Publishers, 1996).

generate (if it can), which is referred to as *biocapacity*. Measures of carbon, fishing grounds, cropland and grazing ground, built-up land, and forest products make up the total ecological footprint, expressed individually, regionally, nationally, or globally, and represent an indicator of the impact and sustainability of our demands on the earth. The Global Footprint Network (GFN), founded in 2003,[30] publishes annual global and national ecological footprint data and calculates "Earth Overshoot Day" each year, the symbolic calendar day on which humanity as a whole is using more per year than the earth can replenish in a whole year. The world first crossed into annual ecological deficit in the 1970s, according to the GFN,[31] and, by 2018, the global overshoot day had reached August 1.[32] However, if the world's population consumed at the same rate as the U.S., the overshoot day would land as early as March 15, a date exceeded only by the tiny countries of Qatar, Luxembourg, United Arab Emirates, Mongolia and Bahrain. The GFN has estimated that 80% of the world's population now lives in countries that are in ecological deficit, i.e., using more resources than their country can renew.[33]

Who's Got the Biggest Footprints?

Consumption rates of food, water, energy, and materials differ vastly across countries (and within countries, of course), both historically and currently. Another way to measure our ecological impacts is to calculate the theoretical number of Earths it would take to satisfy our collective demands. The world as a whole now needs the equivalent of about *1.7 Earths* to satisfy our collective demands, according to the GFN's 2017–2018 aggregate data. According to their estimates, in the 1970s the U.S. had an ecological footprint equal to about 3 Earths (if applied to the world), roughly ten times that of China or India and almost double that of Europe as a whole (Figure 1-2).

Even after rapid development in some countries over the past 25 years, the U.S. still has an ecological footprint at least 2.5 times larger than China's and 8 times larger than India's (using 2014 estimates). This means that, if everyone on the planet consumed at the rate of the U.S., we would now need

---

[30] Global Footprint Network, http://www.footprintnetwork.org/.

[31] Global Footprint Network, Country Trends, http://data.footprintnetwork.org/#/countryTrends?type=earth&cn=5001.

[32] Global Footprint Network, "Earth Overshoot Day," https://www.overshootday.org/.

[33] Global Footprint Network, Data and Methodology, https://www.footprintnetwork.org/resources/data/.

about five "Earths" to sustain us, compared with three for Europe, just over two for China, and still less than one for India, for example (Figure 1-2).

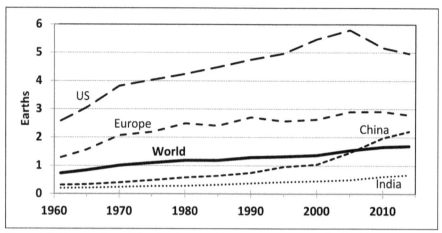

Figure 1-2. The number of Earths that would be required to sustain life if every country consumed at the rate of the individual countries in the plots. The world as a whole now requires approximately 1.7 Earths for our collective survival.[34]

In terms of ecological footprints per person, the GFN uses a measure of global hectares per person (gha). The gha (1 hectare = 2.47 acres) is calculated from the amount of cropland, grazing land, fishing grounds, built-up land, forests, and carbon demand a population requires to maintain their level of consumption and absorption of waste, particularly carbon emissions. According to the GFN, the globally equitable biological capacity per person, i.e., if everyone on the planet consumed at a rate consistent with the long-term biological or carrying capacity, is estimated to be equivalent to *1.72 global hectares per person.* That of an average American is currently 8–10 hectares per person, while the footprint in most European countries is between 4 and 7 hectares per person, indicating that consumption varies significantly among richer countries as well as between richer and poorer countries, which are still mostly less than 2 gha per person (Figure 1-3).

Although the world as a whole is increasingly in ecological overshoot, are some countries' ecological footprints declining while others are increasing? No single picture is evident, but while so-called "emerging economies" such as China, India, and Brazil have increased their per-capita footprints somewhat in the last 10–20 years, richer countries, such as the U.S. and Europe,

---

[34] Data obtained from Global Footprint Network,
http://data.footprintnetwork.org/#/countryTrends?type=BCpc,EFCpc&cn=100.

which have historically taken the lion's share of resources, have *continued to consume at roughly the same high rates* (albeit with a slight reduction in the last 5–10 years or so) and are still well above the per-person footprints in emerging countries (Figure 1-3). India has maintained a low per capita ecological footprint, and although China has tripled its per-capita footprint since about 2000, it has still not reached the levels of the U.S. or Europe.

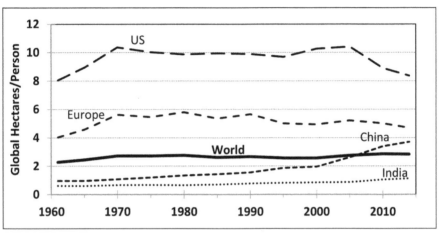

Figure 1-3. Ecological footprints (global hectares per person or *gha*), for India, China, Europe, the U.S., and the world, 1961–2014. The globally equitable biocapacity per person is about 1.7 gha.[35]

Thus, the world's total ecological footprint, as indicated by Earth Overshoot Day, the number of "Earths" needed, and per capita footprints, is getting larger and larger each year. As the per capita data indicate (Figure 1-3), this is due less to the increase in populations in every country and more to per capita consumption rates. *Richer countries have maintained large per capita footprints and thus overall high ecological impacts, despite small increases in populations since 1950, while some "emerging" economies such as China are experiencing rapid rises in both numbers (doubling over the past 70 years) and per-capita consumption.* Meanwhile some other countries, like India, despite experiencing a rapid increase in population (fourfold over the past 70 years) have maintained low per capita footprints and thus little increases in their overall ecological impact (Figure 1-2). (See also Chapter 2 for a discussion of the relative lack of correlation between ecological impacts and population size compared with the correlation between impacts and per capita consumption rates.)

---

[35] Data obtained from Global Footprint Network,
http://data.footprintnetwork.org/#/countryTrends?type=BCpc,EFCpc&cn=100.

As a result, on almost every measure, from arable land and freshwater use to minerals, marine fish stocks, forests, and fossil fuels, trends over the past half-century show accelerating ecological disruption and degradation, while measures of pollution, from fertilizer run-off to oil spills, pesticide pollution, livestock waste, climate disruption, and air pollution, show corresponding, and accelerating, increases. Both international governmental and nongovernmental institutions, from the United Nations to the Worldwatch Institute[36] to the Earth Policy Institute,[37] regularly report the same story: Despite decades of monitoring, repeated reports and warnings, and an abundance of proposed solutions and preventive strategies, we are rapidly reaching a state of what Lester Brown calls a "world on the edge" of ecological and economic collapse.[38]

Ecological footprints don't by themselves tell us about how they correlate with impacts on the wider natural world, nor can they indicate how overconsumption in one part of the world can affect wildlife, forests, and threatened species in quite different parts of the world. However, researchers in Norway have recently developed a novel computer method for mapping consumption impacts, using global economic trade and consumption data, and connecting that with impacts on threatened species and biodiversity "hotspots" worldwide, (i.e., places where biodiversity is severely threatened), even where supply chains end up in very different places from the species they threaten.[39] Their analysis has revealed that the ongoing threat to many endangered species can be traced back to patterns of final consumption of goods and services in far-distant major consumer countries. For example, marine species are most clearly under threat in Southeast Asia, mainly due to pollution, overfishing, and aquaculture impacts, but the predominant drivers are consumers in the U.S. and Europe.

---

[36] See the Worldwatch Institute's annual *State of the World* reports at: http://www.worldwatch.org/bookstore/state-of-the-world.

[37] Earth Policy Institute at: http://www.Earth-policy.org/ (Since 2015, EPI has closed, but reports remain available).

[38] Lester Brown, *World on the Edge: How to Prevent Environmental and Economic Collapse* (New York: W.W. Norton and Company, 2011), http://www.Earth-policy.org/books/wote.

[39] Daniel Moran and Keiichiro Kanemoto, "Identifying Species Threat Hotspots from Global Supply Chain Data," *Nature Ecology & Evolution* 1, 1 (2017): 23, https://doi.org/10.1038/s41559-016-0023.

Affluence and Effluence: Who's Doing What?

As the global ecological footprint indicators described above suggest, many of the world's people are consuming more and more each year. As the per-capita data indicate, this is not simply explained by the exponential increase in our population numbers but by the fact, as shown in Figure 1-3, that some people, mostly but not exclusively in poorer countries, are now consuming more (compared to historically low levels) while others in richer countries continue to consume at very high levels. Exactly who is doing what in the world's poorest countries, the so-called "emerging" economies, and the world's already richest countries? And exactly what being consumed causes the most ecological damage? Let's summarize some examples of the data:

- It takes over six times the amount of land to feed a person in the U.S. on average compared with a person in India; if everyone had the diet of the U.S., the world would need all the habitable land for agriculture and still need almost 40% more.[40]

- The top three greenhouse gas emitters (China, the U.S. and the European Union) generate over 50% of global greenhouse gas (GHG) emissions while the bottom 100 countries generate only 3.5%; the U.S., for example, with about 4.3% of the world's population, generates 15% of the world's greenhouse gases, while India, with about 17.5% of the world's population, generates 6%.[41]

- In the U.S., total per-capita residential energy use and gasoline use have stabilized or decreased slightly over the past 40 years, after increasing rapidly over the 20th century, but average food consumption (in kilocalories) has increased by at least 15% (to almost 4000 kilocalories a day) and the consumption of soft drinks and bottled water has roughly tripled (reaching a combined average of almost 60 gallons per person in 2000 compared with about 23 gallons in 1970). Substantial increases have also been noted in house sizes (from about 1500 to 2250 square feet on average).[42]

---

[40] Hannah Ritchie, "How Much of the World's Land Would We Need in Order to Feed the Global Population with the Average Diet of a Given Country?" Our World in Data, October 3 2017, https://ourworldindata.org/agricultural-land-by-global-diets.

[41] Johannes Friedrich, Mengpin Ge, and Andrew Pickens, "This Interactive Chart Explains World's Top 10 Emitters, and How They've Changed," World Resources Institute, April 11 2017, https://www.wri.org/blog/2017/04/interactive-chart-explains-worlds-top-10-emitters-and-how-theyve-changed.

[42] Richard Diamond, "Changing Trends: A Brief History of US Household Consumption of Energy, Water, Food, Beverages and Tobacco," *Proceedings of the 2004 American Council for an Energy-Efficient Economy Summer Study*, Pacific Grove, CA: 2004, https://eetd.lbl.gov/sites/all/files/publications/lbnl-55011.pdf.

- The richest 20% of the world's population doubled their per-capita consumption of meat and timber, increased their car use fourfold, and increased plastics use fivefold from 1950 to the late 1990s, while in the poorest 20%, consumption barely increased.[43]

- The total number of people in high- and middle-income countries using air travel each year has increased over sevenfold from 1970 to the present (to over 2 billion and 1.2 billion people, respectively), compared with almost no change in air travel in low-income countries, with only 14 million people using air travel by 2014.[44]

- Annual sales in the electronics industry (smartphones, computers, and other gadgets) now exceed $206 billion in the U.S., while less than 30% of such devices are recycled, contributing to an estimated 50 million tons of e-waste globally in 2017 alone.[45] It is the fastest-growing type of solid waste in the U.S., producing millions of tons of plastics and metal waste annually.[46]

- E-waste is generated predominantly in the U.S., China, and Europe, but much of what doesn't end up in landfills is transported to India, Africa, and other poorer countries for processing or disposal (making our ecological footprints even larger).[47]

The most critical areas of concern, in terms of risks of scarcity, loss of life for humans and other life-forms, and irremediable ecological destruction, are the interconnected areas of food and water consumption, energy use and climate breakdown, and conflict and wars. We will look at the intersection of these areas next.

---

[43] Royal Society (London) and U.S. National Academy of Sciences, *Towards Sustainable Consumption: A Joint Statement by the Royal Society and the United States National Academy of Sciences* (London: The Royal Society, 1997). https://royalsociety.org/~/media/Royal_Society_Content/policy/publications/1997/10 193.pdf.

[44] World Bank, World Development Indicators, "Global Air Travel Increase Between 1974 and 2014," http://www.bitsofscience.org/wordpress-3.0.1/wordpress/images/2016/02/global-air-travel-increase-graph.png.

[45] UN Environment Programme and GRID-Arendal, *Waste Crimes, Waste Risks: Gaps and Challenges in the Waste Sector* (Nairobi and Arendal, 2015), http://apps.unep.org/publications/index.php?option=com_pub&task=download&file=0 11703_en.

[46] United States Environmental Protection Agency, "Sustainable Management of Electronics," https://www.epa.gov/smm-electronics.

[47] United Nations University, "Solving the E-Waste Problem (StEP) Initiative" Project Description (2007), https://unu.edu/projects/solving-the-e-waste-problem-step-initiative.html#outline.

Eating the Earth: The Real Cost of Food

Global food production now accounts for about 70% of freshwater use and about 80% of global deforestation.[48] Even if global population levels were to stabilize at current levels, we may be facing unprecedented mass starvation without major changes in our way of producing and consuming food and drink. Why is this? First, agricultural enterprises have continued to move from small-scale farming to concentrated, industrialized agribusiness enterprises. While the food productivity of the land often increased initially, due mainly to the breeding of high-yield crops or livestock and the widespread use of chemical fertilizers and pesticides, food productivity per acre or hectare, in comparison with smaller farm yields, has increasingly leveled off or declined as the soil is depleted or water sources are exhausted. According to the latest UN report on land use, some 20% of the earth's cultivated land is now declining in yields, mainly due to unsustainable water and land-use practices, while 1.3 billion people depend on increasingly marginal lands with little opportunity to take up alternative livelihoods.[49] Soil loss and degradation are among the most urgent and yet neglected rate-limiting factors affecting long-term human survival, as well as the survival of all plant and animal life, which depends directly or indirectly on healthy soils. In addition, today's agricultural practices contribute substantially to global warming (current food production methods may contribute as much as 25% to GHG emissions[50]) and in turn, warming exacerbates impacts on food production due to heat, droughts, floods, and so on.

Second, global meat production has increased about four- to fivefold over the past half-century,[51] and total consumption is predicted to almost double from 2010 to 2050, close to twice the projected increase in global population over the same period.[52] Combined meat and dairy consumption is

---

[48] United Nations Convention to Combat Desertification, *Global Land Outlook*, 1st ed. (2017): 13, https://www.unccd.int/sites/default/files/documents/2017-09/GLO_Full_Report_low_res.pdf.

[49] UNCCD, *Global Land Outlook*, 8.

[50] UNCCD, *Global Land Outlook*, 13.

[51] Hannah Ritchie and Max Roser, "Meat and Seafood Production & Consumption," 2019, Our World in Data, https://ourworldindata.org/meat-and-seafood-production-consumption.

[52] United Nations Food and Agriculture Organization, *World Livestock 2011: Livestock in Food Security* (Rome: UNFAO, 2011), 78-9, http://www.fao.org/docrep/014/i2373e/i2373e.pdf.

expected to increase globally by approximately 70% by 2050.[53] As poorer countries become more affluent, meat consumption typically increases, although the global average is still only about one-third of US consumption rates.[49] Meat production uses about half of the global production of plant protein from grain and pulses, which goes instead into livestock feed, resulting in a loss of about two-thirds of available protein in the conversion from plant to animal. Livestock as a whole accounts for roughly 80% of agricultural land use while producing less than 20% of food for humans. Overall, meat production, particularly of beef,[54] requires up to 100 times the land to produce a kilogram of protein than the equivalent amount of plant protein. In addition, larger-scale animal husbandry can both destroy ecological habitats and species due to deforestation, overgrazing, or land clearance and produce substantial GHG emissions, particularly methane. In this respect, overgrazing by large herds of livestock can do more direct damage to vegetation and ecosystems than those confined in concentrated animal feeding operations, which present a different set of problems, including overcrowding, disease risk, animal welfare concerns, and concentrated waste.[55] According to one new report, *a diet of meat consumption accounts for approximately double the GHG emissions of a vegetarian diet,*[56] and overall the meat and dairy industries produce an estimated 15% of total global GHG emissions,[57] most of it from the 20 largest corporate agricultural producers.[58] A new analysis reports that, while

---

[53] Richard Waite and Daniel Vennard, "Without Changing Diets, Agriculture Alone Could Produce Enough Emissions to Surpass 1.5C of Global Warming," World Resources Institute, October 17, 2018, https://www.wri.org/blog/2018/10/we-cant-limit-global-warming-15c-without-changing-diets.

[54] Gidon Eshel et al., "Land, Irrigation Water, Greenhouse Gas, and Reactive Nitrogen Burdens of Meat, Eggs, and Dairy Production in the United States," *Proceedings of the National Academy of Sciences of the United States of America* 111 (2014): 11996-2001, https://doi.org/10.1073/pnas.1402183111.

[55] George Monbiot, "Farming Livestock for Food Threatens All Life on Earth, and 'Free-Range' Steak is Worst of All," *The Guardian*, June 8, 2018, https://www.theguardian.com/commentisfree/2018/jun/08/save-planet-meat-dairy-livestock-food-free-range-steak.

[56] Peter Scarborough et al., "Dietary Greenhouse Gas Emissions of Meat-eaters, Fish-eaters, Vegetarians and Vegans in the UK," *Climatic Change* 125 (2014): 179-92. https://doi.org/10.1007/s10584-014-1169-1.

[57] J.P. Gerber et al., *Tackling Climate Change Through Livestock: A Global Assessment of Emissions and Mitigation Opportunities* (Rome: United Nations Food and Agriculture Organization, 2013), http://www.fao.org/docrep/018/i3437e/i3437e.pdf.

[58] Juliet Majot and Devlin Kuyek, "Big Meat and Big Dairy's Climate Emissions Put Exxon to Shame," *The Guardian*, November 7, 2017, https://www.theguardian.com/commentisfree/2017/nov/07/big-meat-big-dairy-carbon-emmissions-exxon-mobil.

meat and dairy account for a similar amount of GHG emissions as cars, trucks and aircraft *combined*, as well as other polluting impacts, they provide only a third of our protein needs. The authors argue that the world needs to cut meat, dairy, and egg consumption by well over half if we are to keep global temperature rises to less than 2°C.[59] (See Chapter 9).

Third, the globalization of food importing and exporting means increases not only in GHG emissions via "food miles," storage, and refrigeration but also in the growing or raising of crops and animals in areas of the world that are not suited to support them (e.g., growing water-hungry rice and almonds in dry regions of central California or raising cattle in the Amazon basin). Global markets distort what is grown, the price of food, and food availability for local people, whose land may be bought up and turned over for export-ready agricultural crops or livestock rather than local produce.

Food to Waste, not Eat

The problem of unsustainable food production and overconsumption is exacerbated by waste. Globally, we waste an estimated one-third of our food, or 1.3 billion tons each year, according to a recent UN Food and Agriculture Organization study.[60] Unsurprisingly, the amount of food waste and loss per person in wealthier industrialized economies is about double that in the poorest regions of the world, such as sub-Saharan Africa and South Asia. Loss and waste appear to be fairly uniform across most industrialized countries.[58] In the U.S., these represent about one-third of food produced, at an estimated annual cost of over $160 billion, or about $1500 per person.[61] At one end, consumers collectively throw away almost half of the food bought each year in industrialized countries. At the other end, the many stages from food "production" to retail store incur about double the amount of consumer

---

[59] Marco Springmann et al., "Options for Keeping the Food System Within Environmental Limits," *Nature* 562 (2018): 519-25, https://doi.org/10.1038/s41586-018-0594-0. Avoiding meat and dairy may be the single most effective way to reduce our ecological impact in richer countries to keep temperature rises to less than 2°C. A "flexitarian" diet in the U.S. and other rich countries, substituting 90% less beef and 60% less dairy with more plant protein, would be required to try to meet this goal, according to Springmann et al.

[60] Jenny Gustavsson et al., *Global Food Losses and Food Waste: Extent, Causes and Prevention* (Rome: United Nations Food and Agriculture Organization, 2011), http://www.fao.org/docrep/014/mb060e/mb060e00.pdf.

[61] Elizabeth Royle, "One-third of Food Is Lost or Wasted: What Can Be Done," *National Geographic*, October 13, 2014, http://news.nationalgeographic.com/news/2014/10/141013-food-waste-national-security-environment-science-ngfood/.

waste. Industrialized agriculture, predicated on the large-scale mechanized growth and harvesting of our plant and animal food, produces considerable waste, and after harvest or slaughter, further waste is generated in the processing, packaging, distribution, and transport of food, often shipped over large distances or continents.

Over the last 40 to 50 years, in industrial countries, to the extent we still eat fresh vegetables, cereals, dairy, meat, and fruits, we now "demand" a certain quality, freshness, and "perfect" appearance, a requirement that results in much greater waste. It is a matter of debate as to who or what exactly has driven this cycle. Food safety concerns and regulation have played a role, by and large to the benefit of consumers, and producers and marketers typically insist they are responding to consumer demand for certain standards of quality and appearance. However, the food production and processing industry, now consolidated in large-scale agribusinesses and food-processing corporations (for which we should no longer use the words farm, farmers, or farming), presses for greater profit, and advertising plays a significant role. In addition, the technology of food production and the requirements of long-distance transport and storage result in increasing manipulation of animal and plant breeds and varieties—to produce "perfectly" shaped tomatoes, spotless and shiny apples, bigger chickens, or leaner and redder beef at our supermarkets.

Climate Breakdown: The Existential Crisis

Global warming and the subsequent disruption of the planet's climate now constitute the greatest human-caused threat to virtually every living system on Earth. It is now the most important driving factor projected to result in mass ecological collapse and extinctions, not only of other species but also of humans, within the lifetime of children born today, unless, as the evidence below indicates, radical changes in our ways of life are introduced within the next few years. Starting as early as the 1950s and accelerating in the decades since 1970, a virtual mountain of evidence has documented human-caused global warming and subsequent climate disruption, with its multiple destructive impacts on virtually all parts of the earth and its ecosystems—from the atmosphere to oceans, rivers, soils, forests, animals, plants, and humans.

The most authoritative international source of scientific data relating to climate change is the UN's Intergovernmental Panel on Climate Change

(IPCC),[62] created jointly by the World Meteorological Organization and the UN Environment Programme in 1988. Between 1990 and 2018 the IPCC has produced five major reports and a number of interim reports in response to the information needs of the UN Framework Convention on Climate Change (UNFCCC). These reports, based on the work of thousands of climate scientists and economists, and researchers in related disciplines, document the anthropogenic increases in global temperatures and their consequences, together with analyses and recommendations for mitigation (ways of slowing or reversing climate disruption) and adaptation (ways of adapting to the climate disruption already occurring or predicted to occur given different future emission and mitigation scenarios).

The latest full IPCC scientific report, completed between 2013 and 2014,[63] concluded that the last three decades have been "successively warmer than any preceding decade since 1850," that "many of the observed changes [in climate] are unprecedented over decades to millennia," and that atmospheric concentrations of carbon dioxide, methane, and nitrous oxide are unprecedented in the last 800,000 years. We have already seen an average increase in global temperature of at least 0.8°C (1.4°F) since the mid-19th century, with most of the increase occurring in the last 30 years, and reaching an approximate 1°C increase around 2015 (Figure 1-4).

About half of all cumulative GHG have been emitted in the last 40 years (rising from under 1000 gigatons between 1750 and 1970 to over 2000 gigatons for the period from 1970 to 2011), and the amount of carbon equivalent has risen from 200 to just over 400 parts per million (ppm), overtaking the 350 ppm that many scientists consider the highest concentration consistent with a reasonably stable climate.

Historically, most fossil fuel-generated carbon emissions (which account for 91% of total GHG emissions) have come from mined or drilled coal, oil, and gas. Most recently, emissions have also come from "unconventional" fossil fuel sources such as shale gas and oil from fracking and tar sands, which have a much larger environmental impact from their extraction than does crude oil.

---

[62] United Nations Intergovernmental Panel on Climate Change (IPCC), http://www.ipcc.ch/.

[63] *UNIPCC Fifth Assessment Report (AR5) Synthesis. Summary for Policymakers* (Geneva, November 2, 2014): 3-6, http://www.ipcc.ch/pdf/assessment-report/ar5/syr/AR5_SYR_FINAL_SPM.pdf. (The Sixth Assessment Report is projected for finalization in 2022).

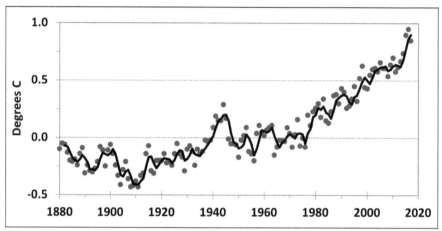

Figure 1-4. Mean deviation in global surface temperature (in °C, solid line) relative to 1951–1980 average temperatures (the 0°C line on the graph), from 1880–present. (Each year's mean deviation from the 1951-1980 average is represented by a dot. The solid line represents a three-year moving average of the annual means.) Data from the US National Aeronautics and Space Administration (NASA).[64]

Only a few transnational corporations or state entities, the "carbon majors," control the lion's share of fossil fuel extraction and production: According to the Carbon Disclosure Project, just 100 companies have been responsible for 62% of global GHG since the start of the Industrial Revolution (including 8 now defunct companies). Since 1988, the year that climate change was publicly acknowledged by the US administration following James Hansen's seminal Senate testimony, just 25 companies or state entities account for 51% of GHG emissions.[65] If fossil fuels were to be extracted over the next 28 years at the same rate as they were between 1988 and 2017, the world would be on track for a catastrophic 4°C increase in average global temperatures by 2100, according to the report.[66] While the relative contribution of oil production has decreased since 1988, those for gas and coal have substantially increased, albeit with some signs of a peak for coal in the last few years.[67]

[64] National Aeronautics and Space Administration, "Global Temperature," 2018, https://climate.nasa.gov/vital-signs/global-temperature/.

[65] Carbon Disclosure Project, *The Carbon Majors Database: CDP Carbon Majors Report 2017* (London: UK: CDP, 2017), 5, https://b8f65cb373b1b7b15feb-c70d8ead6ced550b4d987d7c03fcdd1d.ssl.cf3.rackcdn.com/cms/reports/documents/000/002/327/original/Carbon-Majors-Report-2017.pdf.

[66] Carbon Disclosure Project, *Carbon Majors Report*, 7

[67] Carbon Disclosure Project, *Carbon Majors Report*, 7.

The Global Impacts of Warming

Anthropogenic warming is already causing or exacerbating a range of climate effects, including ocean warming; a 25% increase in ocean acidity; increased melting of sea ice, land ice sheets, snowfields, permafrost, and glaciers, resulting in effects on sea levels, rivers, and freshwater sources derived from glacial sources; dramatic increases in extreme weather events (such as prolonged heatwaves or extreme cold weather events, floods, droughts, wildfires, storm surges, cyclones, and hurricanes—see below); and widespread effects on humans, crops, domestic animals, and the marine, freshwater, and land-dwelling life-forms in the wider natural world. The most sobering conclusions that the IPCC panel reached are as follows:[68]

First, under multiple model emission scenarios, surface temperatures and extreme weather events are "virtually certain" to keep increasing during the 21st century, even under stringent mitigation scenarios. Second, to keep average global warming to 2°C, a goal still associated with continued increases in extreme weather and its associated effects, will require "sustained and substantial" reductions in GHG emissions to maintain total cumulative emissions (since 1870) below about 2900–3000 gigatons. (We have already reached about 65% of this total, half of it in the past 40 years.) Third, an analysis in 2015 concluded that we must now keep 82% of the coal, 49% of the gas, and 33% of the oil in the ground if we are to hope to keep global warming within 2°C, which will necessitate ending fossil-fuel subsidies and investments and promoting renewable energy in the immediate future. The IPCC concludes, "without additional mitigation efforts beyond those in place today, even with adaptation," we are facing almost-certain severe, widespread, and potentially irreversible impacts of climate change by the end of this century.[69]

Are the IPCC models and predictions accurate? Enough data have accumulated to allow their models and estimates to be evaluated against the unfolding reality on the ground. A new major study indicates that climate disruption is occurring to a greater extent and faster than the IPCC models predict, that is, observed effects are occurring at the top of the estimated range of possible impacts or even beyond, thus requiring steeper declines in GHG emissions than previously estimated.[70] The IPCC acknowledged that

---

[68] IPCC *Fifth Assessment Report Summary*, 10.

[69] IPCC *Fifth Assessment Report Summary*, 18-9.

[70] Patrick T. Brown and Ken Caldeira, "Greater Future Warming Inferred from Earth's Recent Energy Budget," *Nature* 552 (2017), 45-50, http://dx.doi.org/10.1038/nature24672.

most of the available climate change models could not model reinforcing feedback loops adequately, and these may be increasingly coming into play as warming accelerates. These "tipping element" feedbacks include the slowing down of the ability of carbon sinks such as oceans and forests to absorb carbon, the release of methane from permafrost melting and the ocean floor, decreased reflection of solar energy due to melting of polar and mountain ice, and rainforest and boreal forest dieback, for example.

International Agreements to Control Greenhouse Gases: Too Little, Too Late?

The earliest attempt to promulgate an international agreement on curbing GHG and related air pollutants was the legally binding Kyoto protocol.[71] The protocol extended the 1992 UNFCCC Rio de Janeiro scientific consensus that climate change was happening and was largely anthropogenic and committing industrialized countries to reduce their GHG emissions.[72] Adopted on December 11, 1997 and entering into force in 2005, the protocol covers the following compounds and groups of GHG: carbon dioxide, methane, nitrous oxide, hydrofluorocarbons, perfluorocarbons, and sulfur hexafluoride. In its first phase, which ran from 2008 to 2012, 37 industrialized countries and the European Union committed to legally binding targets. The second phase, starting in 2012 and due to run to 2020, has yet to be ratified a number of the countries included in the first phase, and several countries have withdrawn or not accepted binding targets. Attempts to extend and expand this protocol to more countries have been largely unsuccessful.

After years of largely stalled attempts in a series of Conference of the Parties to the UNFCCC or "COP" meetings to reach an agreement and to succeed the Kyoto protocol, a new, nonbinding agreement was passed at the 21st COP meeting in Paris in 2015. This committed 195 participating countries to limit global temperature rises to "well below" 2°C (3.6°F) above pre-industrial levels, with an attempt to keep them at or below 1.5°C.[73] Over 180

---

[71] United Nations Framework Convention on Climate Change, *Kyoto Protocol*, Kyoto, Japan, December 11, 1997.
https://treaties.un.org/pages/ViewDetails.aspx?src=TREATY&mtdsg_no=XXVII-7-a&chapter=27&lang=en.

[72] United Nations. *United Nations Framework Convention on Climate Change*, 1992. FCCC/INFORMAL/84 GE.05-62220 (E) 200705. Geneva: United Nations. https://unfccc.int/resource/docs/convkp/conveng.pdf.

[73] United Nations, Charter of the United Nations and Statute of the International Court of Justice, Chapter XXVII Environment, 7.d Paris Agreement, Paris, December 12, 2015, https://treaties.un.org/pages/ViewDetails.aspx?src=TREATY&mtdsg_no=XXVII-7-

individual countries committed to "intended nationally determined contributions" that were designed to collectively ensure that the Paris agreement goal is met or exceeded according to agreed targets and schedules. The Agreement went into effect on November 4, 2016, after ratification by the 55 countries that accounted for 55% of global GHG emissions. (The U.S. Administration has since stated its intent to withdraw from the Agreement, which cannot occur before November 2020.)

The Paris agreement has been strongly criticized on several grounds. First, an increasing number of climate scientists conclude that *even if agreed pledges were fully met, they will be inadequate to maintain warming at 2°C but will lead to warming of at least 3°C by 2100.*[74] At the December 2018 IPCC COP meeting in Katowice, Poland, Johan Rockström of the Potsdam Institute for Climate Impact Research warned that the UN talks had failed to "align ambitions with science", and that we are on track to experience "a very dangerous" 3-4 °C of warming this century,[75] a warning echoed by other scientists at the meeting.

Second, it is clear that *even 2°C of warming will result in catastrophic impacts.* In October 2018, the IPCC released a special interim report[76] (prior to its sixth major scientific report, due in 2022). The new report focuses on the impacts of a rise in temperature of 1.5°C from preindustrial levels, and emphasizes both the urgent need to do everything possible to keep global temperature rise below this level and the difference in impacts if it rises by 2°C or more compared with 1.5°C. For example, extreme heatwaves would be experienced by an estimated 33% of the world's population at 2°C compared with 14% at 1.5°C, and ice-free summers in the Arctic would be 10 times as likely at 2°C compared with 1.5°C. *To limit warming to 1.5°C, the IPCC calculates that GHG emissions must be reduced by at least 45%–50% by 2030 and reach net zero by 2050.* In

d&chapter=27&clang=_en. See also UNFCCC, "What Is the Paris Agreement?," https://unfccc.int/process-and-meetings/the-paris-agreement/what-is-the-paris-agreement.

[74] Joeri Rojelj et al. "Paris Agreement Climate Proposals Need a Boost to Keep Warming Well Below 2°C," *Nature* 534 (2016), 631-9, https://doi.org/10.1038/nature18307. See also David Victor and Charles Kennel, "Climate Policy: Ditch the 2°C Warming Goal," *Nature* 514 (2014), 30-1, https://doi.org/10.1038/514030a. The authors argue both that the goal is unachievable and that other "vital signs" should be used to adequately assess climate impacts and mitigation effectiveness.

[75] Fiona Harvey, "UN Climate Accord "Inadequate" and Lacks Urgency, Experts Warn," *The Guardian*, December 16 2018, https://www.theguardian.com/environment/2018/dec/16/un-climate-accord-inadequate-and-lacks-urgency-experts-warn.

[76] UNIPCC, *Global Warming of 1.5C: Summary for Policymakers*, IPCC SR1.5, October 6, 2018, https://report.ipcc.ch/sr15/pdf/sr15_spm_final.pdf.

other words, *the world has only about a decade to halve global GHG emissions as of 2018.*

This report was quickly followed by an assessment by the UN Environment Programme of the global GHG emissions gap,[77] in which the UN evaluated how close or far each country is from meeting the climate pledges made in the Paris agreement. The report states,

> Current commitments are inadequate to bridge the emissions gap in 2030....if NDCs [nationally determined contributions] ambitions are not increased before 2030, exceeding the 1.5°C goal can no longer be avoided....In fact, global CO_2 emissions increased in 2017 after three years of stagnation.[78]

A preliminary analysis by the International Energy Agency[79] also confirms that the energy sector's carbon emissions are increasing, not decreasing, and in December 2018, coinciding with the UNFCCC's COP 24 meeting in Poland, the Global Carbon Project reported that GHG emissions are projected to rise more than 2% (from 2017 levels) overall to reach an all-time high after three years of little or no increase.[80] While the greatest percentage increases were reported for China and India, richer areas such as the E.U. and the U.S. have not reduced their emissions (the E.U. is projected to record no decrease, while US emissions are expected to increase by over 2%). Per-capita CO_2 emissions are still highly unequal. According to the report, per-capita CO_2 emissions in 2017 were approximately 16 tonnes for the U.S., 7 for 8 countries of the E.U., 7 for China, and close to 2 tonnes for India, compared with an average 4.8 for the world.

Feedback Loops and Tipping Points

Climate scientists have criticized the new IPCC report as underemphasizing the role of tipping points that occur as a result of reinforcing feedback

---

[77] UN Environment Programme, *Emissions Gap Report, Executive Summary*, Nairobi: UNEP, November 2018, https://wedocs.unep.org/bitstream/handle/20.500.11822/26879/EGR2018_ESEN.pdf?sequence=10.

[78] UNEP, *Emissions Gap Report*, 4.

[79] Adam Vaughan, "Energy Sector's Carbon Emissions to Grow for the Second Year Running," (interview with Faith Birol, IEA Director), *The Guardian*, October 8, 2018, https://www.theguardian.com/environment/2018/oct/08/energy-sector-carbon-emissions-grow-second-year-climate-change-coal. Carbon emissions were up by about 1.4% in 2017 and were expected to rise again in 2018. The full IEA report is due to be published in March 2019, as of this writing.

[80] Global Carbon Project, *Carbon Budget and Trends 2018*, December 5, 2018, www.globalcarbonproject.org/carbonbudget.

loops.[81] As noted, the effects of additional warming are typically multiplicative, not linear, due to such reinforcing feedbacks: These feedbacks include the effect of polar icemelt on decreasing the solar reflectivity of these icesheets; melting ice below icesheets causing sudden mass collapse of glaciers and sudden jumps in sea rise; the release of methane and carbon from the melting of permafrost and warming of peatlands and other carbon sources; and the decrease in carbon sinks as trees and soils are affected by warming, combined with the increase in wildfires. In turn, these effects can result in the rapid acceleration of other impacts and "knock-on" effects that have been difficult to model with enough precision so as to predict what the type, magnitude, and timing of impacts will be in coming years.

For example, a new analysis by the Stockholm Resilience Center indicates that interrelated tipping points, or what the authors call "regime shifts" and "cascading effects" due to one-way domino effects and two-way feedbacks, can occur in many ecological systems.[82] They estimate that almost half of ecological collapses (such as coral bleaching, icemelts into oceans, deforestations creating savannahs, loss of biodiversity, soil erosion, and urbanization effects) are interrelated, even at great distances, and could amplify each other. (An example is the melting of Arctic ice resulting in less reflection of the sun's energy and thus more warming, resulting in more forest fires in distant regions that release carbon, thereby generating more warming and more Arctic icemelt.) The authors emphasize the need for integrated rather than compartmentalized analyses, policies and action (such as agricultural policy joined with forestry management) in order to address such interactive processes. Similarly, also in 2018, an international team of climate scientists modeled some of the possible reinforcing feedback effects.[83] They concluded that even if the target of keeping global temperature rises at 2°C or lower are met, such "domino effects," each of which push other Earth systems out of balance in a cascade that cannot be stopped, are likely to accelerate as temperatures reach another degree Celsius of warming from the 1°C increase we have

[81] Fiona Harvey, "'Tipping Points' Could Exacerbate Climate Crisis, Scientists Fear," *The Guardian*, October 9, 2018, https://www.theguardian.com/environment/2018/oct/09/tipping-points-could-exacerbate-climate-crisis-scientists-fear.

[82] Juan C. Rocha et al., "Cascading Regime Shifts Within and Across Scales," *Science* 362 (2018): 1379-83, https://doi.org/10.1126/science.aat7850.

[83] Will Steffen et al., "Trajectories of the Earth System in the Anthropocene," *Proceedings of the National Academy of Sciences of the United States of America* 115 (2018): 8252-9, https://doi.org/10.1073/pnas.1810141115.

already experienced. They also concluded that, in addition to reducing GHG emissions at source, *actively drawing down atmospheric carbon by increasing carbon sinks or carbon capture is urgently required,* and that large-scale social changes are needed to try to stabilize climate in the (now inevitably) warmer world we inhabit.

Overall, despite concerted efforts by the major fossil fuel industries to deny and obfuscate climate science,[84] the intensive lobbying of politicians who are also often the recipients of large campaign contributions from these industries, and restrictions placed on environmental government agencies' research, publications, and regulations, and a lack of media attention, the warnings from climate scientists have been getting louder. In 2017, a group of over 15,000 scientists from 180 countries endorsed a warning that, without drastic action, climate disruption would accelerate quickly, as evidenced by rapid sea rise, ocean acidification and dead zones, and extreme weather events.[85]

In sum, the world is far from meeting even the 2°C target in the Paris agreement, and even if the current level of national pledges at Paris were to be met, the world is on track for closer to 3°C warming by 2100.[86] Meanwhile, as the IEA's latest report indicates (see above), per-capita GHG emissions in richer countries remain high and so far show few signs of the steep decreases that will be needed to avoid runaway climate breakdown.

Climate Catastrophe at Ground Level

Bald numbers and models don't convey much about the reality of the climate crisis. First, global warming is affecting different parts of the earth at

---

[84] There are multiple reports of efforts by the major fossil fuel industries to suppress or obfuscate climate science and the impacts of fossil fuel burning, in some cases using cover organizations such as the Heartland Institute, despite having knowledge of the global warming potential of GHG going back to the 1970s. (See, for example, Bill McKibben, "What Exxon Knew About Climate Change," *New Yorker,* September 18, 2015, https://www.newyorker.com/news/daily-comment/what-exxon-knew-about-climate-change.) Climate change denial is not confined only to these industries but is also found, for example, among people committed to small government or continued growth. See, for example, Jean-Daniel Collomb, "The Ideology of Climate Change Denial in the United States," *European Journal of American Studies* 9 (2014), http://www.doi.org/10.4000/ejas.10305.

[85] William Ripple et al., "World Scientists Warning to Humanity: A Second Notice," *Bioscience* 67 (2017): 1026-8, https://doi.org/10.1093/biosci/bix125.

[86] Fiona Harvey, "World's Climate Pledges Not Yet Enough to Avoid Dangerous Warming – UN," *The Guardian,* October 30, 2015, https://www.theguardian.com/environment/2015/oct/30/worlds-climate-pledges-likely-to-lead-to-less-than-3c-of-warming-un.

different rates and to different degrees. The greatest warming effects are occurring at the poles, as the Arctic warms at about twice the rate of the rest of the world, but there is almost nowhere around the globe where measurable warming and associated climate effects have yet to be felt. Record-breaking temperatures are now regularly recorded all over the world, even in years without an El Nino warming effect.[87] Until recently, it was almost impossible to imagine that human activity could change the average temperature of a massive body like the surface of the earth—and the ecological disruption it then causes—and what can happen at ground level when that change starts to accelerate. As the IPCC reports and other analyses described above emphasize, the difference between keeping warming to 1.5°C instead of 2°C is not just incremental; it represents *many* millions fewer human deaths, millions fewer climate refugees, and millions fewer extinctions.

We are already seeing a substantial increase in the frequency and severity of extreme weather events from close to 1°C of warming (Figure 1-5).

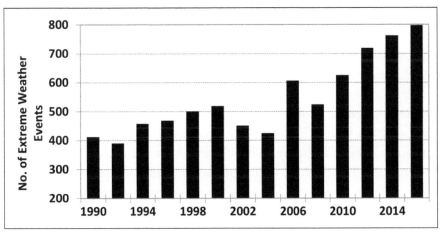

Figure 1-5. Number of extreme weather events 1990–2016. Data from Lancet Countdown: Tracking Progress on Health and Climate Change.[88]

As the now almost-weekly reports of wildfires; drought-related crop failures; and ever-increasing floods, hurricanes, coastal storm surges and landslides remind us, increasingly damaging impacts of climate disruption are

[87] Henry Fountain, Jugal K. Patel, and Nadja Popovich, "2017 Was One of the Hottest Years on Record: and That Was Without El Nino," *New York Times,* January 18, 2018, https://www.nytimes.com/interactive/2018/01/18/climate/hottest-year-2017.html.

[88] Nick Watts et al., "Lancet Countdown on Health and Climate Change: Shaping the Health of Nations for Centuries to Come," *Lancet* 392 (2018), 2479-2514, published online Nov 28, 2018, http://dx.doi.org/10.1016/S0140-6736(18)32594-7. Supplemental data.

no longer confined to low-lying islands in the Pacific or flood-prone countries like Bangladesh. As the latest US multiagency climate assessment indicates,[89] both extreme weather events and average climate conditions are threatening communities, agriculture, infrastructure, and ecosystems almost anywhere in the country, and as the report admits, neither current mitigation efforts (such as reducing emissions and increasing clean energy sources), nor adaptation measures (such as strengthening coastal defenses or improving irrigation efficiency), are currently sufficient to avoid substantial impacts.

Who's Getting Hit Hardest?

Climate breakdown and all forms of ecological devastation disproportionately impact poorer countries and poorer people in all countries and regions. Overall, this means greater impacts on poor whites, people of color, indigenous people, and women and children. They are not only people who are among the least responsible for climate disruption, but also among the least able to mitigate or adapt to or recover from these impacts and the most vulnerable to food and water insecurity, emerging disease risk, and infrastructure loss.[90] The Stern review,[91] released in 2006, estimated that climate-related impacts were then costing 5%–20% of global Gross Domestic Product (GDP) compared with mitigation costs of about 1% of GDP, and noted that poorer countries are typically more exposed to adverse climate-related events, are more vulnerable to the impacts of those events, and have less capacity to adapt to them than richer countries. Over 60% of people in sub-Saharan African countries, of whom around 40% may be undernourished or prone to disease, depend on the rural agricultural sector, which is highly vulnerable to climate effects. For example, Ethiopia experiences extreme variability in its natural water supply but has only 1% of the artificial water storage capacity of the U.S. Similarly, up to a billion people in the Amazon and elsewhere depend on forests for their livelihoods, many of which are under threat from deforestation, drought, and fire.[92] Meanwhile, in the U.S. and elsewhere, those who

[89] US Global Change Research Program (USGCRP), *Fourth National Climate Assessment Vol. II: Impacts, Risks, and Adaptation in the United States*, eds. D.R. Reidmiller et al. (Washington, DC: USGCRP), https://nca2018.globalchange.gov/.

[90] Nick Watts et al., "The Lancet Countdown on Health and Climate Change: From 25 Years of Inaction to a Global Transformation for Public Health," *Lancet* 391 (2017), 581-630, https://doi.org/10.1016/S0140-6736(17)32464-9.

[91] Her Majesty's Treasury (U.K.), *The Economics of Climate Change: The Stern Review* (Chair, Nicholas Stern), (London: Her Majesty's Treasury, 2006), vi.

[92] *The Economics of Climate Change*, 93-115.

can afford it are beginning to move to higher, drier, or less fire-prone areas, while others are left behind with sinking property values, giving rise to those new but increasing 21st-century phenomena of "climate migration" and "climate displacement" among "climate refugees," while, in safer areas, "climate gentrification" takes over.[93]

The cumulative evidence of climate research and the multiple impacts of climate disruption lead us to the inevitable conclusion: The world has so far largely failed to rein in the rise in GHG emissions, despite repeated and persistent efforts by the UN and many other scientific, governmental, and nongovernmental bodies and grassroots organizations. The chances of maintaining global temperatures "well below" 2°C compared with preindustrial levels by 2100, as stated in the Paris agreement, are considered by many scientists to be a "pipe dream."[94] James Hansen, one of the world's pioneering climate scientists, concluded in 2012 that it may be "game over" for the planet if exploited tar sands were added to the fossil fuels already being burned.[95] We may indeed be almost past the point of no return already, where multiple feedbacks result in an exponential rise in carbon release and ecological collapse. This is emphatically *not* a reason to throw up our hands, however, nor to deny or sugarcoat the scientific realities. Every effective step we take to mitigate (stabilize and reduce) climate disruption reduces the chances that it will result in incalculable catastrophe, human suffering, and the suffering and mass extinctions of most life-forms on Earth. And every effective step we take to adapt to the climate disruption already underway reduces its impact and gives us more breathing space to reduce GHG emissions and mitigate their further impact. But all these efforts, unlike many attempted or proposed to date, must not only actually work but be equitable and sustainable over the long term. In the next chapter, we will critically examine the potential success and failure of various "fixes" that have been implemented or proposed to curb climate and ecological breakdown, including, for example, taxation,

[93] See, for example, Benjamin Goulet, "Forced to Move: Climate Change Already Displacing U.S. Communities," KCET Earth Focus blog, April 26, 2018, https://www.kcet.org/shows/earth-focus/forced-to-move-climate-change-already-displacing-us-communities.

[94] Michael Oppenheimer, quoted in Chelsea Harvey, "Hundreds of Scientists Slam Trump for Threatening to Abandon Paris Climate Accord," *Washington Post*, September 21, 2017, https://www.washingtonpost.com/news/energy-environment/wp/2016/09/21/375-u-s-scientists-slam-trump-for-threatening-to-abandon-paris-climate-accord/?utm_term=.4e66dd9d85a3.

[95] James Hansen, "Game Over for the Planet," *New York Times*, May 9, 2012, http://www.nytimes.com/2012/05/10/opinion/game-over-for-the-climate.html.

carbon capture, and geoengineering, among other approaches to the ecological crisis.

Climate and Conflict: The "Threat Multipliers"

The climate crisis, and the ecological crisis in general, interconnect with conflict and war in three ways. One is the impact of climate chaos and ecological destruction on resources and on many parts of the wider natural world, creating climate or ecological refugees and conflict over e.g., diminishing food and water. Second is the role of conflict and war in creating ecological devastation through its massive use of resources and destruction of life and landscapes, water, food supplies, and habitats. Third is the "opportunity costs" of militarism, i.e., the vast amounts of money, energy, human potential, and materials spent on wars and the preparation for wars, which mean that these resources are unavailable for other purposes, including mitigation of the climate crisis and ecological restoration. In other words, *wars and conflict both cause and are caused by the climate crisis and ecological destruction* in an interacting feedback loop that intersects with other causal factors, such as resource grabbing, or political and economic causes of conflict and the forced movement of people.

In 2017, the World Economic Forum's annual Global Risks report,[96] which considers major risks to the global economy, concluded from a survey of 750 members of their "stakeholder community" that climate disruption (including extreme weather events, water crises, major ecological disasters, and failure of mitigation and adaptation efforts) now ranks as the top global risk to economic development and political and social stability in terms of likelihood and/or impact—even outranking weapons of mass destruction. Several groups have attempted to estimate the security implications of climate disruption, including the US Department of Defense (DoD) and various military, national security, and intelligence agencies.[97] Their primary focus is

---

[96] World Economic Forum, *The Global Risks Report 2017*, 12th ed. (Geneva: World Economic Forum, 2017), http://wef.ch/risks2017.

[97] See, for example, U.S. Department of Defense (DoD), *National Security Implications of Climate-Related Risks and a Changing Climate*, July 23, 2015, https://archive.defense.gov/pubs/150724-congressional-report-on-national-implications-of-climate-change.pdf?source=govdelivery; DoD Center for Climate and Security Working Group on Climate, Nuclear and Security Affairs, *A Framework for Understanding and Managing the Intersection of Climate Change, Nuclear and Security*, eds. Christine Parthemore and Janne Nolan, DoD Center for Climate and Security, November 2017, https://climateandsecurity.files.wordpress.com/2017/11/working-group-on-climate-nuclear-and-security-affairs_report-one_2017_11_15.pdf.

on protecting "US national interests" and "national security," and DoD and military researchers have fully recognized that "climate change is a US national security concern."[98] They have concluded that without a concerted effort to control global warming, various impacts of severe climate disruption will act as a series of both direct threats and "threat multipliers," or "stress multipliers," threatening not only the lives and livelihoods of people in other regions but the stability and security of the U.S. itself.

The DoD has identified three major types of climate-related threats to US security: increases in *disasters* (e.g., floods, droughts, heatwaves, wildfires, sea rise, extreme weather events, and emerging diseases); increases in *conflicts* over vital resources (food and water); and increases in *"refugee flows,"* each of which is more likely to impact regions already "prone to instability."[99] A current example is that of Syria, where an unprecedented drought between 2007 and 2010 contributed both to the displacement of up to two million Syrians, predominantly farmers and herders, in an already volatile region and to the ensuing civil war that erupted in 2011.[100,101] While military and security agencies have developed detailed strategic plans for both domestic and international efforts to adapt to climate impacts over several years,[102] they have warned of the lack of preparedness of other parts of the US government to reduce or protect against such threats, including coordination plans dropped by the current administration.[103]

---

[98] Carolyn Pumphrey, ed. *Global Climate Change: National Security Implications* (Carlisle, PA: Strategic Studies Institute, May 2008), 7, https://www.globalsecurity.org/military/library/report/2008/ssi_pumphrey.pdf.

[99] DoD, *National Security Implications*, 3, 8.

[100] Caitlin Werrell and Francesco Femia, "A Responsibility to Prepare: Why the US National Security Community Takes Climate Risks Seriously," *Department of Defense Center for Climate and Security Briefer*, No. 35 (April 7, 2017), 3, https://climateandsecurity.files.wordpress.com/2012/04/a-responsibility-to-prepare_why-the-u-s-national-security-community-takes-climate-risks-seriously_briefer-35.pdf.

[101] Caitlin Werrell et al., "A Responsibility to Prepare: Governing in an Age of Unprecedented Risk and Unprecedented Foresight," *Department of Defense Center for Climate and Security Briefer*, No. 38 (August 8, 2017), 4-5, https://climateandsecurity.files.wordpress.com/2017/12/a-responsibility-to-prepare_governing-in-an-age-of-unprecedented-risk-and-unprecedented-foresight_briefer-38.pdf.

[102] Werrell, *DoD Center for Climate and Security Briefer*, No. 38, 4.

[103] Francisco Femia and Caitlin Werrell, "Responsibility to Prepare: A Whole of Government Approach to Climate and Security in Three Steps," *Department of Defense Center for Climate and Security Briefer*, No. 34 (March 31, 2017), 1-2,

Of increasing significance is the way that armed conflicts can both generate and be generated by so-called "resource wars," which often result from
the excessive exploitation of resources and the degradation of forests, soils,
food and water supplies by local or nonindigenous forces. These conflicts
frequently lead to further ecological destruction and resource depletion in a
reinforcing feedback loop, as a number of historical and more recent accounts have shown.[104] Resource *scarcity*, whether from earlier conflict or via
climate impacts or other forms of environmental degradation, is now predicted to be a major cause of civil and interstate armed conflict, and it may now
be a bigger driver than resource "grabbing" in regions with fertile arable land,
minerals, or commercially valuable crops, according to one analysis.[105] It is
not clear whether population pressure *per se* is a contributing factor in some
conflicts, although one review suggests that it is a relatively weak driver of
resource-related conflict in the absence of other factors.

Water Wars

Conflict over water, vital for life, is the most critical area of concern for
both human survival and that of other life-forms. There are three interrelated
aspects to the global water crisis: one, the availability and control of freshwater sources for agriculture, industry, and other nondrinking purposes; two, the
availability and control of unpolluted drinking water for human consumption;

---

https://climateandsecurity.files.wordpress.com/2012/04/responsibility-to-prepare_a-
whole-of-government-approach-to-climate-security-in-3-steps_briefer-341.pdf.

[104] For historical examples of resource wars in the colonial and postcolonial eras, see, for
example: Adam Hochschild, *King Leopold's Ghost: A Story of Greed, Terror, and Heroism in
Colonial Africa* (New York: Mariner Books, 1998) and Eduardo Galeano, *Open Veins of Latin
America: Five Centuries of the Pillage of a Continent* (New York: Monthly Review Press, 1998).
Several current conflicts also originate partly in the attempt to control increasingly scarce
resources (e.g., conflicts in the Middle East and the civil war in Syria, exacerbated by
climate impacts), and in land and resource "grabs" by transnational corporations in Africa
and elsewhere [see, for example, Michael Klare, *Resource Wars: The New Landscape of Global
Conflict* (New York: Metropolitan Books, 2001); Phillipe Le Billon, "The Political Ecology
of War: Natural Resources and Armed Conflict," *Political Geography* 20 (2001): 561-84,
https://doi.org/10.1016/S0962-6298(01)00015-4.]Food shortages and crop destruction
have also contributed to earlier civil wars in Ethiopia, Sudan, Chad, Mozambique, and
Angola, according to a 1989 analysis: Johan Jorgen Holst, "Security and the Environment:
A Preliminary Exploration," *Bulletin of Peace Proposals* 20 (1989): 123-8,
https://doi.org/10.1177/096701068902000202, quoted in Nils Gleditsch, "Armed Conflict and the Environment: A Critique of the Literature," *Journal of Peace Studies* 25 (1998):
381-400, https://doi.org/10.1177/0022343398035003007.

[105] Christa Brunnschweiler and Erwin Bulte, "Natural Resources and Violent Conflict:
Resource Abundance, Dependence, and the Onset of Civil Wars," *Oxford Economic Papers*
61 (2009): 651-74, https://doi.org/10.1093/oep/gpp024.

and three, the availability of water for other life. Almost all the attention has been put on the first two aspects, despite the fact that ignoring the vital need for water in the wider natural world disregards both the right of all life to exist and our dependency on the whole web of life for our own survival. Added to the overall ecological crisis are the extreme weather patterns and changes in freshwater distribution and availability caused by global warming, with flooding or severe droughts in many regions and record-breaking levels of snowpack and glacial melting in others. For example, many of the great rivers of Asia arise from the snows and glaciers of the Himalayas, providing a major source of freshwater for an estimated 1.5 billion people in eight countries, their animals, and crops. In some areas, increased rates of withdrawal due to factors such as population increases or changes in meat consumption, crop type, or water management practices, combined with shrinking glaciers, changing rainfall patterns, and thus diminishing or fluctuating flow rates in these rivers, are now exceeding the replenishment rate by unsustainable amounts.[106] Agricultural demands on freshwater have also increased beyond replenishment levels in many countries due to groundwater depletion, primarily due to withdrawals for irrigation, a trend that is expected to continue in coming decades.[107]

In many countries, scarcity of water *availability* has been exacerbated by a crisis of *accessibility*, caused by disputes over extractive water rights and, critically, the privatization of water sources. This crisis has contributed to several conflicts and the rise in climate refugees and will undoubtedly become an ever-growing cause of conflict this century.[108] The privatization of water doesn't just affect people in poor countries: In virtually every country, corporations have bought up rights to provide drinking water and/or wastewater management to local communities; to tap into freshwater sources like springs and artesian wells; and/or to withdraw massive volumes of municipal water to "filter," bottle, and sell still and soda (sparkling) water and soft drinks back

---

[106] National Academy of Sciences of the United States of America, *Himalayan Glaciers: Climate Change, Water Resources and Water Security* (Washington, DC: National Academies Press, 2014). https://www.nap.edu/resource/13449/Himalayan-Glaciers-Report-Brief-Final.pdf.

[107] Carol Dalin et al., "Groundwater Depletion Embedded in International Food Trade," *Nature* 543 (2017): 700-4, https://doi.org/10.1038/nature21403.

[108] See, for example, the chronology of water-related conflicts compiled by the Pacific Institute, http://www2.worldwater.org/chronology.html. While conflicts over water can be traced back millennia, the number and scale of such conflicts and the impact of water scarcity on both human and wildlife populations are likely to increase in this century.

to the public. Such practices add greatly increased costs, plastic pollution, and increased energy consumption (from bottle manufacture to transport and marketing) to the problem of who controls water supplies.[109]

Maude Barlow has been one of the most prominent defenders of the right to clean water around the world, and has warned of the consequences of water privatization. She has documented the growing trend to treat public water not as a right and a part of the ecological commons, but "like any other tradable good, with its use determined by the principles of profit."[110] By the mid-2000s, some 10 transnational corporations (such as Suez and Vivendi Environment of France and RWE-AG of Germany) dominated the growing market, controlling the supply of drinking water and wastewater treatment to over 300 million people worldwide. In addition, far from being a choice for consumers in richer countries, bottled water has fast become the only source of potable water in many water-scarce countries, controlled by bottling companies such as Nestlé, Coca-Cola, and PepsiCo.[111]

The Ecological Costs of War

The preparation for and the actual pursuit of armed conflict or war contribute to a country's ecological impact first, in the direct use of materials and energy, from military equipment and weapons to personnel; and second, in the direct and indirect damage caused to life, property, infrastructure, land, water sources, and agriculture via bombing, shelling, fire, blast, chemical weapons, scorched-earth practices, the burning of food supplies or other deliberate forms of environmental destruction, together with debris and pollution remaining after the conflict. It is extremely difficult to quantify the ecological impacts of the preparation and prosecution of armed conflict and war. Nevertheless, Arthur Westing, a senior research fellow at the Stockholm International Peace Research Institute (SIPRI), has produced detailed analyses of the ecological impacts of the second war in Indochina, weapons of mass

---

[109] In the U.S. alone, the largest overall market (though not in per-capita global consumption), bottled water consumption has continued to increase sharply, reaching almost 13 billion gallons in 2016, https://www.statista.com/topics/1302/bottled-water-market/.

[110] Maude Barlow and Tony Clarke, "The Lords of Water," in *Troubled Water: Saints, Sinners, Truth and Lies*, eds. Anita Roddick and Brooke Shelby Biggs (Chichester, UK: Anita Roddick Publications, Ltd., 2004), 16. See also Maude Barlow and Tony Clarke, *Blue Gold: The Battle Against the Corporate Theft of the World's Water* (London: Earthscan, 2002) and Vandana Shiva, *Water Wars: Privatization, Pollution and Profit* (Brooklyn: South End Press, 2002; reprinted by North Atlantic Books, 2016).

[111] Maude Barlow and Tony Clarke, "Evian Backward Is Naive," in *Troubled Water*, 62.

destruction, and major wars, particularly in the 20th century, compared with nonconflict-related ecological use and damage by human populations.[112] While the focus of such analyses has typically been on environmental impacts of direct consequences to human populations, rather than on wildlife or geophysical regions (except studies of the impact of the two atomic bombs dropped on Hiroshima and Nagasaki), they show how the large number of regional and two major global conflicts over the past century, which used "conventional" weapons, have had devastating ecological consequences on forests, grassland, agricultural crops, livestock, wildlife, soils, and water as well as directly on people, whether combatants or civilians.[113]

Military Spending and Its Ecological Cost

Military expenditures in different countries give an indirect indication of the consumption of material and energy resources on the one hand and the potential opportunity costs of those expenditures on the other. In 2016, total global annual military expenditures reached almost $1.7 trillion, according to the SIPRI.[114] The U.S. has been by far the biggest military spender worldwide in the post-World War II era (Figure 1-6), with costs totaling over $700 billion in 2016 alone. (This number includes the base budget and "overseas contingency operations (OCO)/global war on terror" funding, but not veterans' benefits, homeland security, and related costs.) At 37% of the global total, this is more than the next seven countries—China, Russia, Saudi Arabia, India, France, the U.K., and Japan—*combined*, according to the SIPRI data.

The Congressional Research Service estimates that the cost of U.S. military operations since September 11, 2001 has exceeded $1.7 trillion dollars, based on DoD appropriation figures.[115,116] However, an analysis by the Wat-

---

[112] Arthur Westing (SIPRI), *Ecological Consequences of the Second Indochina War* (London: Taylor and Francis, 1976); Arthur Westing (SIPRI), *Weapons of Mass Destruction and the Environment* (London: Taylor and Francis, 1977); Arthur Westing (SIPRI), *Warfare in a Fragile World: Military Impact on the Human Environment* (London: Taylor and Francis, 1980).

[113] For example, in World War II, agricultural production among European and Japanese combatant nations fell by an estimated average of 38%, with an average rate of recovery of only about 8% per year in the immediate postwar period, as one indicator of the ecological destruction brought about by the conflict (see Westing, *Warfare in a Fragile World*, 65.)

[114] Nan Tian et al., *Trends in World Military Expenditures, 2017* (Stockholm: SIPRI, May 2018), https://www.sipri.org/sites/default/files/2018-04/sipri_fs_1805_milex_2017.pdf.

[115] Lynn M. Williams and Susan B. Epstein, *Overseas Contingency Operations Funding: Background and Status* (Washington DC: Congressional Research Service Report R44519, February 7, 2017), https://fas.org/sgp/crs/natsec/R44519.pdf.

[116] Steven Kosiak, *Is the US Military Getting Smaller and Older, and How Much Should We Care?* (Washington DC: Center for a New American Security Report, March 2017), using DoD

son Institute for International Affairs suggests that the actual costs of the "war on terror," including international military operations, veterans' benefits, interest on debt payments, and related spending at the Departments of Homeland Security and State, are approximately $5.9 trillion.[117]

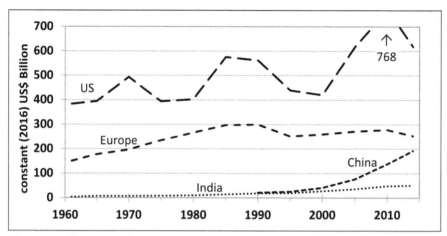

Figure 1-6. Military spending (constant 2016 US$ in billions) for the U.S., Europe, China, and India, 1960–2016. Data from the Stockholm International Peace Research Institute (SIPRI).[118] Note that figures for China prior to 1989 are not available.

Arms sales to other countries account for billions of dollars each year. For example, the U.S., with the largest share of global arms sales,[119] made over $82 billion in new major arms sales offers in 2017.[120]

The "opportunity cost" of military spending in the U.S. amounts to billions of dollars each year, accounting for 53% of governmental discretionary

budget estimates from US Office of Management and Budget Fiscal Year 2017 data; https://www.cnas.org/publications/reports/is-the-u-s-military-getting-smaller-and-older.

[117] Neta C. Crawford, "Costs of War: United States Budgetary Costs of the Post 9-11 Wars Through FY2019: $5.9 Trillon Spent and Obligated," (Providence, RI: Watson Institute for International and Public Affairs, Brown University, November 14, 2018), https://watson.brown.edu/costsofwar/files/cow/imce/papers/2018/Crawford_Costs%20of%20War%20Estimates%20Through%20FY2019%20.pdf.

[118] SIPRI, Military Expenditure Database, 1949-2017, https://www.sipri.org/databases/milex.

[119] Pieter D. Wezeman et al., *Trends in International Arms Transfers 2017* (Stockholm: SIPRI, March 2018), 1, https://www.sipri.org/sites/default/files/2018-03/fssipri_at2017_0.pdf.

[120] William Hartung, *Trends in Major US Arms Sales in 2017: A Comparison of the Obama and Trump Administrations. Trend Report* (Washington, DC: Center for International Policy, March 2018), 1, https://securityassistance.org/sites/default/files/US%20Arms%20Sales%202017%20Report.pdf.

spending in 2016 (just for the DoD's base budget of approximately $616 billion), and far outstripping the discretionary spending available for other sectors such as health, education, science, transport, infrastructure, and the environment.[121] For example, the U.S. Environmental Protection Agency's 2016 fiscal-year budget was about $8.14 billion, roughly 75 times less than the "base" military budget alone, and at least 85 times less than the estimated base plus overseas contingency operations spending for that year.[122] Even if the question of the justification of these expenditures is put aside for the moment, they represent enormous levels of consumption of materials and energy, incalculable levels of potential or actual destruction when deployed, and an enormous opportunity cost in terms of Federal or state monies that could be directed, among other programs, toward mitigation of the real threats to security that the climate and ecological crises represent.

In sum, we are clearly at increasingly high risk of causing what many scientists are calling the sixth mass extinction on the earth, and the first by our own hand. We are in the process of destroying much of the wider natural world, and even the very means of our collective survival, and taking many of the animals and plants we depend on or live alongside with us, through a combination of a failure to preserve and conserve the commonwealth of life, overconsumption on the part of some while others go hungry and live in poverty, and the immense economic and ecological costs of conflict, wars and the preparation for wars, all of which exacerbate each other.

This failure, as I will explore in the next chapters, is in large measure a function of the habitual way we think about the world—the technological, economic, social, and cultural paradigms by which we live, which place short-term economic growth and gains over longer-term concerns—and therefore how we approach the various "fixes" that we hope will solve our predicament but that often repeat errors of the same thinking that got us into the crisis in the first place. We are also used to thinking that change happens incremental-ly: As in the boiling-frog analogy, we are often unaware that change is *accelerat-ing*, not progressing linearly, until it is almost too late. We also have that re-markable human ability to adapt to (almost) anything, which enables us to survive imposed horrors but also can dampen our responses to looming catastrophes. At a deeper level, as we will explore, our failure is attributable to

---

[121] National Priorities Project, "A Militarized Budget," April 30, 2017, https://www.nationalpriorities.org/analysis/2017/militarized-budget-2017/.

[122] US Environmental Protection Agency, "EPA'S Budget and Spending," https://www.epa.gov/planandbudget/budget.

how we consider what is important: what are the ultimate purpose, meaning, and values of our lives, and what really sustains us.

As we face this existential crisis, we must now pose the questions of when and how, not whether, irreversible global climate breakdown and ecological collapse is likely to happen if we now fail to take radical action, and how many, not how few, human lives and other life-forms would be lost. Even if we disagree on the scale or timing, or even if we are indifferent to the fate of other forms of life and the beauty of what we are losing—in the mistaken belief that we are not dependent on nature, not only for our vital needs but also for our spiritual and cultural wellbeing—ignoring our new reality is to take an unprecedented risk with our own future lives, our children's and grandchildren's lives, and the lives of all beings on Earth, and to throw the dice as we gamble on the fate of the earth as we know it.

Chapter 2

Fixes That Fall Short

Trade and growth are now priorities for all [government] posts.... Some economic security-related work like climate change and illegal wildlife trade will be scaled down.

—Tim Hitchins[1]

If your ladder is leaning against the wrong wall, every step you take just gets you to the wrong place faster.

—Stephen Covey[2]

The environmental crisis cannot be solved by good engineering..., cannot be solved by economic planning, cannot even be solved by cosmetic changes in our conception of development and change. It requires a very radical transformation in our consciousness.

—Seyyed Hossein Nasr[3]

In the late 18th century, Thomas Malthus proposed that populations tend to grow in response to prosperity rather than maintain a high standard of living, until the point where the increase would greatly exceed the capacity of the earth to support it.[4] Since Malthus's time, there have been numerous attempts to answer the deceptively simple question, "How many people can

---

[1] Leaked notes for a speech to the "Prosperity UK" conference of 26 April 2017 by Tim Hitchens, director of economic and consular affairs, UK Foreign Office; reported by Rachael Revesz, "U.K To "Scale Down" Climate Change and Illegal Wildlife Measures to Bring In Post-Brexit Trade, Secret Documents Reveal,"*The Independent*, April 9, 2017, https://www.independent.co.uk/news/uk/politics/uk-government-to-scale-down-climate-change-and-illegal-wildlife-measure-a7674706.html.

[2] Stephen R. Covey, *The Seven Habits of Highly Effective People Personal Workbook* (New York: Touchstone Press, 2004), 41.

[3] Seyyed Hossein Nasr, "The Spiritual and Religious Dimensions of the Environmental Crisis," in *A Sacred Trust: Ecology and Spiritual Vision*, eds. David Cadman and John Carey, Temenos Academy Papers No. 17 (London: The Temenos Academy, 2002), 119.

[4] Thomas R. Malthus, *An Essay on the Principle of Population* (Oxford: Oxford World's Classics, 1798), 8, 13 et seq.

the Earth support?," a question that, as we saw in Chapter 1, depends on whether the world's ecological footprint lies within or exceeds the long-term capacity of the earth to sustain and renew what we consume, waste, and destroy.[5]

In 1972, the publication of Barry Commoner's *The Closing Circle* and a subsequent dialog with Paul Ehrlich and John Holdren resulted in introduction of the equation $I = f(PAT)$, where environmental Impact (I) is a function (f) of Population (P) × Affluence (A) × Technology (T).[6] As an early attempt to account for the combined effects of major causes of environmental impacts, this equation has been taught for decades in environmental studies courses. It has arguably focused attention on the idea that we can "solve" our ecological predicament by a combination of reducing population numbers and/or relying on technological or economic fixes. We need to ask: Have the approaches used to date worked? The damning evidence of ecological overshoot and breakdown described in Chapter 1 overwhelmingly indicates that we are failing, catastrophically in many areas, to live within the carrying capacity of the earth, and that, as we saw, there are vast differences in footprints and impacts across the globe. Do we continue along the same path, increasing our efforts to implement the fixes we've tried? Or is there something deeper that is wrong with the fixes? Let's begin by examining the approaches used to date in the three areas outlined by the famous equation, starting with population and technology, and moving to economic fixes, and explore why they have been largely inadequate to prevent or ameliorate the ecological crisis.

The Population Fix: Misunderstanding the Issues

We are indeed experiencing a rapid and accelerating increase[7] in global population. The shortest observed doubling time of the world's population has been about 37 years, which occurred between 1963 and around the year

---

[5] See, for example, Joel E. Cohen's classic papers, "Population Growth and the Earth's Carrying Capacity," *Science* 269 (1995), 341-6, https://doi.org/10.1126/science.7618100; and *How Many People Can the Earth Support?* (revised ed.) (New York: W.W. Norton & Company, 1996).

[6] Barry Commoner, *The Closing Circle: Nature, Man and Technology* (New York: Bantam Books, 1972); Paul Ehrlich and Paul Holdren, "Critique: One-dimensional Ecology," *Bulletin of the Atomic Scientists* 23 (May 1972), 16, 18-27; and Barry Commoner, "Response," *Bulletin of the Atomic Scientists* 23 (May 1972), 17, 42-56.

[7] This is due to the *exponential* nature of population growth. Imagine a 64-square chessboard. Put one grain of sand on the first square, two on the next, four on the next, eight on the next, and so on. There are 255 grains on the last square on the first line, but by the time the very last square is reached, the mountain of sand contains 18.4 *quintillion* grains.

2000, the year when the global population reached about 6 billion. Since then, the doubling time has lengthened slightly to just over 40 years, but it still takes only about 13 years to add a billion more people. Over the past 50 years, the world has added over 3.6 billion people, and we are on track to reach 8 billion before 2050.[8]

It has been tempting for many to focus almost exclusively on global population size as the defining problem of ecological unsustainability. Paul Ehrlich's early books[9] undoubtedly helped popularize the idea that "overpopulation is our No. 1 environmental problem,"[10] despite his own argument that the impact of population growth could not be considered separately from affluence and consumption. Some have argued for active "population control" measures, particularly in countries where birth rates are relatively high, such as in parts of Africa and Asia. Even leaving aside the fact that low-income countries contribute comparatively little to the world's ecological and carbon footprints,[11] even with higher birth rates, and profound ethical concerns about the idea of population "control," and how it has often been applied disproportionately to poor people, people of color, or indigenous peoples, the argument ignores the fact that it is an ineffective strategy to address the ecological crisis.[12] Even in countries that have gone through the "demographic transition" from high to low birth and death rates so that the *rate of growth* has slowed significantly, the overall population continues to increase for a long period before stabilizing.

The same thing applies to the global population.[13] Even though overall birth rates[14] and death rates[15] and thus overall growth rates have already

---

[8] Demographic data from https://ourworldindata.org/world-population-growth.

[9] Paul Ehrlich, *The Population Bomb* (New York: Ballantine, 1968); and Paul Ehrlich and Anne Ehrlich, *The Population Explosion* (New York: Simon and Schuster, 1990).

[10] Quote from the subtitle of the hardback cover of Ehrlich, *The Population Explosion*, 1990.

[11] David Satterthwaite, "The Implications of Population Growth and Urbanization for Climate Change," *Environment and Urbanization* 21 (2009): 558, https://doi.org/10.1177/0956247809344361. For example, low and high income countries increased in population by about 50% and 7% respectively between 1980 and 2013 but contributed about 12% and 30% of carbon emissions during that time. Satterthwaite argues that the "P" variable in the I=f(PAT) equation should be replaced by "C" for consumers, as many populations consume little.

[12] George Monbiot, "The Population Myth," September 9, 2009, https://www.monbiot.com/2009/09/29/the-population-myth/.

[13] For example, in 1965, the global population was 3.3 billion, the growth rate was 2.03% per year, adding 68 million people to the population. In 2000, the number of people added was 75 million, when the world's population was about 6.1 billion, although the overall growth rate had almost halved, to 1.23% per year.

decreased significantly across the world and are projected to continue to decline, the total global population is projected to go on increasing for decades to come, as shown in Figure 2-1.

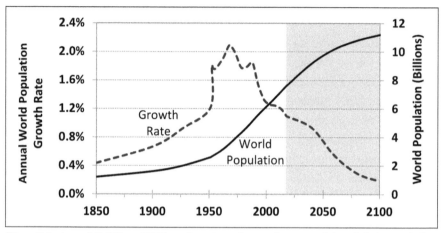

Figure 2-1. Actual (1850 to 2017) and projected growth rates of the global population (based on global birth and death rates) and world population in billions, 1850 to 2100. Data from WorldoMeters.info and WorldinData.org.[16]

What the demographic data show is that *global populations cannot be stabilized by decreasing birth rates by the latter part of the 21st century, even if drastic and rapid methods of fertility reduction were implemented*, and certainly not in the time we may have left if we are to avoid the worst impacts from ecological devastation.

To emphasize this conclusion, demographers and others have modeled population projections based on hypothetical decreases in birth rates. For example, in 2004, Meadows and colleagues (see Chapter 1) ran a scenario of

---

[14] Data from Max Roser, "Fertility Rate," 2018, Our World in Data, https://ourworldindata.org/fertility-rate. Based on data from United Nations, Department of Economic and Social Affairs, Population Division, *World Population Prospects: The 2017 Revision*, https://esa.un.org/unpd/wpp. The data show that overall live birth rates have halved from about 5 per woman in 1950 to 2.5 in 2015.

[15] Global Burden of Disease (GBD) 2017 Mortality Collaborators, "Global, Regional and National Age-Sex-Specific Mortality and Life Expectancy 1950-2017: A Systematic Analysis for the Global Burden of Disease Study 2017," *Lancet* 392 (2018): 1684-735, https://doi.org/10.1016/S0140-6736(18)31891-9.

[16] Data (1850-2018) from WorldoMeters.Info, "World Population by Year," http://www.worldometers.info/world-population/world-population-by-year/, based on data from *World Population Prospects 2017 Revision* data (medium-fertility variant) and (2015-2100) from Max Roser (2018) "World Population Growth," Our World in Data, https://ourworldindata.org/wp-content/uploads/2013/05/updated-World-Population-Growth-1750-2100.png, also based on UN Population Division data.

their World3 model (Figure 2-2) in which global family size was set and maintained at only *two children per family* after the year 2002 (i.e., based on the global population at the time of about 6 billion).[17] The world's population *growth rate* slows, but demographic momentum still results in a peak population of 7.5 billion by the year 2040 before declining quite rapidly, compared with a peak of 8 billion without the restriction on family size, all other conditions being equal. In other words, the two-child limit reduced the peak population level by less than 10% and delayed ecological collapse by only a few years, if no other limits on our current growth and consumption patterns were imposed.

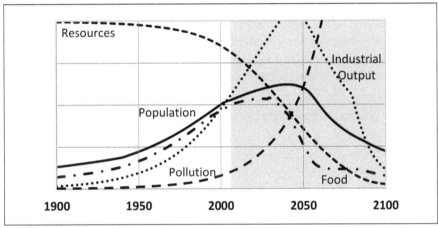

Figure 2-2. World3 model (2004) assuming two children per family from 2002; otherwise conditions are as for Scenario 2 (see Chapter 1), a close to business-as-usual scenario. Peak population occurs around 2040 at about 7.5 billion, a reduction of about 10%. Reproduction of Scenario 7 in Meadows et al.[18] using Vensim simulation of World3.[19]

Meadows' findings are supported by more recent models developed by Bradshaw and Brook using 2013 global population data and taking into account trends in mortality reduction, the rate of unplanned pregnancies, and other factors.[20] Their models show that even if a draconian one-child policy were imposed worldwide (as of 2013), global population levels would peak at

[17] Donella Meadows, Jorgen Randers, and Dennis Meadows, *Limits to Growth: The 30-Year Update* (White River Junction, VT: Chelsea Green Publishing Company, 2004), 238-41.

[18] Meadows, Randers, and Meadows, *Limits to Growth: The 30-Year Update*, 241.

[19] The data for the plot were generated using the Vensim version of the World3 model, and run on the Vensim Model Reader x 32. Used with permission. Both are available at http://www.vensim.com.

[20] Corey J.A. Bradshaw and Barry W. Brook, "Human Population Reduction Is Not a Quick Fix for Environmental Problems," *Proceedings of the National Academy of Sciences of the United States of America* 111 (2014): 16610-5, https://doi.org/10.1073/pnas.1410465111.

about 8.9 billion in 2056 (compared with about 9.25 billion without such as policy) and would only return to 2013 levels of 7 billion by 2100. Even a hypothetical catastrophic increase in mortality due to a global war or pandemic would not necessarily impact population levels substantially. While welcoming observed reductions in fertility due to, for example, women's empowerment and education, the authors conclude that:

> ...our models clearly demonstrate that the current momentum of the global human population preclude any demographic "quick fixes."...[fertility reduction] cannot be argued to be the elephant in the room for immediate sustainability and climate policy...society's efforts toward sustainability would be directed more productively toward adapting to the large and increasing human population by rapidly reducing our footprint as much as possible through technological and social innovation, devising cleverer ways to conserve remaining species and ecosystems, encouraging per capita reductions in consumption of irreplaceable goods, and treating population as a long-term planning goal.[21]

Meanwhile, while birth rates in richer countries have declined, overall levels of affluence and consumption in these countries have not (see Chapter 1). Their consumption rates per person still greatly exceed those of poorer regions of the world with larger and faster growing populations, and even of those countries, such as China, where consumption is now rising.

The Technology Fix: Miracle or Myth?

Our tendency has been to believe that technological "fixes" can and will solve most if not all of our resource and pollution problems, in the hope that we won't have to give up our affluent material lifestyles to maintain a habitable planet. Typically, technological fixes tend to be "end-of-pipeline" rather than preventive or precautionary approaches.

First, producers and environmentalists alike have assumed that improving efficiency will lead to overall decreases in consumption of nonrenewable resources while maintaining our current lifestyles. However, as William Jevons first observed, consumption actually tends to *increase* over a given period, due to increased demand—giving rise to the well-known Jevons paradox.[22] (For example, if my car gets 20 miles to the gallon, I may only drive 100 miles a week, using 5 gallons, but if I get a car that gets 30 miles per gallon, I may

---

[21] Bradshaw and Brook, "Human Population Reduction," 16613-5.

[22] See, for example, Blake Alcott, "Jevons' Paradox," *Ecological Economics* 54 (2005): 9-21, https://doi.org/10.1016/j.ecolecon.2005.03.020; also see John Polimeni et al., *The Jevons Paradox and the Myth of Resource Efficiency Improvements* (London: Earthscan, 2008).

decide to go on longer road trips, amounting to say 200 miles a week and using nearly 7 gallons.) The effect Jevons predicted (also known as the "rebound effect") can dampen or override the decrease in resource use and even *increase* the rate at which resources are consumed, unless the rise can be obviated by other means. (A related example of paradoxical effects of increased efficiency can be found in Leopold Kohr's well-known essay on the speed of populations.[23] Kohr showed that the ability and desire to go faster requires more freeways, more straight and wide roads requiring more land use, etc., which encourages more and more people to drive on them with ever-increasing expectations of shorter times to get from A to B. Eventually traffic jams and bottlenecks choke traffic flow, thereby decreasing the efficiency and speed of travel at great cost to the economy and environment.)

Second, all technologies require energy and material inputs, potentially produce pollution, and can carry substantial safety or health risks. These *should* be taken into account in a total ecological budget and risk-benefit analysis but are often neglected. In the fossil-fuel sector, for example, the energy return over energy invested (EROEI) for oil has become less favorable as easily extracted oil has given way to harder-to-extract "unconventional" sources such as tar sands or the fracking of shale gas and oil. Eventually, the *net* energy becomes negative for some sources, i.e., it takes more energy to provide a given energy source (if the costs of extraction, refining, production, transport, clean-up etc. are counted) than the energy yield of the final product.[24] However, in practice, if the costs of extraction and production and profit from the final product accrue to different entities, if inertia hampers the decision-making process, or if policy interests focus only on short-term gains, then production tends to continue well after the point where more energy is invested than gained.[25]

The promise of technological "solutions" has also been held out as a way to clean up ecological damage already caused or anticipated, particularly in the area of greenhouse gas (GHG) emissions. All such approaches involve not only energy inputs but also pollution impacts of their own, some of them of unknown severity. For example, "unconventional" fossil fuels, such as fracked gas and oil or tar sands, which have been promoted as "bridging"

---

[23] Leopold Kohr, "The Velocity of Populations," *Land Economics* 34 (1958): 178-81.

[24] Shaun Chamberlin, *The Transition Timeline: For a Local, Resilient Future* (Totnes, Devon, UK: Green Books, 2009), 122, based on data of Nathan Hagens and Kenneth Mulder (www.theoildrum.com).

[25] Chamberlin, *Transition Timeline*, 122-3.

energy sources until "clean energy" becomes sufficiently widespread and cheap, carry substantial pollution risks during both extraction and burning, and still cause substantial increases in GHGs, particularly from methane emissions, which has much larger warming effects over the short term than does carbon dioxide.[26]

As climate disruption has gathered pace, carbon capture and storage (CCS) has been proposed to deal with rapidly increasing GHG levels, either by capturing carbon from fossil fuel and related sources, or by preferentially burning biomass rather than fossil fuels and capturing and storing the resultant carbon. As noted in Chapter 1, the UN's Intergovernmental Panel on Climate Change (IPCC) report of 2014 warned that active carbon-removal strategies may now be needed to meet climate goals, which require global carbon emission reductions of 40%–60% by 2050.[27] James Hansen and colleagues have also concluded that carbon removal will now be required, given the current rate of GHG emissions.[28] However, despite promising small-scale experiments with carbon capture and much exaggerated or misleading media coverage,[29] questions of scalability, how and where to store the carbon captured, and the possibly prohibitively high energy and cost inputs to operate carbon capture and storage plants have yet to be addressed.[30]

[26] The numerous analyses of the costs and benefits and risks of fracking and other unconventional fuels are beyond the scope of this discussion; however, given the need to radically and urgently reduce GHG emissions, these fuels are adding to, not solving the climate crisis. Nor do I discuss of the costs and benefits of nuclear energy here. Nevertheless, the failure to invest heavily in clean energy and alternatives to our current ways of generating and using energy, combined with the multigenerational risks that nuclear plants and waste carry mean that, in my view, nuclear energy represents a technology that could have and should have been avoided.

[27] UNIPCC Fifth Assessment Report (AR5) Synthesis. Summary for Policymakers (Geneva, November 2, 2014), 21, http://www.ipcc.ch/pdf/assessment-report/ar5/syr/AR5_SYR_FINAL_SPM.pdf.

[28] James Hansen et al., "Young People's Burden: Requirement of Negative Carbon Emissions," Earth System Dynamics 8 (2016), 577-616, http://doi.org/10.5194/esd-8-577-2017.

[29] See, for example, David Roberts, "Sucking Carbon Directly Out of the Air Won't Solve the Climate Crisis," Vox, July 16, 2018, https://www.vox.com/energy-and-environment/2018/6/14/17445622/direct-air-capture-air-to-fuels-carbon-dioxide-engineering.

[30] James Hansen, "Get Out of Jail Free Card: Carbon Capture," June 12, 2018, http://www.columbia.edu/~jeh1/mailings/2018/20180612_CarbonCapture.pdf. Hansen and colleagues cast serious doubts on whether CCS can significantly reduce GHG levels both because of unproven technological feasibility and also prohibitive costs, and conclude it should not be viewed as a way to avoid reducing GHG emissions at source.

In addition, the idea of using large-scale geoengineering approaches to mitigate climate disruption has gained momentum.[31] Gwynne Dyer, for example, has argued that the climate crisis is too urgent to rely on emission reductions. He advocates including major geoengineering interventions in "short-term" interventions to bring down temperatures while we continue attempts to reduce carbon emissions. Such solutions include seeding clouds with chemical agents to increase rainfall or increasing the amount of solar energy reflected back from the earth into space (known as "albedo enhancement") by stratospheric injections of sulfur[32] or other aerosols. Such interventions are not only unproven at the scale that would be required to hold temperatures to within survivable limits but also could be extraordinarily risky to parts of the natural world, prohibitively expensive, require large amounts of energy to produce or deploy, or cause other consequences such as resource wars. (For example, seeding the atmosphere with stratospheric aerosols could decrease rainfall and increase the risk of drought and food shortages in tropical parts of the world, thereby increasing the risk of conflict.[33])

The apparent promise of geoengineering has been heavily criticized, and not only on technical grounds of feasibility, cost, or effectiveness. For example, Vandana Shiva, a scientist, author, and long-term ecological activist, argues that the geoengineering approach is symptomatic of the same thinking that got us into the ecological predicament—it is a "one-dimensional," short-term way of thinking that ignores ecological complexity, assumes that we can control nature, and effectively wages "war on a planetary scale" from places of power, instead of focusing on ecological resilience and damage prevention.[34] Al Gore has described geoengineering as applied to the climate crisis as "insane, utterly mad," pointing out that "the hubris involved in thinking we can come up with a second planet-wide experiment that would exactly counteract the first experiment is delusional in the extreme."[35]

---

[31] See, for example, Gwynne Dyer, *Climate Wars: The Fight for Survival as the World Overheats* (London: Oneworld Publications, 2008, 2011).

[32] P.J. Crutzen, "Albedo Enhancement by Stratospheric Sulfur Injections: A Contribution to Resolve a Policy Dilemma?" *Climatic Change* 77 (2006), 211-9, https://doi.org/10.1007/s10584-006-9101-y.

[33] Augusto Ferraro, Eleanor Highwood, and Andrew Charlton-Perez, "Weakened Tropical Circulation and Reduced Precipitation in Response to Geoengineering," *Environmental Science Letters* 9 (2014) 014001 (7 pp), http://doi:10.1088/1748-9326/9/1/014001.

[34] Interview with Vandana Shiva and Gwynne Dyer, *Democracy Now!* July 8, 2010.

[35] Al Gore, quoted in John Queally, "Geoengineering Global Cooling: 'Insane, Utterly Mad and Delusional,'" *Common Dreams*, January 16, 2014, http://www.commondreams.org/headline/2014/01/16.

The Economic Fix: Having Our Cake and Eating It?

Let's now turn to the problem of affluence and overconsumption, in terms of its twin impacts on the depletion of nonrenewable parts of the wider natural world and the ecological damage resulting from pollution. The impacts of our ecological footprints have been addressed by two main approaches. One is the idea that we can have "sustainable economic growth" and "sustainable development," without changing the underlying economic paradigms that have helped drive the ecological crisis, and the other is the idea that by putting a price on nature—the monetary damage caused by human activity and the "value" of "ecosystem services" provided by nature—we can bring these into the realm of the market economy, to cost them, to tax them, or to buy and sell them, and thereby encourage the transition toward using less damaging goods and services.

First, I will examine what different organizations and economists have meant by the term "sustainable" growth or development and whether it is either possible or desirable, and if so, under what conditions. I will also examine what is driving economic growth and the consumption that goes with it, and what the consequences of the growth paradigm have been.

The "Sustainable Growth and Development" Problem

In richer countries, the assumption—and aim—appears to be, *In what ways can we maintain economic growth and our current overall levels of consumption despite diminishing resources and increasing pollution?* In other words, can we "decouple" economic growth from ecological limits? In poorer countries, the economic assumption is, supposedly, *How can we reach the level of material development already achieved by richer countries?* How can development be decoupled from ecological limits? Rather than questioning the paradigm of growth *per se*, the concept of "sustainable" growth and development has, over the past 40 or so years, become the dominant narrative. It raises a multitude of thorny ethical and practical questions: What is "sustainable" for humans, other forms of life, and the earth? Can we (and should we) in the richer countries attempt to maintain our current level of consumption and our lifestyles by cleverer technologies and greater efficiencies, rather than significant absolute reductions in our levels of consumption? Can poorer countries and "emerging economies" reach types of development similar to those historically enjoyed by richer countries (and do they all want to) while avoiding global ecological and economic collapse? And what would be "equitable" development, on a global basis, given that the richer industrialized countries have dominated the use and exploitation of the wider natural world for the past several hundred years and are responsible for the lion's share of ecological destruction? What in fact constitutes human needs and what constitutes "limitations" on our relative needs and wants, and how can they be more equitably distributed? What about the vast and increasing disparities in wealth and thus consumption within countries as well as between them? And what about the rights of other species to live, even if they are not useful to humans as "resources" or "eco-system services" (bearing in mind, as scientific studies of the complexity of ecological webs have shown, that it is not clear which species and parts of the wider natural world are intimately bound up with providing our "resources" and which are not)? In sum, is the very idea of "sustainable" development and growth, as currently conceived, either possible or desirable, or is it actually contributing to the ecological destruction that will sooner or later prevent the continuation of sustainable life for poor and rich alike?

Over the past 30 to 40 years, "sustainable growth" and "sustainable development" have become common terms, yet they are defined in various ways, leading to diverse interpretations. A commonly used definition was that developed by the United Nations' World Commission on Environment and Development, which after more than 20 years of input produced a landmark report, *Our Common Future* (commonly known as the Brundtland report), in 1987. The report defined sustainable development as "development that meets the needs of the present without compromising the ability of future generations to meet their own needs," and it enshrined two key concepts:

> the concept of **needs**, in particular the essential needs of the world's poor, to which overriding priority should be given; and
>
> the idea of **limitations** imposed by the state of technology and social organization on the environment's ability to meet present and future needs.[36]

The authors, while acknowledging the multiple challenges of population growth, world poverty, conflict, and ecological degradation, nevertheless boldly asserted that "we see the possibility for a new era of *economic growth* [my emphasis], one that must be based on policies that sustain and expand the environmental resource base...to relieve the great poverty that is deepening in much of the developing world."[37] They continued, "Technology and social

---

[36] United Nations World Commission on Environment and Development (UNWCED, Chair, Gro Harlem Brundtland), *Our Common Future*, General Assembly Report A/42/427 (Geneva: United Nations, 1987), 24-5. http://www.un-documents.net/our-common-future.pdf.

[37] UNWCED, *Our Common Future*, 18.

management can be both managed and improved to make way for a new era of *economic growth* [my emphasis]."[38] Although the authors fully recognized the (then-current) level of demands on the environment by the (then) global population, they were optimistic that a combination of technological innovation and increased efficiency would continue to permit reductions in energy and material use for a given level of output, allowing for "sustainable development" to proceed. They paid comparatively little attention to the idea of reducing levels of consumption in richer countries, other than a brief review of pricing incentives to switch to more efficient technologies or renewable energy sources. Instead, a strong emphasis was put on reducing population growth in "developing" countries, via women's education and government contraceptive policies, for example. They also paid little attention to the wider natural world except as resources for human needs and sinks for our waste.

Subsequent to the Brundtland report, the UN Development Programme produced a series of 17 "sustainable development goals" that aimed to "end poverty, protect the planet and ensure that all people enjoy peace and prosperity."[39] In 1992, the U.N. held a conference in Rio de Janeiro on "the Environment and Development," also known as the Earth Summit, from which a Declaration on Environment and Development was adopted by 178 member states, comprising a set of 27 principles known as the Rio principles. In addition, an action plan, "Agenda 21," emerged to voluntarily guide member states' and other international agencies' actions on sustainable development.[40] These principles enshrine the goal that all human beings have the right to "a healthy and productive life in harmony with the natural world," and that States should work together to:

> protect and restore the health and integrity of the Earth's ecosystems…and reduce and eliminate unsustainable patterns of production and consumption, and promote appropriate demographic policies.[41]

---

[38] UNWCED, *Our Common Future*, 24.

[39] United Nations Development Programme, Sustainable Development Goals, http://www.undp.org/content/undp/en/home/sustainable-development-goals.html.

[40] United Nations Conference on Environment and Development, Rio de Janeiro, July 3-14, 1992: *Agenda 21*, https://sustainabledevelopment.un.org/content/documents/Agenda21.pdf.

[41] United Nations Department of Information, *Earth Summit: Agenda 21, The United Nations Program of Action from Rio*, UN Publication No. E93.111, December 1994, 9-10. https://www.dataplan.info/img_upload/7bdb1584e3b8a53d337518d988763f8d/agenda21-earth-summit-the-united-nations-programme-of-action-from-rio_1.pdf.

However, while significant progress has been reported on implementation of some of the Agenda 21 goals, including the creation of several international legal instruments and commissions,[42] it has been difficult for many member states to come close to achieving the goals based on the Rio principles in the 20 years since the summit. A comprehensive analysis of progress commissioned for the UN Division for Sustainable Development in 2012[43] reported wide variation and limited overall progress on most of the goals and, tellingly, on three of the principles—changing consumption patterns, promoting human settlement development, and protecting the atmosphere—reported either no progress or negative progress. As described in Chapter 1, the fact that the world's ecological footprint has increased by more than one-third since the Rio summit, and that the U.S. still consumes an average of 90 kg of resources per day compared with 45 kg for Europeans and only 10 kg for people in Africa,[44] speaks to little or no progress on sustainable consumption and production or their equitable distribution, with continued overconsumption in some parts of the world and deep poverty in others. (The authors also point out that despite an estimated 30% increase in efficiency in the use of resources, we are using 50% more than we did 20 years ago.) Also telling is the absence of principles addressing the fundamental structures of the global economy, globalization, and trade and the repeated but failed attempts by other UN bodies to bring the question of sustainable development into transnational corporation negotiations or the World Trade Organization's deliberations.[45]

What's Wrong with Economic Growth?

What is most noticeable on re-examining the Brundtland report some 30 years later is the extent to which the global community has failed to come to grips with the multiple problems the authors identified. Brundtland identified the two key issues that need to be addressed—*needs* and *limitations*—yet con-

---

[42] These include the UN's Framework Convention on Climate Change, the Forestry Principles, the Convention on Biological Diversity, the Convention to Combat Desertification, and the Straddling Fish Stocks Agreement.

[43] UN Department of Economic and Social Affairs (UNDESA), *Review of Implementation of Agenda 21 and the Rio Principles: Synthesis.* Prepared by the Stakeholder Forum for a Sustainable Future, January 2012, https://sustainabledevelopment.un.org/content/documents/641Synthesis_report_Web.pdf.

[44] UNDESA, *Review of Agenda 21*, 7.

[45] UNDESA, *Review of Agenda 21*, 8.

cluded that economic growth was possible and desirable to allow development without clearly advocating a reduction in growth in the most affluent
countries. The world has continued to pursue economic growth in both rich
and poor countries, with little or no regard for ecological limits, few attempts
to address vast inequalities between and across countries, and minimal effort
put toward how to ensure that people's needs are met while overconsumption
is curbed. Arguments continue about whether the solutions recommended
were unrealistic, either because of technological limitations and unrealistic
notions that overall economic growth can coexist with long-term ecological
sustainability or because of government or social inertia.

What's wrong with this picture? Even at the time of the Brundtland report, environmental economists such as Herman Daly were pointing out that
the Commission's optimistic recommendation to expand the world economy
by a factor of five to ten was *ecologically impossible*—even four times would be
too much—and that such attempts would "move us from unsustainability to
imminent collapse."[46] Yet the International Monetary Fund happily celebrat-
ed forecasts of 3.6% and 3.7% global economic growth in 2017–8, "an acceleration from the 3.2% recorded in 2016," an upturn "heralded by many policy
makers and economists,"[47] as if we were still living on an infinite planet.

In addition, most corporate and government policies recommended or
deployed to date have not advocated significant reductions in either economic
growth or material consumption on the part of richer countries, or noneconomic means of reducing environmental impacts. Some economists and
energy corporations have also justified current approaches, such as the continued use of fossil fuels in poorer countries, on the grounds that development would be impossible without them, and that "keeping fossil fuels in the
ground" amounts to denying such countries the means to lift themselves out
of poverty. While energy and other materials are clearly essential requirements
for development and the reduction of absolute levels of poverty, organizations such as the World Bank[48] are beginning to recognize, first, that the

---

[46] Herman Daly, "Sustainable Growth: An Impossibility Theorem," in *Valuing the Earth:
Economics, Ecology, Ethics,* eds. Herman Daly and Kenneth Townsend (Cambridge, MA:
MIT Press, 1993), 269.

[47] Josh Zumbrum, "IMF Raises Global Economic Outlook for This Year and 2018," *Wall
Street Journal,* October 10, 2017, https://www.wsj.com/articles/imf-raises-global-
economic-outlook-for-this-year-and-2018-1507640400.

[48] Stephane Hallegatte et al., *Shock Waves: Managing the Impacts of Climate Change on Poverty,*
World Bank Climate Change and Development Series (Washington: World Bank, 2016),
http://www.doi.org/10.1596/978-1-4648-0673-5.

impacts of climate change and ecological devastation now far outweigh any short-term benefits of economic growth based on nonrenewables and fossil fuels, especially in poorer countries; and second, that development must increasingly be envisaged in terms of renewable energy and more reliance on local energy production and related strategies.

In sum, *economic growth, as Meadows' models have shown and many economists have concluded, cannot continue as before and cannot be "decoupled" from either the limits imposed by the consumption of nonrenewable resources or those imposed by now widespread global ecological destruction.*[49] As Herman Daly wrote two decades ago:

> The term 'sustainable development' makes sense for the economy, but only if it is understood as 'development without growth'—i.e., qualitative improvement of a physical economic base that is maintained in a steady state by a throughput of matter-energy that is within the regenerative and assimilative capacities of the ecosystem…. To delude ourselves [that] growth is still possible and desirable if only we label it 'sustainable' or color it 'green' will just delay the inevitable transition and make it more painful.[50]

Next, let's examine what is driving the economic growth paradigm, and the assumption that growth as we have known it is desirable and a net good, by examining the experience of richer countries, where average consumption is high and economic growth has continued apace.

What's Driving Growth?

The paradigm of economic growth, based predominantly but not exclusively on a capitalist economic model of private ownership and profit, has dominated the macroeconomic systems of Western countries for the past century. It has spread, through the globalization of trade, to many parts of the world, and, despite the increasingly obvious physical limits to growth and the extent of ecological destruction described in Chapter 1, there are few signs that this paradigm has been challenged at the macroeconomic level. International bodies such as the International Monetary Fund, World Bank, and Organisation for Economic Cooperation and Development still call for economic growth and development; and a country's increasing Gross Domestic Product (GDP) is still a standard measure of economic growth, considered by many to be synonymous with progress and future economic stability.

---

[49] See, for example, Daly, "Sustainable Growth," 267-73; Meadows, Randers, and Meadows, *Limits to Growth: The 30-Year Update*, 240; and Naomi Klein, *This Changes Everything: Capitalism vs. the Climate* (New York: Simon and Schuster, 2014), 86-9.

[50] Daly, "Sustainable Growth," 268.

Herman Daly has pointed out that economic growth, as pursued by both capitalist and socialist economies, is "an aberration." Human societies have spent 99% of their histories in a steady-state according to Daly; economic growth has existed for only the last two centuries, and as a primary goal only since the 1920s.[51] However, conventional economic thinking, particularly in capitalist economies, has assumed until recently that continued economic growth is not only a necessity but also a marker of social progress, i.e., a net good, and is sustainable into the indefinite future.

Classical economic theories of market-based capitalism focus on a self-contained, circular model of the production and sale of goods and services and their purchase by consumers, together with the circular exchange of labor and wages, profits, and capital. This system (along with macroeconomic mechanisms such as the maintenance or manipulation of the money supply) is required to maintain growth. It largely ignores, as we will discuss below, not only the limits of the earth but also so-called externalities—including ecological impacts—as well as "noneconomic" aspects of our lives, those nonquantifiable or noncommodifiable aspects of quality of life, from voluntary work to aesthetic, cultural, and spiritual needs. Most industrialized and economically mature societies have become dependent on economic growth, and, over the past 70 or so years, on increasingly globalized trade. At a macroeconomic level, growth is maintained or increased by governmental fiscal mechanisms and by financial and banking practices that maintain or increase the supply of money in the system, and permit banks to lend money while maintaining only a small reserve themselves. Once economic systems have become dependent on growth to fuel the economy, they are driven by a need to increase consumption. It becomes increasingly difficult to break the cycle without causing economic crashes, mass unemployment, and large-scale disruption of goods and services, at least in the short term.

Is More, Bigger, Faster, and Newer, Better?

The irony of arguments about whether we can all have economic growth and development lies in the largely unquestioned assumptions that economic growth is a good (if only we could increase the efficiency of our resource use and fix our pollution problems with technology) and implies that the material accumulation of goods and services is more important than cultural, spiritual,

---

[51] Herman Daly, "The Steady-State Economy: Toward a Political Economy of Biophysical Equilibrium and Moral Growth," in *Valuing the Earth: Economics, Ecology, Ethics*, eds. Herman Daly and Kenneth Townsend (Cambridge, MA: MIT Press, 1993), 331.

or moral considerations. In other words, both mainstream economics and society as a whole in richer countries have largely operated on the assumption that more is better, bigger is better, faster and newer are better, and that people in other countries by and large want what we have. Underlying the above assumptions is a more profound question: *What is the purpose of greater wealth, or the greater accumulation of goods? And who and what are benefiting from, or paying the price for, economic growth?*

Inasmuch as growth depends on the continuous, expanding consumption of goods and services, what drives this cycle of consumption? A simplistic model of the "market" in capitalist economies—where consumers, as "rational actors" with perfect knowledge and choice, generate demand for goods and services and the market supplies them—ignores several ways in which demand is created and perpetuated, as well as the wider social and ecological impacts of the economic system. On the one hand, for most privately owned businesses, the goal is not just to maintain a reasonable profit margin to cover wages and capital investment but also to *maximize* profits, often over the short term, and to maximize returns for owners and investors. Therefore there are incentives to a) maximize demand and consumption and b) minimize costs, whether of material inputs, wages, or ecological costs that cannot be externalized (see below).

In classical economic theory, the concept of "consumer sovereignty" is predicated on the idea that in a (hypothetical) market, the consumer is free to make choices, and the law of supply and demand works to set prices. As everyone who operates in the real world knows, we are all in fact constrained by multiple factors, not least of which is how much *knowledge and choice* consumers have.[52] In addition, economists since the 19th century have realized that demand beyond the level of essentials, such as food, shelter, and clothing, for which demand is inflexible, is subject to "diminishing marginal utility," i.e., satisfaction decreases with each additional unit of a good or service (for example, the first chocolate or new dress or vacation is wonderful, the second good, but the third, fourth, etc. become less and less satisfying and more boring). This incentivizes business to *create* a continuous demand for nonessential products and services, rather than simply respond to demand. Creating demand has become a highly sophisticated science, through advertising and a range of psychological methods of persuasion; by building in obsolescence, as most of us notice particularly in the area of electronic appliances

---

[52] E.J. Mishan, *Growth: The Price We Pay* (London: Staples Publishing, 1969).

and technological gadgets; by creating novelty and fashions, from food fads to clothing to automobiles and wearable exercise monitors; and by convincing us that *convenience*, like the idea of more, bigger, newer, and faster is better, is always highly desirable. In fact, we are paying a very heavy social and ecological price for convenience, speed, and our throw-away lifestyles, but in ways that we are distanced from or encouraged to ignore or justify.[53]

Many of these psychological tricks play on our susceptibility to a sense of *competition, comparisons,* and *expectations.* For example, Barry Schwarz describes numerous studies that suggest that when faced with multiple choices, we *cannot* choose, because none of the choices seems perfect or we feel that a particular good or experience isn't what we expected while another might have been.[54] Many of us are also highly susceptible to competition and comparisons, whether it's whether we might have paid too much for an item to what our friends or someone on our social media seems to be buying or experiencing and getting great pleasure from. Critically, comparisons and expectations also play a wider societal role. As the authors of *The Spirit Level* argue, people in very unequal societies often experience a greater sense of dissatisfaction and unhappiness than those in more equal societies, even at comparable levels of overall (i.e., population-level) consumption,[55] suggesting that people are disturbed as much by where they fit on the "ladder" of consumption as by their absolute level of material consumption. Further, in many cases, people who live in highly unequal societies are disturbed by the social injustice that is evident around them.

Thus it turns out that "more, bigger, faster, newer" is not necessarily better due to factors from too many choices, diminishing utility, comparisons, and expectations to economic inequalities. These factors can encourage a reinforcing cycle: We consume more but get less and less satisfaction out if it. Yet we are as much driven or persuaded that consuming more will increase

---

[53] Many of these social and ecological costs are incurred at a distance, for example by people, often in a distant countries, where child and sweatshop labor are normal, where our mountains of discarded electronic waste accumulate or our plastic containers wash ashore, or where wildlife is decimated to make way for plantations. Closer to home, we are now beginning to make the connections between, for example, the convenience of ordering goods and services online and buying too much stuff, while facing lost full-time jobs, empty stores on Main Streets and High Streets, and the growth of monopolistic companies and the "gig" economy.

[54] Barry Schwarz, *The Paradox of Choice: Why More is Less* (New York: Harper Perennial, 2005).

[55] Richard Wilkinson and Kate Pickett, *The Spirit Level: Why Greater Equality Makes Societies Stronger* (London: Bloomsbury Press, 2010).

our satisfaction as we are actively driving our own consumption. At the same time, particularly in rich countries like the U.S., we are encouraged to see consumption and economic growth as the primary measure of success and happiness, while ignoring larger issues such as vast inequalities, our cultural and spiritual needs, and the ecological costs of overconsumption. So we need to inquire, on a countrywide level, whether economic growth does in fact increase our subjective sense of wellbeing and happiness, and if so, at what level? And what other factors are important?

Is Economic Growth Making Us Happier?

The seminal works on happiness and economic growth by Richard Layard, an economist at the London School of Economics,[56] and Peter Victor, a prominent Canadian ecological economist,[57] strongly suggest that, after a certain level of individual income (or at a national level, GDP), the broad answer is "no."[58] For example, data from U.S. surveys suggest that there has been little or no increase in people reporting that they were "very happy" in the U.S. over the 50 years since World War II, despite a doubling of real GDP per capita over the same period (see Figure 2-3, overleaf). According to data reviewed by Victor, this pattern is broadly similar across a range of countries.[59] While such measures of wellbeing and happiness are somewhat crude, Layard's and others' work provides an example of limits; inasmuch as self-reported happiness is not strongly linked to increases in GDP, the assumption that "more growth is better" can be challenged.

---

[56] Richard Layard, "Has Social Science a Clue?: What Is Happiness? Are We Getting Happier?" Lionel Robbins Lecture Series, London, March 3-5, 2003, http://eprints.lse.ac.uk/47425/; Richard Layard, *Happiness: Lessons from a New Science* (London: Allen Lane, 2005).

[57] Peter Victor, *Managing Without Growth: Slower by Design, Not Disaster* (Cheltenham, UK: Edward Elgar Publishing, 2008), 124-6.

[58] The assumption that more goods, wealth or economic status will bring more happiness, pleasure, and satisfaction, or that the power and control that they (supposedly) confer will bring greater security, or peace of mind, has of course been challenged over the centuries from theological, sociological, psychological and (unorthodox) economic viewpoints. For example, Gerald Smith quotes from the writings of the early 20th-century economist Richard Tawney, who cautioned that capitalism and industrialization should not be idolized, and that economic activity, productivity, and wealth should be subordinated to a social purpose. If riches and power became the "master not the servant," Tawney warned, we would increasingly witness the ascendancy of greed, power, self-aggrandizement, and waste, and argued, even then, for a "principle of limitation." [Gerald Alonso Smith, "The Purpose of Wealth," in *Valuing the Earth: Economics, Ecology, Ethics*, eds. Herman Daly and Kenneth Townsend, (Cambridge, MA: MIT Press, 1993), 183-209.]

[59] Victor, *Managing Without Growth*, 126-7.

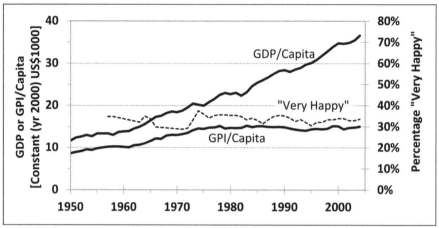

Figure 2-3. Per-capita real Gross Domestic Product (GDP), Genuine Progress Indicator (GPI), and percent of people reporting that they were "very happy," U.S., 1950–2014. GDP and GPI data from Redefining Progress, 2007[60]; happiness data from Smith (1979) and the National Opinion Research Center.[61] Based on graphs in Victor, 126, 129.

One reason for this lack of correlation is the fact that GDP and indeed economic measures as a whole fail to account for the negative costs of growth and the many other factors that determine wellbeing or happiness or the health of the planet.[62] If other indices are used, such as the Genuine Progress Indicator (GPI),[63] which factors in social (e.g., welfare, education, crime) and ecological costs and benefits (e.g., pollution, carbon and ecological footprints, loss of arable and wetlands), this measure of progress has, like the happiness data described above, increasingly diverged from GDP over the past 50 or more years and flatlined over that period (Figure 2-3). The GPI is

---

[60] John Talberth, Clifford Cobb, and John Slattery, *The Genuine Progress Indicator: Executive Summary.* Redefining Progress, February 2007, http://rprogress.org/publications/2007/GPI2006_ExecSumm.pdf. Data from report reproduced at https://ase.tufts.edu/gdae/CS/GPI.pdf.

[61] Tom W. Smith, "Happiness: Time Trends, Seasonal Variations, Intersurvey Differences and Other Mysteries," *Social Psychology Quarterly* 42 (1979), 18-30, (data from 1945-1971), and National Opinion Research Center, General Social Survey, Final Report, *Trends in Psychological Wellbeing,* 1972-2014 (Chicago: NORC, April 2015), http://www.norc.org/PDFs/GSS%20Reports/GSS_PsyWellBeing15_final_formatted.pdf. (Note: the dashed line on the graph represents a 2-year moving average.)

[62] As many critics have pointed out, GDP also includes on the "plus" side the costs of activities such as cleaning up ecological damage, the aftermath of climate disasters, etc., which are now becoming a burgeoning and increasingly predatory business that Naomi Klein describes as "disaster capitalism" in Naomi Klein, *The Shock Doctrine: The Rise of Disaster Capitalism* (Toronto: Random House, 2007).

[63] Talberth, *Genuine Progress Indicator,* 2007.

now used or being planned for use in several countries and a few U.S. states.[64],[65] Measures such as the GPI also indicate that countries like the U.S. have shifted to a period where the costs of economic growth increasingly outweigh the benefits.[66]

Other data also indicate that income and standard measures of growth become less and less important after a certain basic level of security is reached. Other, noneconomic factors become relatively more important, according to data from the Organisation for Economic Co-operation and Development (OECD)'s Better Life Index,[67] the Social Progress Index,[68] and the UN's *World Happiness Report* for 2018,[69] the latter of which ranks 156 countries according to criteria that include both economic variables and healthy life expectancy, social support, freedom, trust, and generosity. Scandinavian countries (Norway, Finland, Denmark, and Iceland) and Switzerland have consistently been among the top-ranked countries since 2011, the year of the first report, ranking highly on each of the six major variables. However, although the per-capita GDPs of the U.S. and the U.K. are closely comparable to those of the Scandinavian countries, their happiness rankings were much lower, at 18th and 19th, respectively.

Flooring the Accelerator: Deregulation, Wealth and Power, for Some

A distinct shift has occurred in economic policy in the U.S. and other capitalist economies over the past 30 to 40 years, toward more privatization and the deregulation of the financial and business sectors, lower corporate taxation, fewer controls over the movement of industries and business and capital, the use of tax havens, and so on. These measures, along with weaken-

---

[64] Marta Ceroni, "Beyond GDP: US States Have Adopted Genuine Progress Indicators," *The Guardian*, September 23, 2014, https://www.theguardian.com/sustainable-business/2014/sep/23/genuine-progress-indicator-gdp-gpi-vermont-maryland.

[65] Genuine Progress in the States, http://www.gpiinthestates.org/.

[66] Herman Daly, *Beyond Growth: The Economics of Sustainable Development* (Boston: Beacon Press, 1996).

[67] OECD, *How's Life? 2017: Measuring Well-being* (Paris: OECD Publishing, 2017), https://doi.org/10.1787/how_life-2017-en.

[68] Michael Porter and Scott Stern with Michael Green, *Social Progress Index 2017* (Social Progress Imperative, 2017), http://www.socialprogressindex.com/assets/downloads/resources/en/English-2017-Social-Progress-Index-Findings-Report_embargo-d-until-June-21-2017.pdf.

[69] UN Sustainable Development Solutions Network, *World Happiness Report 2018*, eds. John H. Helliwell, Richard Layard, and Jeffrey D. Sachs, http://worldhappiness.report/ed/2018/.

ing of labor and environmental laws, have exacerbated inequality while concentrating power into ever-fewer hands. Naomi Klein, for example, argues that it is this aspect of capitalism—and the power it exerts over the political system—that is largely driving the climate crisis. She writes, "we have not done the things that are necessary to lower emissions because those things conflict with deregulated capitalism, the reigning ideology for the entire period we have been struggling to find a way out of this crisis. …[Actions to avert catastrophe] are extremely threatening to an elite minority that has a stranglehold over our economy, our political process, and most of our major media outlets."[70] Similar characteristics are also a feature of many non-capitalist or centrally-planned economies, and in oligarchies or plutocracies where high levels of corruption and concentrations of power and wealth accrue to a small minority, and act as accelerators (or justifiers, depending on the narrative) of economic growth, while exacerbating its negative impacts on people and nature.

In sum, we can no longer assume that continued economic growth beyond a certain point yields increasing wellbeing and happiness. Instead, it exacts ever-increasing costs, from ecological destruction to the neglect and corruption of cultural, moral, and spiritual needs. First, economic growth works in a reinforcing cycle—whereby short-term profits drive growth, growth drives consumption, consumption drives growth, and employment becomes dependent on growth and consumption—meaning that short-term profits and wealth accumulation too often trump long-term and ecological considerations. Second, if we look at ecological and carbon footprint data, many of us in richer countries and beyond clearly have, either willingly or by persuasion, become virtually addicted to consumption. Precisely because of "diminishing marginal utility," and arguably a corresponding diminishment of the nonmaterial dimensions of our lives, we seek more and more stuff, more and more experiences, and more and more elusive sources of pleasure and meaning. Like alcoholics and drug addicts, where we find the drug works less and less and causes more and more damage to our bodies and spirits, we nevertheless seem to be unable to stop, even as the warning signals become harder and harder to ignore.

Almost 50 years ago, E.F. Schumacher challenged the rationale for economic growth, namely, the idea that "universal prosperity is possible; that its attainment is possible on the basis of the materialist philosophy of 'enrich

---

[70] Klein, *This Changes Everything*, 18.

yourselves'; and that this is the road to peace."[71] The evidence he presented demonstrated than none of these propositions was likely to be fulfilled,[72] and subsequent events have emphatically supported his arguments. Rather, Schumacher believed that the only wise path to economic security and peace was an "economics of permanence."[73] In Parts II and III, we will explore how we might change the paradigm of destructive growth and inequality to a new, nonviolent economics in which needs, not greed, and our unity with the wider natural world, become the order by which we live.

Pricing Nature: Conservation or Commodification?

Much of the natural world—from land, water, air, terrestrial life, seeds, and forests to life-forms in the rivers and oceans—has been treated as exchangeable property or commodities for centuries. We must look largely to remaining indigenous societies or certain religious traditions to find people for whom the answer to the question, "Who should own the earth and all that lives on it?" is "No one."[74] Fewer and fewer areas of the earth's lands, waters, animals, and plants are now economically unclaimed and wild or existing as "commons" for the use of all. Land ownership and the mineral, animal, plant, or riparian "rights" that accompany it, have been a major economic driver of shifts in many agricultural and industrial economies and in land and water use, profoundly affecting the course of development of a country or region,[75] the distribution of wealth and capital, and, when extended to colonial and postcolonial ownership, the global economy.

---

[71] E.F. Schumacher, *Small is Beautiful: Economics as if People Mattered* (New York: Harper and Row, 1975), 22.

[72] For example, Schumacher estimated, based on observed rates of increasing per-capita consumption of fossil fuels in rich and poor countries and their respective population increases over 30 years, that they would become vastly more scarce and costly long before the world's poor could afford them or gain enough capital to spur the large-scale development of "alternative" fuels.

[73] Schumacher, *Small is Beautiful*, 30.

[74] Among the indigenous peoples of Australia, the Americas, and other regions, the idea of ownership of the land and all that grows and moves on it was a foreign concept—the land, waters, air, and life were a sacred commons for all to use as a gift from the Source or Spirit.

[75] For example, a series of parliamentary Enclosures Acts in England, particularly in the 18th and early 19th centuries, legalized ownership and consolidation of parcels of roughly a quarter of the total agricultural land traditionally used for common purposes such as livestock grazing or hay gathering, and helped to drive increasing numbers of rural dwellers to cities to become poorly paid workers in the new Industrial Revolution.

In Garrett Harding's well-known but controversial essay, "The Tragedy of the Commons"[76] (based on the original idea by economist William Forster Lloyd), he posited that common resources—any resource to which access is unrestricted—are always at risk of ruinous exploitation if every user, acting in their "rational" self-interest, maximizes their individual use of that commons, such as overgrazing a village green (or in one of Harding's more controversial examples, having as many children as desired). His argument has been used to support the idea of private ownership, despite abundant evidence that privatization hasn't prevented ecological exploitation and degradation of the commons, or unequal control and distribution of resources, but rather the opposite. If anything, the tragedy is not of the commons, but of the unrestrained exploitation of private ownership. Elinor Ostrom[77] and others, in studies of the ways in which various communities voluntarily share their common land and resources, have pointed out that social and moral constraints and communal responsibility act to prevent the overuse of "commons" by one or a few people or a dominant group, especially where the community is cohesive enough to both recognize and honor its human members and its mutual dependency on the commons in question. In addition, natural commons, including the atmosphere and open oceans, obviously cannot be parceled out and claimed either by individual governments or by private owners, and thus must be dealt with by international agreements and treaties, which have been notably difficult to achieve and monitor.[78]

If the claims of private ownership of land, minerals, forests, and economically useful life-forms have led to the overuse and exploitation of what become "resources" for human use, and thus part of the economy, what can constrain this overuse and the ecological destruction that ensues? Rather than moral restraint based on environmental and spiritually grounded ethics, which may be enshrined in the kind of voluntary constraints pointed out by Ostrom

---

[76] Garrett Harding, "The Tragedy of the Commons," *Science* 162 (1968): 1243-8, https://doi.org/10.1126/science.162.3859.1243.

[77] Elinor Ostrom, *Governing the Commons: The Evolution of Institutions for Collective Action* (Cambridge, UK: Cambridge University Press, 1990).

[78] The difficulties of regulating the global commons can be illustrated by efforts to regulate territorial waters, global marine seabed rights, and fishing rights by the UN, starting in 1956 and culminating, after a series of conferences and treaties and 10 years of negotiations, in the Convention on the Law of the Sea (1982) and the establishment of the International Seabed Authority. The treaty met with considerable resistance from industrialized nations, despite widespread support for the goals. See Arthur Westing, *Global Resources and International Conflict: Environmental Factors in Strategic Policy and Action* (Oxford, UK: Oxford University Press, 1986), 189.

and others, or a regulatory approach supported by public agreement, one approach among economists focuses on pricing the costs of ecological destruction on the one hand and the pricing of nature's "services" on the other. Both approaches, as we will see, involve a central dilemma. According to our conventional economic and technological thinking, what isn't quantifiable or monetized is often ignored, invisible, or considered not valuable. Yet attempts to price nature, whether damage or so-called ecosystem services, continue to regard nature as a collection of tradable objects subject to the vagaries of pricing, commodity pricing, and the short-term requirements of the market, in contrast to the deep ecology and economy perspectives that we will explore in Parts II and III.

Pricing Ecological Destruction

Unless the costs of ecological damage are included in the costs of production and use of goods and services, they are considered as economic *externalities,* a concept introduced in the 1960s. Externalities include damage to human health and damage to the "commons," including the atmosphere, nonterritorial oceans, rivers, public lands, wildlife, and future generations as well as costs to private property, goods, or services. In theory, if externalities can be costed and included (internalized) in the price of a good or service, the higher market prices of highly polluting goods and services will result in lower consumption and use and an increased drive to greater efficiency or "greener" products and services. Externalities can be embedded in prices via taxes, by businesses passing on the costs of regulations, or by producers passing on additional costs associated with voluntarily producing less-damaging products or services. In variants of direct pricing, quotas can be set and traded, as for carbon or other pollutants, or "offsets" can be bought and traded for sustainable projects elsewhere that theoretically offset the pollution damage. The latter idea has become an increasingly accepted method of reducing environmental damage and excessive use of polluting or scarce resources via a tradable market or pricing mechanism.

Market-based mechanisms such as "cap-and-trade" theoretically allow overall caps to be placed on sources of pollutants and trading of quotas within those caps. For example, the emissions trading scheme (ETS) for certain GHGs was introduced in the European Union starting in 2005 as part of its implementation of the Kyoto protocol (see Chapter 1). A fierce debate has ensued as to whether the cap-and-trade system, and the EU's ETS system in particular, can work in principle or practice. A number of analyses have concluded that the ETS has largely failed, based on clear evidence from various analyses that it has done very little to curb carbon emissions, even after considerable modifications designed to price emissions and set caps more stringently as it has become clear that global warming continues to accelerate.[79]

Carbon offsetting has also been used by businesses and consumers in the form of, for example, a small fee added to the price of a plane ticket, with the money theoretically going to e.g., ecological conservation schemes such as forestation. These schemes have been heavily criticized as being effectively a permit to pollute, as they are notoriously difficult to monitor effectively and thus easy to scam, while encouraging polluting activities to continue with the claim that compensatory actions are being taken elsewhere and in a time frame that adequately neutralizes the initial carbon emissions. For example, Erin Deranger, a founder and executive director of the group Indigenous Climate Action and a member of the Athabaskan Chippewa First Nation, described in a 2018 interview how the Yukon Nation had recently signed an agreement to allow corporations to buy the carbon sequestration potential of their indigenous territory. In Deranger's view,[80] this commodifies ancient lands and forests that were "always there" and part of nature, effectively allowing corporations to buy a permit to continue to pollute (and presumably cedes control of the land or forest from the indigenous people to the corporation).

Economists and activists who critique such pricing, taxing, and trading systems are concerned that they will lead to increasing commodification of natural systems, and that the trading of polluting permits, or even the potentially regressive effects of taxes on pollution, add to the inequitable burden of such costs on poorer people and countries unless specific policies are introduced to prevent them. In addition, to be effective, many actions to curb

[79] Ben Schiller, "Europe's CO_2 Trading Scheme: Is It Time for a Major Overhaul? *Yale Environment 360*, April 26, 2011, https://e360.yale.edu/features/europes_co2_trading_scheme_is_it_time_for_a_major_overhaul; Adela Putinelu, "Are Carbon Markets an Effective Way to Address Climate Change? *Climate Home News*, October 16, 2012, http://www.climatechangenews.com/2012/10/16/does-emissions-trading-really-work/; Frederic Branger, Oskar Lecuyer, and Phillippe Quiron, "The European Emissions Trading Scheme: Should We Throw the Flagship Out with the Bathwater?" *WIREs Climate Change* 6 (2015), 9-16, https://doi.org/10.1002/wcc.326.

[80] Erin Deranger, in an interview with Amy Goodman on *Democracy Now!*, September 14, 2018, https://www.democracynow.org/2018/9/14/effective_tool_to_limit_greenhouse_emissions.

pollution that crosses borders, such as greenhouse gases, can be done only within international agreements, cooperation, and comparable regulations, to discourage corporations from moving production to countries or regions with less-stringent pollution controls or from profiteering and "gaming" the system—a part of the "race to the bottom" of transnational businesses seeking to minimize the costs of production and labor in countries with weak or corrupt governance. One of the key questions is whether market-based systems, such as tradable energy quotas, carbon taxes, or revenue-neutral fee-and-dividend mechanisms, as recently suggested by Hansen and others for carbon,[81] can effectively reduce consumption and pollution without stronger regulation, reductions in source emissions, and/or the advance of alternative ways of living, together with deeper shifts in our thinking and priorities. The question remains to be answered, given the increasingly drastic steps required even to maintain global warming to 2°C (see Chapter 1). In addition, while a revenue-neutral carbon tax, which has been introduced in British Columbia, for example,[82] appears to be favored by citizens and a number of economists, it raises issues such as to whom or what the resulting revenue would go— whether equally to everyone as a tax cut, or to fund renewable energy, or to offset the disparate impact on poorer people, etc. Many economists are concerned that such taxes will impact economic growth, or claim that we can tax carbon and maintain growth (if such taxes are used to cut corporate tax rates, according to some analyses[83]), but, as described above and explored further in Chapter 9, the business-as-usual assumption that "growth" is imperative has been and must be challenged if we are to have a sustainable future.

The other key question is *Cui bono?* Who benefits, and who pays, and when? Cost-benefit analyses can attempt to put a price on nature, then add up the sum of, say, pollution costs vs. human benefits, but they often omit two vital aspects: First, how those costs and benefits are distributed both now and

---

[81] Bibi van der Zee, "James Hansen Rails Against Cap and Trade Plan in Open Letter," *The Guardian*, January 12 2010, https://www.theguardian.com/environment/2010/jan/12/james-hansen-carbon-emissions.

[82] Leyland Cocco, "How to Make a Carbon Tax Popular? Give the Proceeds to the People," *The Guardian*, December 4, 2018, https://www.theguardian.com/world/2018/dec/04/how-to-make-a-carbon-tax-popular-give-the-profits-to-the-people.

[83] Robert Murphy, "Amplifying Oren Cass's Critique of a Carbon Tax, Part 1," Institute for Energy Research, September 6, 2017, https://www.instituteforenergyresearch.org/uncategorized/amplifying-oren-casss-critique-carbon-tax-part/.

into the future (epitomized by the fact that the poor, people of color, and women bear a disproportionate part of the costs of ecological damage while reaping fewer of the benefits of growth and wealth, and the fact that long-term ecological costs are often ignored in favor of short-term gains), and how to include the intrinsic rights of humans and the wider natural world to live in an unpolluted world, irrespective of economic considerations, such as being forced to choose between employment or a healthy environment or work-place. (These issues will be considered further when exploring the intersec-tion of the ecological and justice movements, and other ways that the inequi-table distribution of costs and benefits has been taken into account, in Chap-ters 6 through 10.)

"Ecosystem Services"—Should We Price the Gift of Life?

The second approach to pricing nature is to put an economic value on its many aspects, variously referred to as "natural capital," (a term coined in the bestselling book by Paul Hawken and Amory and Hunter Lovins in 1999)[84] or "ecosystem services," a term first widely used in the early 2000s by the UN in their Millennium Ecosystems Assessment.[85] These "services," from materi-al and biological resources and the earth's capacity to absorb, neutralize, or transform pollutants and support vital cycles of life to the aesthetic value of nature, are typically considered in four groups: provisioning (food and water), regulating (e.g., maintaining the balance of atmospheric gases, temperature, and elemental cycles, and controlling disease), supporting (e.g., nutrient cy-cles), and cultural (e.g., esthetic and spiritual value).

Proponents of pricing ecosystem services (PES), which include some conservationists as well as economists, argue that it is a way to take into ac-count the hitherto-uncounted value of nature to humans and thereby encour-ages its protection. But there are several serious objections to this approach, not only from some economists who are concerned about the practicalities, but also from others from those concerned with moral, spiritual, or ecojustice viewpoints.[86] First, as I will emphasize further in forthcoming chapters, the

---

[84] Paul Hawken, Amory Lovins, and Hunter Lovins, *Natural Capitalism: The Next Industrial Revolution* (London: Earthscan, 1999).

[85] UN Millennium Ecosystem Assessment. *Ecosystems and Human Well-being: Synthesis.* Washington, DC: Island Press, 2005.
https://www.millenniumassessment.org/documents/document.356.aspx.pdf.

[86] See, for example, Nicolas Kosoy and Esteve Corbera, "Payment for Ecosystem Services as Commodity Fetishism," *Ecological Economics* 69 (2010): 1228-36,
https://doi.org/10.1016/j.ecolecon.2009.11.002; Richard Connif, "What's Wrong with

entirety of nature, indeed the cosmos, is a single, integrated, interdependent whole. It is not possible to separate any one part as having more or less fundamental or inherent value than another. The impossibility—and danger—of trying to place a monetary value on the infinite web of life and the physical systems that support all life and that ensure human survival, or even selected strands of that web, is clear. What price sunlight, oxygen, nitrogen, carbon, hydrogen, and all the elements we need for life? What price the myriad homeostatic cycles and mechanisms, so elegantly described by the Gaia hypothesis, that have allowed the earth to maintain the very narrow conditions necessary to support life as we know it? What price chlorophyll, mitochondria, DNA, phytoplankton, krill, and the other building blocks and foundational life-forms that support all other life? Or the bacteria and fungi that compost dead vegetation, the dung beetles that roll away droppings, the earthworms that enrich our soils, the wild insects that pollinate our flowers and crops, or the rock formations that purify the water we use from our wells?

If we fail to understand that sooner or later, pulling out one strand can cause large parts of the web to collapse, are we not potentially encouraging the view that some parts are valuable, monetizable, and exchangeable while others can be ignored or devalued? And what price can we place on the spiritual and cultural value of nature? Finally, and critically, as I will argue in Part III, what about the deep ecology perspective *that sees all life-forms as fundamentally having the intrinsic, not just instrumental, right to exist,* much as we have theologically, ethically, and formally (such as in the UN Declaration of Human Rights) granted humanity the basic right to live, whether people are economical "productive" or "useful" or not, however imperfectly we honor that right in practice?

Second, the commodification of nature's "services," including as an opportunity to expand, invest in or market "green" products or capitalize on nature's "value," leads precisely to the same problems we already see in the trading of human-produced goods and services: The richest can buy and trade or invest in a range of "ecosystem services" and resources as they do today with minerals, food, land, commodities and so forth, while the poor are less able or unable to do so.[87] Without some form of ethical constraints, how will

---

Putting a Price on Nature?" *Yale Environment 360*, October 18, 2012, https://e360.yale.edu/features/ecosystem_services_whats_wrong_with_putting_a_price_on_nature.

[87] For example, the UK Government established an outside "Ecosystems Market Task Force," whose mandate was to advise government departments on "opportunities for UK

the pricing of "ecosystem services" limit the continued overuse and exploitation of nature? Do these services become subject to the laws of supply and demand, so that they can be dumped, destroyed, monopolized, or inequitably distributed according to the dictates of the market for those services? (For example, carbon offsets arguably enshrine the "rights" to destroy an ecosystem "service" by theoretically "offsetting" or paying for its restoration elsewhere.) And what about the vast inequities we already see in who benefits and who pays for human-produced goods and access? Would they not also apply to the distribution of these "ecosystem services"? And how do economists propose to take into account future generations, whether of humanity or of nature? If we regard almost all of nature as property, as business and financial opportunities, on the order of billions of dollars, aren't we claiming that we can "solve" the ecological crisis with the same thinking and systems that got us into this mess in the first place? As George Monbiot puts it, "Commodification, economic growth, financial abstractions, corporate power: Aren't these the processes driving the world's environmental crisis? Now we are told that to save the biosphere we need more of them."[88] Finally, what happens to our moral, esthetic, and spiritual sense of the earth and all the life-forms and processes we depend on when we commodify more and more of the wider natural world? Do we not risk losing something precious and actually vital to our wellbeing as well as to our physical survival—the very soul of our relationship with the gift of life on Earth, its numinosity and wonder?

The types of population-, technology-, and economics-based interventions attempted or promised thus far generally have not and will not, in their present forms, "solve" our ecological predicament, even if we ignore what they cost culturally, ethically, and spiritually. Clearly, economic and technological interventions and policy changes will be required in whatever approach to

---

business from expanding green goods, services, products, investment vehicles and markets which value and protect ecosystem services." See Ecosystems Market Task Force, *Realising Nature's Value: The Final Report of the Ecosystems Market Task Force* [to the UK Department for Environmental and Rural Affairs], March 2013, https://assets.publishing.service.gov.uk/government/uploads/system/uploads/attachment_data/file/316101/Ecosystem-Markets-Task-Force-Final-Report-.pdf.

[88] George Monbiot, "Putting a Price on the Rivers and Rain Diminishes Us All," *The Guardian*, August 6, 2012, https://www.theguardian.com/commentisfree/2012/aug/06/price-rivers-rain-greatest-privatisation. Monbiot also quotes the UK government task force as talking about "…harnessing City financial expertise to assess the ways that these blended revenue streams and securitizations enhance the ROI [return on investment] of an environmental bond," as an example of the business-as-usual thinking behind the trading of ecosystem services.

our predicament is proposed, but they must involve a radical shift in the business-as-usual paradigms of growth, profit, consumption, globalization, and reliance on end-of-pipeline technological fixes. They must include ethical concerns, including social inequality, the rights of other life-forms, and the moral and spiritual dimensions of our predicament. But even these terms do little to convey something much deeper. What are we for? What do we love? How do we learn to live in interconnection and love with the life that gives us life? Do we think of that wildlife refuge, a wilderness lake or a quiet spot in a city park as a resource to be owned, bought and sold, or as something beyond price, to be protected not because its value is known but precisely because its true worth is incalculable?

In sum, have we, again, been applying the same "solutions" and fixes that have helped bring about our ecological crisis, while ignoring the underlying causes? Have we, in other words, been like drivers rushing toward a cliff edge of ecological devastation, with our feet firmly on the accelerator of economic growth, and merely strapping on seat belts as we go in the hope that they will save us, and instead of stopping to ask where we are going? And have we forgotten to ask what really sustains us?

Economists Peter Brown and Geoffrey Garver have proposed that we need to add another term for ethics (E) to the famous I=PAT equation, so that it becomes I=PAT(E).[89] As I will explore in later chapters, any interventions and approaches to address our impacts on the wider natural world need to be grounded in a deeper understanding of the underlying cultural, moral, and spiritual dimensions of the causes and conditions of our predicament and a re-examination of our very ways of thinking and being in the world—our habitual technological, social, economic, political, and accepted ethical frames. They also call for our ability to translate principles into practical action, i.e., in ways that don't eschew technology, science, economics, or policies but re-frame them. We need new, practical moral and spiritual economics and technology that are grounded in integration, not separation and distancing, and that will require a boldness and vision that matches the predicament of our time.

---

[89] Peter G. Brown and Geoffrey Garver, *Right Relationship: Building a Whole Earth Economy* (San Francisco: Berrett-Koehler Publishers, Inc., 2009), 76.

Chapter 3

Science, Technology, and Religion: Driving Our Predicament?

Man's place in the physical universe is to be its master. It is his place, by controlling the natural forces with his intelligence, to put them to work to his purposes and to build a future in his image.

—Willard Libby[1]

We are not entranced with the universe, with the natural world. We are entranced instead with the domination of the natural world, with bringing about violent transformation.

—Thomas Berry[2]

In 1961 the World Council of Churches' Third World Congress stated, "The Christian should welcome *scientific discoveries as new steps in man's dominion over nature* [my emphasis]."[3] However, a cautionary note followed:

> Science and technology are instruments in the hands of man. They can be used for good or evil purposes....[T]he abuse or conservation of natural resources [is an] example...It is not good that man should be subdued by nature or enslaved by technology. Nor is it good that nature should be subdued by man, if the mastery merely feeds his rebellious pride. But it is good that man increase his knowledge and should use his growing mastery of nature for the benefit of mankind and the glory of God.[4]

By 1979, the Congress's optimistic view of and endorsement of science in its role of "mastering nature" had begun to be seriously questioned. That year

---

[1] Willard Libby (Nobel Laureate in Chemistry, 1960), quoted in Brian Easlea, *Fathering the Unthinkable: Masculinity, Scientists, and the Nuclear Arms Race* (London: Pluto Press Ltd, 1983), 168.

2 Thomas Berry, interview with Derrick Jensen, in Derrick Jensen, *Listening to the Land: Conversations About Nature, Culture, and Eros* (White River Junction, VT: Chelsea Green Publishing Company, 2004), 36.

[3] World Council of Churches, *The New Delhi Report of the Third Assembly of the World Council of Churches 1961*, ed. W.A. Visser t'Hooft (New York: Association Press, undated), 96.

[4] World Council of Churches, *New Delhi Report*, 97.

the World Council of Churches held a conference on "Faith, Science, and the Future" at MIT, attended by scientists and delegates from churches around the world.[5] The goal elaborated at the conference was the promotion of a "just, participatory and sustainable society." A group representing the poorer countries began a report with the statement "We denounce science and technology."[6] As the theologian John Cobb Jr. recounts, this seemed like an astonishing denunciation to many of the other participants. Surely, science and technology were "almost unquestioned goods on which we could rely for progress." Ian Barbour summarized the critique of science at the meeting:

> ... the traditional image of the value-free, neutral scientist, dedicated only to the pursuit of science, came repeatedly under attack.... The critique was directed mainly against the ways in which technology and applied science contribute to the concentration of economic and political power, and increase the gaps between the rich and the poor nations (and between rich and poor within nations).[7]

The overall charge made at that conference—notably from the poorest countries—was that science and technology are contributing both to the increasing disparities in wealth and power between the rich and poor of the world and to global ecological destruction. That charge has been echoed in recent decades by many environmental justice and peace advocates and concerned scientists, in both faith and nonfaith communities.

Critiques of the ecologically destructive aspects of modern science refer not only to its technological applications but also to the scientific method itself and its view of nature. They are based largely on two principal theses: one, that this is due to the historical separation of religion and science (faith and reason), whereby nature came to be viewed as an machine or object to be controlled and manipulated, rather than as an integral part of creation to be considered as hallowed and sacred; and second, that it is due to an anthropocentric, masculine and patriarchal worldview, which emphasizes domination, hierarchy, control, competition, and a fear of nature. These views are intertwined, and both also point to theological grounds by which domination of women and of nature came to be justified. Let's look at the history of these

---

[5] World Council of Churches, *Faith and Science in an Unjust World, Report of the World Council of Churches' Conference on Faith, Science, and the Future*, Massachusetts Institute of Technology, Cambridge, MA, July 12-24, 1979 (Philadelphia: Fortress Press, 1980).

[6] John B. Cobb Jr., "Envisioning a Just and Peaceful World," *Religious Education* 79 (1984): 488, https://doi.org/10.1080/0034408400790402.

[7] Ian Barbour, "Justice, Participation and Sustainability at MIT," *Ecumenical Review* 31 (1979): 380, https://doi.org/10.1111/j.1758-6623.1979.tb02528.x.

ideas to see how they explain the role of science and religion in our ecological predicament.

The Scientific Worldview: A Brief History

Although many aspects of the European scientific worldview can be traced to Plato, Aristotle, and the Greek philosophers, the birth of what we usually think of as modern science in the West is traceable to the 17th century and the Age of Enlightenment in Europe. This was the time of Galileo (1564–1642), building on the earlier observations of Copernicus (1473–1543), and the natural philosophers Francis Bacon (1561–1626), dubbed the first empiricist; Rene Descartes (1596–1650); and Isaac Newton (1643–1727). "Mechanistic" modern science was born, and religion and science would gradually come to occupy separate realms in a new way.

By the 17th century, the accepted notion was of a difference in kind, not in degree, between the "natural" and the "supernatural." New experimental methods applied *only* to natural phenomena, and they eschewed speculation or investigation into the nature of the soul or God.[8] Further, Rene Descartes famously posited an absolute division between mind and matter, leading to "Cartesian dualism," while Francis Bacon appeared to have no hesitation in asserting power and control over nature, thereby creating a new perspective in which science overturned the ancient organic worldview.[9]

By the time of the Reformation, social institutions (and later, science), became increasingly secularized, developing, as Rex Ambler puts it, "a very earthly faith in the possibility of human liberation though material pro-gress."[10] According to John Cobb Jr., the influence of Calvinism and Kantian philosophy reinforced the idea of the natural world as the realm of science.[11] Meanwhile, a religious focus remained on the covenantal relationship of humanity with God and the salvation of the individual soul, continuing well into the 19th century, at least in Protestant theology.

---

[8] T. Spratt, *History of the Royal Society of London* (London: Royal Society, 1667), http://quod.lib.umich.edu/cgi/t/text/text-idx?c=eebo;idno=A61158.0001.001.

[9] Carolyn Merchant, *The Death of Nature* (San Francisco: HarperSanFrancisco, 1982), 86, 164. First published in 1980.

[10] Rex Ambler, "Befriending the Earth: A Theological Challenge," *The Friends Quarterly* 26 (1990), 10.

[11] John B. Cobb Jr., "Protestant Theology and Deep Ecology," in *Deep Ecology and World Religions: New Essays on Sacred Grounds,* eds. David Landis Barnhill and Roger S. Gottlieb (New York: State University of New York Press, 2001), 213-4.

This new worldview had clear repercussions on the developing roles of science and scientific thought in the study of the human and wider natural worlds. God, or any spiritual force or nonmaterial power, is either rendered absent from the natural world (having, like a watchmaker, made and set the universe 'ticking' at the beginning of creation and then left it to run) or was never present in the first place. For example, Richard Dawkins, in *The Blind Watchmaker*,[12] argues that life and evolution are self-organizing, without a "purpose" or "mind," and that they require no postulated divinity or creator to explain their genesis, organization, or evolution. The evolution of life-forms, however complex, could be explained as the cumulative effect of the processes of random mutation and natural selection. Science had no need to postulate an overseeing "watchmaker" or Creator. Humanity, instead of being in awe and fear of natural forces, now sought to know, predict, manipulate, and control them for our own purposes.

Nature as Machine: Modern Critiques of Science

The charge laid against science, both by the Romantic movement and later by 20th-century critics of science, is first, that science became dualistic, in the sense of confining its realm to studying and manipulating the material, observable world and separating this from the realm of the supernatural, sacred, divine, nonmaterial, or metaphysical world, about which it remained largely silent. To the extent that nature became viewed as devoid of a creator or no longer imbued with intrinsic sacredness or divinity—or, as Dawkins argued, as a self-organizing system, subject only to the forces of evolution—the reality or otherwise of a separate spiritual or religious realm was largely irrelevant. Second, through the discovery of physical laws that govern physical processes from the movement of planets to the behavior of atoms; attempts to observe phenomena "objectively"; the study of discrete, isolated biological phenomena and physical forces, primarily under experimental conditions; and the attempt to manipulate, predict, and control nature, science created a paradigm or worldview that became characterized as both *mechanistic* and *reductionistic*. Viewing the material world largely as a machine or object results in the objectification of humans and the wider natural world. Reducing or reifying it to its constituent material parts renders nature "nothing but" a set of observable, measurable, and manipulable phenomena, and

---

[12] Richard Dawkins, *The Blind Watchmaker: Why the Evidence of Evolution Reveals a Universe Without Design* (London: Penguin Books, 1986).

reinforces the notion that they/we are little more than functioning, utilitarian machines and mechanisms that can be controlled, modified or even replicated by laboratory systems or robots. Third, as scientists began to study smaller and smaller parts of things in isolation—organisms, cells, molecules and atoms—it became easier to lose sight of systems, interactions, patterns, processes, and interrelationships, and this can lead to erroneous or incomplete conclusions about how things fit and work together in interdependent wholes. It is difficult, if not impossible, to see "the pattern that connects," as Gregory Bateson has put it.[13] Finally, the tendency toward reductionism and mechanism encouraged humans to control and exploit what was considered a largely inanimate or insentient natural world.

This tendency was reinforced, at least in the West, by biologically, culturally, or religiously grounded beliefs in four interrelated concepts: dualism, in this context the belief in a separate non-material human soul; *anthropocentrism*, a belief in the uniqueness of humans; the *hierarchical* structure of life on Earth; and the primacy of *domination*, conquest and competition. Many scientists, particularly in the late 19th century, while recognizing the process of evolution, nevertheless regarded humans as qualitatively different from our nearest primate ancestors or at the apex of evolution, while diverging in views about the existence of a soul, whether human or in other life-forms. Both views reinforced the notion that humans were superior to other animals and life-forms, and that nature was for our use, i.e., that humans had the right and might, either by dint of divine mandate from God or evolutionary superiority, to conquer, dominate, and "subdue" nature for our own purposes. Critics of science have argued that these beliefs have led to a sense of hubris and entitlement among scientists as they pursue a Promethean quest to exploit nature.

There have been numerous revolts against mechanistic science, including before and during the Romanticism movement of the early 19th century (by William Blake among others) and up to the present day. However, as John Brooke and Geoffrey Cantor point out, despite a simplifying tendency in such narratives—for example, that a mechanistic view of the world is largely responsible for both the social and ecological crises we face today[14]—the charge that these tendencies in science have played a role in ecological destruction (and in the development of weapons of mass destruction) has also

---

[13] Gregory Bateson, *Mind and Nature: A Necessary Unity* (New York: Bantam Books, Inc., 1980), 8-9.

[14] John Brooke and Geoffrey Cantor, *Reconstructing Nature: The Engagement of Science and Religion* (Edinburgh: T. and T. Clark, 1998).

been made today both by philosophers, physicists, biologists and scientists such as Carl Gillett, Arthur Koestler, Thomas Nagel, Fritjof Capra, and Steven Rose[15] and by feminist scientists and ecofeminists (see below).

The modern critique of scientific dualism and mechanistic reductionism partly rests on shifts in scientific discoveries and fields of study such as quantum physics, the study of consciousness, and the modern science of ecology. Sharp distinctions between what have been viewed as the material and non-material worlds, between energy and mass, mind and matter, began to dissolve, and the mechanistic worldview began to change. Sir Arthur Eddington (1882–1944), an astronomer, physicist, mathematician, and Fellow of the Royal Society, wrote as early as the 1920s:

> …we no longer have the disposition which, as soon as it scents a piece of mechanism, exclaims, 'Here we are getting to bedrock. This is what things should resolve themselves into. This is ultimate reality.'… Perhaps the most essential change is that we are no longer tempted to condemn the spiritual aspects of our nature as illusory because of their lack of concreteness…. Mind is the first and most direct thing in our experience; …the problem of experience is not limited to the interpretation of sense impressions…consciousness is not wholly, nor even primarily, a device for receiving sense impressions…. What I attempt to dispel is the feeling that in using the eye of the body or the eye of the soul, and incorporating what is thereby revealed in our conception of reality, we are doing something irrational and disobeying the leading of truth which as scientists we are pledged to serve.[16]

In addition, advances in fields such as anthropology, primatology, genetics, biological sciences and psychology began to reveal closer similarities between humans and other species, while the field of ecology, emerging as a distinct field in the 19th century, began to unravel the extent of the interdependency of myriad life-forms. Each of these developments is now contributing to the emergence of a more integrated and holistic worldview, which will be explored further in Chapter 5.

---

[15] See, for example, *Beyond Reductionism: New Perspectives in the Life Sciences*, eds. Arthur Koestler and J.R. Smythies (Boston: Beacon Press, 1971); Steven Rose, *Lifelines: Biology Beyond Determinism* (New York: Oxford University Press, 1998); Thomas Nagel, "Reductionism and Antireductionism" in *The Limits of Reductionism in Biology*, Novartis Foundation Symposium #213 (Chichester, UK: John Wiley and Sons, 1998), 3-14, http://www.isnature.org/Events/2009/Summer/r/Nagel1998-Rednism%26AntiRednism.pdf, Thomas Nagel, *Mind and Cosmos: Why the Materialist Neo-Darwinian Conception of Nature is Almost Certainly False* (New York: Oxford University Press, 2012); Carl Gillett, *Reduction and Emergence in Science and Philosophy* (Cambridge, UK: Cambridge University Press, 2016).

[16] Arthur Eddington, *Science and the Unseen Worlds*, Swarthmore Lecture 1929 (London: George Allen and Unwin, Ltd., 1929), 20-21, 24, 26, 31.

Feminist Critiques: A Different Vision

The feminist critique of the dominant scientific paradigm, particularly with respect to its view of the natural world, rests primarily on the following grounds. First, this paradigm has allowed for the desacralization of nature and paves the way for its conquest. Second, it ignores or devalues nonmaterial, abstract qualities that cannot be quantified, measured, or manipulated, including truth, beauty, love, morality, and the spiritual. Third, by privileging rationality and objectivity, it devalues subjective ways of knowing. Fourth, by claiming to be "value-neutral," it ignores the cultural, political, racial, gender-based, and historical biases inherent in deciding what is studied, how it is studied, and how data are interpreted and applied[17] (and of course, what work gets funded).[18] Fifth, it has always been an overwhelmingly masculine endeavor that has regarded nature as female and to be subjugated, and has pursued science as an enterprise to conquer and dominate others and nature.[19]

From the time of Aristotle, the "rational" male was considered superior to the "nonrational" female, in part because to be female was to be a "mutilated" male, in Aristotle's view. For centuries, women were considered incapable or unsuited to the pursuits of natural philosophy and science. While this view has lost credibility, certain fields of science are still heavily male-dominated. The problem of not enough women in science is not simply a matter of unequal opportunity but also that sciences reflect and reinforce masculine ways of thinking and being in the world and male priorities regarding what science and technology are developed and used for. This in turn has profound implications for how we approach the ecological predicament. Inasmuch as the idea of objectifying, conquering, controlling, and manipulating nature—of regarding it as a machine to be used, devoid of feeling, autonomy, or sacredness—is more typical of a masculine worldview than a feminine one, we need to integrate feminine ways of thinking and being in the

---

[17] For example, women scientists are increasingly represented in primatology. A number have challenged predominantly male anthropological and sociobiological interpretations of primate behavior as overemphasizing male domination and control and female submission at the expense of recognizing a far greater degree of diversity and complexity in behavior. See, for example, Donna Haraway, *Primate Visions: Gender, Race and Nature in the World of Modern Science* (New York: Routledge, 1989).

[18] See, for example, Sheldon Krimsky, "Do Financial Conflicts of Interest Bias Research? An Inquiry into the 'Funding Effect' Hypothesis," *Science, Technology and Human Values* 38 (2012): 566-87, http://journals.sagepub.com/doi/abs/10.1177/0162243912456271.

[19] Brian Easlea, *Fathering the Unthinkable: Masculinity, Science, and the Nuclear Arms Race* (London: Pluto Press, 1983), 19 et seq.

world with how we regard our human relationship to the wider natural world.[20] Let's look further at the feminist critique of how science is viewed and the way it is conducted with respect to nature.

Carolyn Merchant, in *The Death of Nature*, argues that the Enlightenment and the beginning of a masculine modern science marked the end of the sacredness and numinosity of the natural world. Science both appropriates and denies nature, the feminine, the sacred, and the nonrational. Francis Bacon, she writes, had little hesitation in creating a new world in which science effectively became the new priesthood.[21] Brian Easlea writes that Bacon, one of the leading natural philosophers of this period, viewed nature as female, portrayed as a bare-breasted, veiled woman in one of the statues of the time. Nature was not merely to "reveal her secrets"; "she" was to be plundered, penetrated, or in later cases, killed off and reduced to mere matter.[22] Nature was to be controlled, and by the power of men. Bacon also spoke of "the truly masculine birth of time" and the achievement of "the dominion of man over the universe," and of "turning with united forces against the Nature of things, to storm and occupy her castles and strongholds, and extend the bounds of the human empire, as far as God Almighty in his goodness may permit."[23] Rene Descartes wrote that "we shall become the masters and possessors of nature."[24] As Easlea points out, Descartes, in a radical philosophical shift, is credited with "killing off" the idea of Nature not only as female, but *as life itself*, and of creating a vision of a "clockwork" universe, which consisted only of the disembodied human (male) mind and an infinity of matter characterized only by physical properties. God gradually disappeared from view; nature was female, but also a machine.[25] Easlea argues that perhaps the ultimate result of this worldview is the pursuit of nuclear weapons as a prime example of "masculine behaviour in pursuit and application of scientific inquiry."[26] And, as ecofeminists such as Carolyn Merchant, Vandana Shiva and others have argued, our plundering of the earth has also reflected a

---

[20] A number of writers have pointed out that it is not simply a masculine worldview, but a Eurocentric worldview characteristic of white, majority male, scientists in the West. Asian science and indigenous views of the natural world, for example, were and are grounded in very different paradigms.

[21] Merchant, *The Death of Nature*, 83, 111, 164.

[22] Easlea, *Fathering the Unthinkable*, 20.

[23] Francis Bacon, quoted in Easlea, *Fathering the Unthinkable*, 19, 20, 21.

[24] Easlea, *Fathering the Unthinkable*, 23.

[25] Easlea, *Fathering the Unthinkable*, 22-3.

[26] Easlea, *Fathering the Unthinkable*, 5.

predominantly masculine scientific view of the wider natural world (see below and also Chapter 11).

"A Feeling for the Organism"

Feminist scientists have argued that a masculine way of thinking, particularly with regard to the wider natural world, profoundly influences the *way* science is done, and this in turn affects how it is interpreted and applied. For example, Evelyn Fox Keller and others[27] have argued that the methodology of science—with its emphasis on reductionism and the "value-free," impartial, or objective observer—reflects a masculine way of thinking that excludes participation. Keller argues for a way of seeking knowledge, a "dynamic objectivity," that acknowledges the independent integrity of the world while relying on a participatory experience that connects us to it.[28] She gives an example of this way of practicing science from the research of Barbara McClintock. McClintock discovered "jumping genes" (the ability of genes to transpose themselves or "jump" from one position to another on a chromosome or from one chromosome to another) in her work with corn plants, a discovery that geneticists had previously dismissed as impossible. She had made this discovery by becoming deeply involved with each plant she was studying. Keller writes:

> ...[Barbara McClintock] tells us one must have the time to look, the patience to 'hear what the material has to say to you,' the openness to 'let it come to you.' Above all, one must have a 'feeling for the organism.'... 'No two plants are exactly alike...I start with the seedling, and I don't want to leave it. I don't feel as if I know the story if I don't watch the plant all the way along.... I know every plant in the field...I know them intimately...'[29]

Keller, herself a physicist whose later work has focused on the philosophy of biology and the role of gender in science, observes:

---

[27] See, for example, Evelyn Fox Keller, *Reflections on Gender and Science* (Hartford, CT: Yale University Press, 1985); Ruth Bleier, ed., *Feminist Approaches to Science* (New York: Pergamon Press, Inc., 1986); Nancy Tuana, ed., *Feminism and Science* (Bloomington: Indiana University Press, 1989); Sandra Harding, *The Science Question in Feminism* (Ithaca, NY: Cornell University Press, 1986) and *Whose Science? Whose Knowledge? Thinking from Women's Lives* (Ithaca, NY: Cornell University Press, 1991); Evelyn Fox Keller and Helen E. Longino, *Feminism and Science* (New York: Oxford University Press, 1996); Vandana Shiva, *Staying Alive: Women, Ecology and Development* (London: Zed Books, 1989), particularly Chapter 2: "Science, Nature and Gender," 14-37.

[28] Keller, *Reflections*, 115.

[29] Evelyn Fox Keller, *A Feeling for the Organism* (New York, San Francisco: W.H. Freeman and Co., 1995), 198.

> This intimate knowledge…is a prerequisite for her extraordinary perspicacity….
> For McClintock, reason—at least in the conventional sense of the word—is not
> by itself adequate to describe the vast complexity—even mystery—of living
> forms…. Organism is for [McClintock] a code word—not simply a plant or an-
> imal…but the name of a living form, of object-as-subject.[30]

Barbara McClintock also described a way of creative knowing that was
beyond the knowing of the traditional scientific method. Keller describes her
as asking, "Why were you so sure of something when you couldn't tell anyone
else?…you were sure in what I call a completely internal way…"[31] Keller also
quotes Einstein: "…only intuition, resting on sympathetic understanding, can
lead to [the laws that govern nature];…the daily effort comes…straight from
the heart."[32]

What these scientists are saying is that such ways of knowing or learning
about the natural world are not confined to mysticism, poetry, and nonscien-
tific endeavors and can, and should, be integral to scientific study and its
applications.[33] In addition, feminist scientists are arguing that exclusively
rational, reductionistic and mechanistic approaches, associated with the (dominant) masculine aspect, need to be *complemented by and integrated with* these
deeper ways of seeing, understanding and applying science. These ways are
more closely associated with what we think of as the feminine aspect, described further in Chapter 4, and are not necessarily or exclusively the domain
of either women and men but exist in varying degrees in both. As will be
explored in Parts II and III, such an integral view allows us to better understand and interact with the wider natural world as a living, sentient, sacred
and precious gift and in ways that align with, rather than dominate, nature.

Science, Technology, and Ecological Destruction

While applications of science and technology have contributed beneficial-
ly to human life (e.g., in public health and medicine, in industry and commerce, in decreasing mortality and back-breaking physical labor, and in adding comforts and convenience to our lives), the critical questions become: In

---

[30] Keller, *A Feeling*, 198, 199, 200.

[31] Barbara McClintock, quoted in Keller, *A Feeling*, 203.

[32] Albert Einstein, quoted in Keller, *A Feeling*, 201.

[33] I have often experienced something similar, when examining the miracle of a *Paramecium*
under a microscope, or studying the way that the cells in a fertilized egg communicate to
form the first stages of a new life, or the way a dung beetle labors diligently to roll its ball
of dung, taking its humble but vital part in the great cycles of life and death. Listening to
the earth can bring knowledge, understanding, humility, and wonder in equal measure.

what ways are they now contributing to the ecological crisis? Is the ecological devastation we are now seeing (as described in Chapter 1) a question of potentially beneficial applications of science and technology having been distorted by social, political, or economic forces, or is there something wrong with the way we are applying them that have to do with deeper paradigms at work, including the moral and spiritual dimensions? Let's explore these questions further, focusing on two areas that have major potential impacts on the wider natural world: agriculture, and energy production and use; and, in the following chapter, on the twin impacts of weapons of mass destruction and climate breakdown.

A substantial proportion of Western science and technology over the past century or more has been directed towards capital-intensive, larger-scale enterprises that accumulate wealth, are resource-intensive, are privately controlled by larger and larger corporations, and are predicated upon industrial expansion and growth and profit, goals which, to the extent they are pursed without regard for human wellbeing or the preservation of nature, contribute to an increasing disparity between rich and poor and the exploitation of the wider natural world, both within and across countries. Historically, the export of Western science and technology was regarded as almost universally beneficial for developing countries, by bringing them the benefits of more efficient methods of agriculture, new technologies, and modern infrastructure. However, by the late 1970s, this view began to be challenged, as in many cases, such technologies were actually benefiting Western businesses and industries and were inappropriate—economically, culturally, and ecologically—with sometimes disastrous results for indigenous societies and ecosystems. For example, the experiments of the first "Green Revolution," starting with developments in agricultural production efficiency in the 1930s and leading to international application in the 1960s, revealed some fundamental flaws in the rosy picture of global agricultural development that it was supposed to promote. According to numerous critiques,[34] the "revolution" increased the dominance of transnational companies over the agricultural production of the poorer countries it was designed to assist, and increased their dependency on Western technology and markets. Tractors, dependent on Western manufac-

---

[34] See, for example, Nick Cullather, *The Hungry World: America's Cold War Battle Against Poverty in Asia* (Cambridge, MA: Harvard University Press, 2010); Vandana Shiva, *The Violence of the Green Revolution: Agriculture, Ecology and Politics* (London: Zed Books, 1991); Prabhu Pingali, "Green Revolution: Impacts, Limits, and the Path Ahead," *Proceedings of the National Academy of Sciences of the United States of America 109* (2012): 12302-8, https://doi.org/10.1073/pnas.0912953109.

turers for parts and imported fuel for operation, often lay idle in fields; and crop varieties that depended on expensive pesticides and chemical fertilizers and imported seeds were largely unaffordable by local populations. It also frequently promoted types of agriculture that were unsuited to the climate, terrain, and needs of the people, and were primarily directed at cash crops for export rather than food for the local population.

Though rarely articulated, an underlying assumption was that a goal of sustainable, equitably distributed or *subsistence* agriculture under local control was not sufficient or desirable. Development along Western lines presupposed that a growth economy and ever-increasing material wealth and surplus production was the goal. Economic growth, a stable food supply, a decrease in absolute poverty, and material wealth have indeed been the goals of many recipient countries, but the way that technology has been introduced often primarily increased the wealth and political power of only a small minority within the country and the wealth of transnational corporations, while providing cheap food and goods for richer countries. In sum, numerous technological methods that Western countries have often promoted have failed to foster sustainability and community self-reliance compared with more slowly evolved, ecologically sensitive, locally adapted ways of living among indigenous populations.

Large-scale energy technologies, as with large-scale agricultural technologies, have significant ecological as well social and political impacts. For example, since energy generation from fossil fuels has a finite future, and is at least partly (if not largely) responsible for regional conflicts in some parts of the world, nuclear energy has returned to center stage as governments consider their energy options. Nuclear energy presents formidable technical and ethical problems, such as the production of additional sources of plutonium and enriched uranium that can be diverted for weapons development (in addition to those produced in dedicated weapons reactors), the problem of radioactive waste disposal, and the risk of accidents or sabotage.

These and other examples present profound ethical and practical dilemmas. On one hand, many large-scale technological solutions to the energy crisis, as in areas such as water and food provision, follow a similar pattern to the one we have illustrated above with agriculture—they reproduce a pattern of dominance by transnational companies, centralized control, dependency on long-distance transport and import of energy, an inequitable distribution of power and wealth, a lack of self-reliance, a reduced need for local labor, a lack of flexible adaptability to local needs and conditions, and an increased potential for ecological destruction compared with "soft" energy paths. On the other hand, proponents argue, what right have we to refuse to share available scientific and technological developments with other communities or countries? There is a middle way. It *is* possible for communities to increase their material wellbeing without necessarily investing in large-scale modern technologies such as nuclear power, centrally generated electricity, and modern agricultural methods, to take a few examples, and retaining local control over their land, agricultural and manufacturing processes and labor, while using appropriate technologies as needed. (Examples of how this is being done are explored in Part III.)

The theologian John Cobb Jr., commenting on that first World Council of Churches conference on Faith, Science, and the Future in 1979 described above, argued that science and technology have made the rich richer and more powerful and the poor poorer and less powerful than they would otherwise have been, because the rich and powerful employ scientists and technologists to "fulfill their desires."[35] As illustrated by the above examples, some applications of technology and science not only primarily serve the needs of some in the donor community or country rather than the recipient community but also can, if inappropriately applied, actively damage local economies; distort or destroy centuries-old, slowly evolved, and locally adapted agricultural and health practices; reduce the need for local labor; damage or destroy local ecologies; and promote the idea that Western or newly developed methods are superior to traditional methods. They can also promote unsustainable practices over the long term in areas ranging from agriculture to healthcare, to industry and infrastructure development, as well as dependency on the part of political and economic institutions.

Cobb's charge raises the deeper ethical question of whether it is the scientists' responsibility only to discover, leaving the moral and ethical dilemmas of applying these discoveries to the world at large, a view held by Robert Oppenheimer, the physicist in charge of developing the first atomic bomb. He said, "*It is good to turn over to mankind at large the greatest possible power to control the world* [my emphasis] and to deal with it according to its lights and values."[36] I believe that is no longer justifiable, if it ever was, for scientists and technologists to "turn over" responsibility for discoveries and inventions to society at large, particularly since they have the means to develop ever more potent

---

[35] Cobb, "Envisioning a Just and Peaceful World," 488, 489.

[36] Oppenheimer, quoted in Easlea, *Fathering the Unthinkable*, 90.

ways to destroy and manipulate human, animal, and plant life and the very nature of the planet. Scientists have a moral obligation to understand the social, ecological and related implications of their work and to conduct their work with integrity, knowing that trust is absolutely critical to this work. Also, as members of society, we can choose to work or not to work in or for certain sectors; we can be critical and awake to the dangers of allowing our own and societal biases to influence the choice, interpretation, and application of our work. Further, we have an obligation to participate in taking responsibility for how science is applied and its social, economic and ecological impacts by being part of policymaking, as long as a clear line is maintained between an unbiased search for facts and discoveries—i.e., what we can know or not know at a given point about, for example, the toxicity of a substance to human health and other life-forms—and policies about, say, controlling pollutants or research priorities that are based on these facts and discoveries.[37]

Religions As Drivers of the Ecological Crisis

As evidenced by surviving artifacts, images, and writings of almost every group of peoples who have lived on the earth, despite vast differences in historical periods and in rituals, language, and ways of relating to the "supernatural," humans have sought to know and understand their relationship with powers and forces greater than themselves. They have variously named these forces or powers gods, God, or spirits and have worshiped, feared, or propitiated and felt governed, comforted or guided by, loved by, or punished by these powers. From ancient times, people have often thought of God or gods or spirits as residing in nature—in the heavenly bodies, in rocks, rivers, animals, plants, trees, the wind, and the earth itself. The deities or spirits in these bodies may have power and use that power for good, evil, or both. Others have thought of a Creator God who is both immanent in nature and transcendent or beyond form, whose manifestations are the visible form through which we know God's greatness and beauty and goodness. Some think of many gods in human, animal, plant, or other natural forms underneath a Godhead; an invisible, infinite divine Mind; a higher consciousness; or a Mystery that is beyond form. Some believe that God endowed human beings with unique capacities or a soul that no other living beings on the earth share,

---

[37] For example, I both conducted studies of the health effects of lead and, with others, was involved in policy work to recommend safe environmental levels and standards based on the precautionary principle. See J.M. Ratcliffe, *Lead in Man and the Environment* (Chichester, U.K.: Ellis Horwood Ltd.; New York: Halsted Press, 1981), 99.

while others believe that each sentient being shares the same fundamental divinity. Others have thought of a transcendent Creator God who made all things but who no longer resides in them, or, in more modern times, of a self-organizing cosmos in which deities and supernatural forces are relics of superstitions and earlier prescientific worldviews.

We don't know precisely if, or the extent to which, any older civilizations or societies, either en masse or among small groups of individuals, may have regarded the cosmos and nature as a kind of "accidental" universe—i.e., subject only to the forces of physics and chemistry and with the self-organizing potential to produce life-forms that do not require the existence of a nonphysical spiritual power or consciousness to explain them—but it appears that the particular mechanistic form of this worldview emerged only relatively recently with the ascendance of natural philosophy and science in the West, as described above.[38] With the emergence of a scientific worldview and a belief in a self-organizing universe, various expressions of secularism, agnosticism, and atheism gradually became more prominent in the West. Only in recent decades have some philosophers, process theologians, ecotheologians, and scientists sought an emergent synthesis in which newly interpreted spiritual and religious thought and a scientific worldview form new, integral views of the story of the cosmos and our place in it (Chapter 5).

In what ways have these various religious beliefs and worldviews contributed to the destruction of the natural world or, conversely, to its preservation? Have these traditions changed over time with respect to their views of the natural world?[39] The focus here will be primarily on the traditional and modern Christian interpretations of the role of humans in relation to the natural world—interpretations that have had far-reaching consequences for our view of the divine-human-nature relationship due to their dominant influence in Western culture and the spread of that influence to much of the world—but will also refer to Jewish interpretations of this relationship, particularly as reflected in the Hebrew Bible (the Tanakh) shared with Christiani-

---

[38] Eurocentric views of science tend to omit consideration of the cosmologies and sciences developed in China, Arabia, India, and other civilizations long before the European Enlightenment.

[39] The relationship between major faith traditions and ecology—Buddhism, Judaism, Islam, Taoism, Hinduism, Jainism, Confucianism, and Indigenous traditions, as well as Christianity—have been the subjects of an excellent series of volumes entitled *Religions of the World and Ecology*, edited by Mary Evelyn Tucker and John Grim and published by the Harvard University Center for the Study of World Religions and Harvard University Press.

ty as the Old Testament. (Recent religious interpretations of the role of humans in nature, in the light of the ecological crisis, are explored in Chapter 7.)

God, Humans, and Nature: Whose Earth Is It?

A number of ecotheologians and others consider that historical and present-day interpretations of Christian theology (despite considerable variations in theology and interpretations of scripture across denominations and among theologians) reveal a worldview that is fundamentally *dualistic, anthropocentric* or *androcentric*, and *hierarchical*. Historically, this worldview has contributed to a dualistic concept of the cosmos in which God is the creator of but separate from the manifest creation; where humans are superior to, and separate from, the wider natural world as the only beings with an immortal soul separate from the physical, temporary body; and (particularly in Christianity rather than Judaism) an emphasis on an eternal life beyond life on Earth. It is a worldview that has also contributed to the domination of nature by humanity on the one hand, and to an instrumental, if yet sacralized, view of nature on the other.

The cosmos, the earth, and nature have been traditionally viewed as the creation of a transcendent God, according to interpretations of the first creation story in the book of Genesis. In this foundational story, familiar to most Jews and Christians, "In the beginning, God created the heaven and the earth" (Genesis 1: 1, King James Version). In six days, light, day and night, the heavens, stars, earth, waters, plants, and animals were created, and God saw that it was good, and commanded his creation to be fruitful and multiply (Genesis 1: 2-25). On the sixth day, God created humans "in our image, after our likeness: and let them have dominion over the fish of the sea, and over the fowl of the air, and over the cattle, and over all the earth, and over every creeping thing that creepeth upon the earth" (Genesis 1: 26), and "subdue it" (Genesis 1: 28).

Varied interpretations of these verses have led to widely different views of nature and our relationship with the natural world. For example, early and medieval Christians, including Augustine, Thomas Aquinas, and Christian mystics such as St. Bonaventure and St. Francis, largely viewed nature as a manifestation and expression of God's goodness, and thus as sacred. As Elizabeth Johnson points out, medieval theologians viewed God-Humans-

Nature as a "metaphysical trinity," each imbued with sacredness.[40] There is a subtle but important difference between regarding nature as a creation of a transcendent God and thus sacred and worshiping nature as God. In traditional Judaism, for example, Hava Tirosh-Samuelson writes that God was believed to have created the natural world and commanded humans to be thankful for it, bless it, and take care of it as part of the covenant between God and the people of Israel. But "to venerate the natural world for its own sake or to identify God with nature is precisely the pagan outlook that Judaism rejects as idolatrous."[41] An injunction against worshiping nature as God, in this interpretation, is also shared by some strands in Christianity (see below). It does not exclude a regard for nature as part of God's creation and clearly coexists with a responsibility to care for the wider natural world, a view that, as described further in Chapter 7, is carried into today's concern for earthcare by Jewish, Christian, Muslim and other religious traditions.

With respect to the God-human relationship, Christianity was historically principally concerned with human life and its destiny and regarded "the world" as something to ignore or something sinful and to be actively withdrawn from.[42,43,44] The natural world became in some aspects a backdrop for the human drama, a stage created by God for the use of humanity, but in other aspects an adversary. Partly under the influence of Greek philosophy, early Christians developed an apocalyptic view of the world, believing that it was essentially fallen, corrupt, and soon to end. The response was a belief in a heavenly world beyond the earthly plane, and a soul, separate from the body, which was to be preserved, liberated, or saved into the next, eternal world. Rex Ambler quotes Martin Luther, whose view of the creation story in Genesis was that it "plainly teaches that God created all these things in order to

---

[40] Elizabeth Johnson, "Losing and Finding Creation in the Christian Tradition," in *Christianity and Ecology*, eds. Dieter T. Hessel and Rosemary Radford Ruether (Cambridge, MA: Harvard University Press, 2000), 6.

[41] Hava Tirosh-Samuelson, "Introduction. Judaism and the Natural World," in *Judaism and Ecology*, ed. Hava Tirosh-Samuelson (Cambridge, MA: Harvard University Press, 2002), xxxiv; see also Moshe Sokol, "What are the Ethical Implications of Jewish Theological Conceptions of the Natural World?" in *Judaism and Ecology*, 261-82.

[42] Wesley Granberg-Michaelson, "Creation in Ecumenical Theology," in *Ecotheology: Voices from South and North*, ed. David Hallman (Maryknoll, NY: World Council of Churches/Orbis Books, 1994), 96.

[43] Rex Ambler, "Befriending the Earth: A Theological Challenge," *The Friends' Quarterly* 26 (1990): 8.

[44] Cobb, "Protestant Theology," 213-4.

prepare a house and an inn, as it were, for the future man."[45] Ambler also points out that the Manichees (a widespread movement that was prominent from the third to seventh centuries CE) represent an early example of a dualistic sect that regarded the body and even nature itself not merely as separate or of little consequence, but actually as sources of evil in the world. The writings of Augustine, however, evidence a different view, when he criticizes the Manichees for their failure to appreciate the natural world for its own sake, as a glorification of God, in words that sound almost modern: "[The Manichees] do not consider how admirable these things [of nature] are in their places, how excellent in their own natures, how beautifully adjusted to the rest of creation, and how much grace they contribute to the universe by their own contribution, as to a commonwealth…"[46]

The natural world, even though viewed as God's creation, became infected with the view of the "world" as a realm of temptation, corruption, suffering, and sin and became a source of anxiety, fear, and rejection. The Christian doctrine of original "sin" is associated with worldliness and the lusts of the flesh, and thus the physical realm, the body, and the natural world take on the projected aspects of a corrupt and tempting environment. Ecofeminists have also pointed out the correspondence between the perceived view of the female body in Christianity (and other religious traditions) as a source of sin and temptation and the way (female) nature can be conflated with "sin" and "worldliness" (see Chapter 4).

Last, we have always had to deal with the uncontrollable forces of nature and the wider natural world and with death and suffering on the physical plane, and we have responded to these realities in various ways, from placating angry gods, to narrating a story of vengeance and punishment by a creator God, to rejecting the idea of a benevolent God or any divinity. (For example, Thomas Berry believes that the collective trauma of the Great Plagues of the late 1340s and early 1350s, in which around one-third of the population of Europe perished, radically altered the way they viewed their relationship with the natural world and with death.) We eventually see the beginnings of an imperative to control rather than placate the gods of nature that would see its expression in the scientific revolution and would take the perceived relationship between humanity and nature in a radically different direction.

---

[45] Martin Luther, "Lectures on Genesis," in *Works, Vol. 1*, ed. Jaroslav Pelikan (St. Louis, MO: Concordia, 1955), 47, quoted in Amber, *Befriending*, 8.

[46] Augustine of Hippo, *The City of God*, 11.22, quoted in Amber, *Befriending*, 12.

Christian Views of Nature—Roots of the Ecological Crisis?

In 1967, Lynn White Jr., a historian of science and technology, wrote a controversial landmark essay, "The Historical Roots of Our Ecological Crisis,"[47] in which he claimed that Western Christianity bore "a huge burden of guilt" for the ecological crisis. He argued that, as far back as the 7th to 11th centuries, Europeans were beginning to develop their powerful tradition of science and technology (based in large part on the translation of Arabic and Greek science into Latin) and to use a form of technology that would start to significantly alter human relationships with the earth. He argued that a new "exploitative attitude" to nature or "human ecology" was "deeply conditioned by beliefs about our nature and destiny—that is, by religion"[48]—in this case, the Christian worldview. White argued that the concept of God creating humanity in his image promoted a dualistic view of humans and nature which required humans to "subdue" and have "dominion" over all the creatures of the earth. Thus, Christianity assumed human supremacy over the natural world and the right to use it at will for human ends. In addition, in his view, Christianity had destroyed the immanent God of the animistic paganism of the pre-Christian era and thereby essentially desacralized nature. Last, by promoting the idea of linear, historical time, a concept that White argued leads to the notion of linear progress, Christianity had further enabled the eventual global exploitation of the natural world. Other writers, notably eco-feminists, have also argued that "the dominating, 'objective' God is also a hallmark of…European colonizing relationships with the rest of the world."[49]

White's essay provoked, and in some circles continues to provoke, a far-reaching response among Christian and other theologians, laypeople, and ecologists. Some of these responses have been in basic agreement with White's charge that Christianity's view of nature and the human-nature relationship has contributed to the ecological crisis and must be re-examined.[50]

---

[47] Lynn White Jr., "The Historical Roots of Our Ecological Crisis," *Science* 155 (1967), 1203-7, https://doi.org/10.1126/science.155.3767.1203.

[48] White, "Historical Roots," 1205.

[49] Anne Primavesi, "A Tide in the Affairs of Women?" in *Ecotheology: Voices from South and North*, ed. David Hallman (Maryknoll, NY: World Council of Churches/Orbis Books, 1994), 192.

[50] See, for example, eds. P.N. Joranson and Ken Butigan, *Cry of the Environment* (Santa Fe: Bear and Co., 1984); Paul Santmire, *The Travail of Nature* (Philadelphia: Fortress Press, 1985).

Others, however, have pointed out alternative interpretations of the first chapter of Genesis and other Biblical passages that mitigate the apparent mandate to subdue or dominate the earth—including the concept of stewardship expressed in later chapters of Genesis (see below)—and a strong mystical tradition within Christianity that hallows and respects nature.[51] White himself pointed to an "alternative" Christian relationship to nature, exemplified by St. Francis of Assisi, among others.

Nature as Intrinsically Sacred

Christian and other mystics, for example in the Kabbalistic and Hasidic traditions,[52] have shared a view of nature that is arguably characterized not only by a view of nature as sacred because created by God for human use or as a way of preserving its usefulness for humanity, but also by a sense of caring for the natural world *for its own and God's sake.* The 13th-century mystic St. Francis of Assisi is perhaps the most well-known exemplar of this sensibility, and the person with whom we often associate an ecological consciousness, together with his disciple St. Bonaventure. A similar sensibility can also be found in the writings of mystics such as Meister Eckhart, and many women mystics, including Theresa of Avila, Hildegard of Bingen, Julian of Norwich, and Mechtild of Magdeburg.[53] These interpretations emphasize the wonder of creation and the role of humans in celebrating, giving thanks, and praising the natural world in and of itself. While earlier Christians, and the Greeks and others who preceded them, had regarded nature as God's handiwork, or, in Francis's word, as God's "lettering," Francis is one of the earliest known Christian mystics to both ascribe intrinsic worth to all living beings and experience an *equality* between himself and other creatures, regarding the Sun and Moon and living creatures as his brothers and sisters. He may also have been one of the first such mystics to *make the connection between violence done*

---

[51] See for example, Ernest S. Feenstra, "Christian Impact on Ecology," *Science* 156 (1967): 737, https://doi.org/10.1126/science.156.3776.737; Ernest Fortin, "The Bible Made Me Do It," *The Review of Politics* 57 (1995): 197-223, https://doi.org/10.1017/S0034670500026875; Robin Attfield, "Christian Attitudes to Nature," *Journal of the History of Ideas* 33 (1983): 369-86, https://orca.cf.ac.uk/48961/1/Journal%20History%20Ideas_Christian%20Attitudes%20Nature.pdf.

[52] See, for example, Elliott R. Wolfson, "Mirror of Nature Reflected in the Symbolism of Medieval Kabbalah," in *Judaism and Ecology*, ed. Hava Tirosh-Samuelson (Cambridge, MA: Harvard University Press, 2002), 305-31, and Jerome (Yehudah) Gellman, "Early Hasidism and the Natural World," in *Judaism and Ecology*, 369-85.

[53] See, for example, Carol Flinders, *Enduring Grace: Living Portraits of Seven Women Mystics* (New York: Harper Collins Publishers, 1993).

to the natural world and violence done to humanity, a connection that we see in writings of the Quaker John Woolman, Gandhi, and other modern mystics (as I will explore further in Chapters 6, 7, and 9). For example, St. Francis says: "If you have men who exclude any of God's creatures from the shelter of compassion and pity, you will have men who do likewise for their fellow men."[54]

While some scholars have pointed to an attitude, put forward by Augustine and others and prevalent by the Middle Ages, that humans should "improve" on nature through agriculture, inventions, and other means,[55] many examples exist of a nature-enhancing theology within Christianity. God does not sanction unbridled use of nature but sets limits on how it is to be used. Some writers argue that it is *only* a religious biblical narrative that may restrain humans from attempting to control nature: "…it is only when the transcendent God of biblical religion is no longer thought to intervene in the world either as creator or redeemer that the full force of claims for human dominion over nature becomes evident."[56] Rupp argues that it is precisely because of the progressive secularization of the world under the influence of the Enlightenment and modernism that anthropocentrism and domination of nature—associated with Christianity in White's analysis—reach their fullest expression.

Covenant: Using and Preserving the Earth

Other interpretations of Genesis and other texts in the Hebrew Bible cast a different light on the relationship of God to humanity. Larry Rasmussen argues that, in dramatic contrast to preexisting religious worldviews, where humans were in a passive, fated relationship to deities and powers that needed to be appeased and feared, the *new covenant* [57] emphasizes the coparticipatory role that, for the first time, humans were to play in creating a strong moral order in the world: "…we are morally responsible before God for the condition of the world…this was an extraordinary affirmation of human

---

[54] St. Francis of Assisi, quoted in Michael Thompson, "The Care of Our Planet," *The Friends' Quarterly* 26 (1990): 4.

[55] Attfield, "Christian Attitudes," 369-86.

[56] George Rupp, "Religion, Modern Secular Culture, and Ecology," *Daedalus* 130 (2001): 23-30.

[57] Genesis tells of an all-powerful God who causes the Flood, saving only Noah, his family, and pairs of living beings. But God then makes a covenant with Noah, saying: "I will establish my covenant with you, and with your seed after you; and with every living creature that is with you, of the fowl, of the cattle, and of every beast of the Earth with you….neither shall all flesh be cut off any more by the waters of a flood, neither shall there any more be a flood to destroy the Earth." (Genesis 9: 9-11, KJV).

agency and freedom."[58] While acknowledging the incompleteness of the liberation of slaves, women, the body, nature, and mind, Rasmussen writes that early Judaism marked "an ecumenical theology and ethic of life [that] should pursue [the "moral project"] within the space marked by two interwoven themes: the healing, mending, and transforming of the world (*tikkun olam*) and the celebration of the gift of life itself as the gracious creation of a suffering and caring God in an awesome universe."[59]

God, speaking through Moses on Mount Sinai, directed that animals and humans (including slaves) were to rest every seven days and land was to be left fallow every seven years. Animals, birds, crops, and trees were all to be used in ways that allowed them to replenish themselves (see, for example, Exodus 23: 10-12). In Leviticus, God tells the people:

> If ye walk in my statutes, and keep my commandments, and do them; Then I will give you rain in due season, and the land shall yield her increase, and the trees of the field shall yield their fruit. (Leviticus 26: 3-4, KJV)

If the Israelites followed these and other divine laws pertaining both to human relations and relations with the natural world, there would be peace, harmony, and plenty; the land would be fruitful; and there would be no plagues or starvation. If, however, the people "walked contrary to God's way," then sufferings, plagues, wild beasts, and the desolation of the land would be visited upon them. (This warning is repeated in Isaiah, Chapter 24, making it clear that devastation and pollution of the earth would follow as a consequence of the transgression of laws, the violation of statutes, and the breaking of the everlasting covenant.) These texts can be interpreted as a promise to humankind that, if humans kept their side of the covenant, and lived in harmony with each other and the wider natural world, then peace, health, abundance, and harmony would be theirs in perpetuity. But if they broke the covenant, then ecological devastation, disease, and human suffering would result.

In sum, what we see over the course of Christianity's evolution from its roots in Judaism, Greek philosophy, and the "pagan" Greco-Roman mystery traditions are, not unexpectedly, some contradictory strands. On the one hand, it develops as a dualistic anthropocentric, hierarchical, and hegemonic theological strand, allowing or even commanding humanity to dominate and

---

[58] Larry Rasmussen, "Theology of Life and Ecumenical Ethics," in *Ecotheology: Voices from South and North*, ed. David Hallman (Maryknoll, NY: World Council of Churches/Orbis Books, 1994), 113.

[59] Rasmussen, "Theology of Life," 117.

subjugate a nature that, while sacred, is to be used at will.[60] However, this strand coexists with a covenantal theology, which arguably forms the ground for a modern theology of environmental stewardship and the birth of ecotheology as a field concerned with the relationship between religious worldviews and ecological destruction (see Chapter 7). The latter is further blended with and enhanced by a mystical strand throughout Christianity's history, exemplified by St. Francis and others, that speaks to a reverence, compassion, and care for the creation for its own sake and suggests a deeper, more equal, and interdependent view of our relationship to nature.

Over the past 30 to 40 years, several theologians and scholars have argued that our sense of the divine in nature has been largely lost or corrupted. Whether this loss (if it has occurred) results from differences and changes in theological interpretation; the eventual dominance of a secular, mechanistic scientific worldview; or economic and demographic pressures to exploit nature has been a matter of debate, but concern for the consequences of the desacralization of nature has in part prompted the emergence of both ecotheology[61] and of creation spirituality,[62] originated by former Dominican priest Matthew Fox, as distinct fields of theological discourse.

Thomas Berry speaks eloquently of how "…we seldom notice how extensively we have lost contact with the revelation of the divine in nature. Yet our exalted sense of the divine itself comes from the grandeur of the universe, especially from the earth, in all the splendid modes of its expression."[63] As Sally McFague has argued, a sense of the sacredness of all life needs to be consciously restored for us to care for the wider natural world and each other.[64] This view has been echoed by theologians and writers from multiple traditions, who often draw on a range of mystical wisdom traditions in their work.

[60] John B. Cobb Jr., "Ecology, Ethics and Theology," in *Valuing the Earth: Economics, Ecology and Ethics*, eds. Herman Daly and Kenneth Townsend (Cambridge, MA: Massachusetts Institute of Technology Press, 1993), 211-27.

[61] See, for example, Anne Marie Dalton and Henry C. Simmons, *Ecotheology and the Practice of Hope* (Albany, NY: State University of New York, 2010), 19-37.

[62] Matthew Fox, *The Coming of the Cosmic Christ: The Healing of Mother Earth and the Birth of a Global Renaissance* (San Francisco: HarperSanFrancisco, 1988).

[63] Thomas Berry, *The Dream of the Earth* (San Francisco: Sierra Club Books, 1990), 80-1. First published in 1988.

[64] Sallie McFague, *The Body of God: An Ecological Theology* (Minneapolis: Fortress Press, 1993).

Thus, there has arguably been a tension, particularly in Christianity, between a humble gratitude and regard for the gift of a sacred creation and the idea that we are masters of that creation. Whether or not nature is regarded as sacred on account of having been created by God and representing part of a "metaphysical trinity" of God, humans, and nature, a strong strand in traditional Christianity has viewed humans as *ordained* to have dominion over nature. This view of divine order (of nature as subordinate to and in the service of humanity), rather than a desacralization of nature, has arguably contributed the most to the religious justification for the exploitation and abuse of the wider natural world, despite Biblical warnings of the consequences of violating the covenantal relationship between God and humanity.

In sum, the emergence of the modern scientific worldview in the West and the anthropocentric strand in Christianity can both be seen to reinforce the view of nature as object, to be studied, used, and conquered for man's use, albeit from different perspectives. However, as the development of weapons of mass destruction and the ecological impacts of humans on the wider natural world have accelerated, so too have these worldviews been challenged. As the extent of the ecological crisis has become evident over the past 30-40 years, along with other theological shifts, particularly within Christianity but also among other traditions, "the cry of the earth" has joined the concern for the poor with voices of mystics and others to prompt the emergence of variegated earth stewardship, ecojustice, environmental ethics and ecotheology movements across many denominations and faiths (see Chapter 7). These movements also parallel deeper paradigm shifts in science and philosophy, discussed throughout Part II, that embrace a more holistic, or deep ecology perspective that does not divide humans from nature or spirit from matter but understands them to be integral and interdependent parts of a whole and sacred cosmos.

Chapter 4

Violence to Each Other, Violence to the Earth

May we look upon our treasures and the furniture of our houses and the garments in which we array ourselves and try whether the seeds of war have any nourishment in these our possessions or not.

—John Woolman[1]

The fate of the earth and the fate of the oppressed are inextricably linked.

—Sally McFague[2]

…there is a fundamental connection in Western culture, and in patriarchal cultures generally, between the domination of women and the domination of nature, both culturally/symbolically and socioeconomically.

—Rosemary Radford Ruether[3]

We are accustomed to thinking of violence first and foremost as individual acts of violence of one person to another or collectively as acts of war and conflict. We're less accustomed to thinking of ecological damage—the direct or indirect destruction of animals, forests, lands, and oceans—as violence, except perhaps when we consider the mass slaughter of buffalo, elephants, or gorillas; the clear-cutting of vast expanses of Amazonian forest; or the dynamiting of mountaintops in Appalachia. And we are much less accustomed to seeing the connections between war and conflict and ecological destruction, described in Chapter 1, both in terms of direct ecological destruction, via the effects of shelling, bombing, fires, and pollution, for example, and indirectly, via the enormous consumption of natural resources and the opportunity costs

---

[1] John Woolman, "A Plea for the Poor or A Word of Remembrance and a Caution to the Rich" in *The Journal and Major Essays of John Woolman*, ed. Phillips P. Moulton (New York: Oxford University Press, 1989), 255. First published in 1971.

[2] Sally McFague, "A Square in the Quilt," in *Spirit and Nature: Why the Environment is a Religious Issue*, eds. Stephen C. Rockefeller and John C. Elder (Boston: Beacon Press, 1992), 45.

[3] Rosemary Radford Ruether, "Deep Ecology, Ecofeminism and the Bible," in *Deep Ecology and World Religions: New Essays on Sacred Grounds*, eds. David Landis Barnhill and Roger S. Gottlieb (New York: State University of New York Press, 2001), 229.

in money, materials, and human energy that could be diverted to social goods and to conservation and ecological protection. Last, we are less accustomed to thinking of the many forms of human oppression and exploitation (such as the loss of indigenous ways of life, the exploitation of labor or ethnic minorities, or the effects of racism, poverty and political repression) as forms of structural cultural or social violence. In the same way, we have not necessarily considered the slow but irrevocable loss of millions of species, the erosion of soils, the dying of forests and oceans, and the pollution of rivers, as structural violence to nature. Further, until the emergence of the ecojustice movement, we have not fully considered the connections between the impacts of conflict and structural social violence on human societies and the impacts of wildfires, floods, droughts, landslides, tsunamis, pollution, the loss of food, and a lack of clean water, as they kill and injure people and other life-forms in often-parallel and highly unequal ways.

Nevertheless, as the extent and rate of global ecological destruction have accelerated over the past century, we are being challenged to think about violence in these unfamiliar ways, to examine its roots, and to explore how we might seek to prevent and heal our violence to the earth as much as among ourselves. Humans have always, of course, affected the ecologies in which they have lived and moved, from our earliest emergence as small groups of hunter-gatherers to later, settled agriculturalists—with domesticated animals and cultivated crops, and with limited use of organic materials or extraction of minerals for building or goods—to our present-day, technology-dominated consumer societies. Willful ecological destruction, or what I am defining as violence to the earth, is damage that goes beyond the inevitable destruction required to provide our basic needs for food; shelter; warmth; and material, social, and cultural wellbeing; and for abiding in long-term dynamic and sustainable balance with the ecologies and habitats in which each population lives.

Violence to the Earth: The Outer and Inner Landscape

Violence to the earth has both an outer landscape, seen in the many forms of ecological devastation and disharmony we cause to ecosystems and Earth systems (described in Chapter 1) and the economic, political, and technological forces that are driving that destruction, and an inner, landscape, driven in part by some of our dominant scientific and religious ways of thinking (described in Chapter 3), but also involving a yet deeper sociocultural and psychospiritual level, explored here and in following chapters.

From the wanton mass killings of elephants, rhinoceros, beavers, buffalo, sharks, whales, pangolins, armadillos, otters, etc. for fats, fur, jewelry, souvenirs, handbags, and medications; to factory farming; to the overuse of pesticides and chemical fertilizers; and to the pollution of air, water, and soil, we see the outer landscape of that violence. We are now capable of disrupting all levels of life from genes, cells, and microbiota to primates, from pole to pole, and from mountaintop to ocean floor. We have started to unravel the very fabric of life on Earth, and almost no life-forms have escaped our influence. To some extent this violence can be explained in terms of almost unintended consequences of our scientific and technological prowess, as described in Chapter 3, but also by our hubris, our material acquisitiveness, our so-called progress, and our willingness to wage war. Have we, in our Promethean quest to control and dominate each other and nature, opened a Pandora's box of consequences that we can no longer control—including nuclear war and runaway climate breakdown? And to what extent is it a conscious or unconscious act of domination or hostility toward nature, or a reflection of the way we view nature, either as a result of religious or cultural beliefs and a fundamental dualistic belief in our separation from the wider natural world? And how might violence to the earth be connected to a suppression of the feminine aspect in our patriarchal societies?

On one level, violence to each other and nature is the result of a complex array of economic and political forces (described in Chapter 2). These drive, and are driven by, materialism, the desire for power and possessions, enshrined in the economic systems by which we live, but also by subtler forces, including our desire for security and happiness. Further, as the Quaker John Woolman observed as early as the 18th century, our materialism, status seeking and overconsumption also contain with them the seeds of warfare and conflict, which in turn cause more destruction of nature.

To try to understand the underlying causes of our wanton violence to the earth, that goes so much further than what we need for our survival and wellbeing, we must also look at deeper forces, that is, the inner landscape of ecological violence, and its roots in the cultural paradigms and psychospiritual dimensions of our predicament. As explored in Chapter 3, our scientific and technological powers have given us the capability not only to harness nature for our own purposes but also to annihilate ourselves and nature. In this view, nature is reduced to a largely mechanistic realm of objects and matter, of separate parts rather than wholes, divorced from the realm of spirit. Second, our religiously and culturally grounded anthropocentrism—our (masculine) belief in our uniqueness, superiority, rights over other life-forms, and related beliefs in hierarchy, domination, and competition—has given rise to an instrumental view of nature subject to human domination.

But something deeper is also going on that arguably allows for a kind of violence toward nature that is part of that mechanistic and anthropocentric view but goes beyond it. First, until relatively recently, most biologists, agronomists, and people in general regarded other life-forms as largely insentient—incapable of reflection, complex emotions, or even the capacity to suffer or experience physical pain. Second, we may act violently from a perhaps unconscious sense of fear, alienation, and even hatred of nature as something that cannot ultimately be controlled, that has a mysterious power beyond our understanding. The experience of nature in its dangerous and *unpredictable* state—whether as disease, poisonous plants, dangerous animals, extreme weather, earthquakes, volcanic eruptions and so on—helps explain why we might regard nature as hostile or even as an enemy. Almost all of us experience fear around diseases and physical dangers in nature as a part of our survival instincts, and such fears are exacerbated when we don't have the means to control these dangers.[4] Third, as described in Chapter 3, we, particularly in the West, are the inheritors of a hubristic and masculine sense of agency that prompted the scientific endeavors of Bacon, Descartes, and those who followed, to force nature to reveal "her" workings and "conquer" nature. This urge, as well as a virility that permeates the relentless quest to push forward the frontiers of science, as in the pioneering thrusts of European settlers and colonists, has been translated in modern times into a kind of scientific and technological hubris that produces miracles of engineering, medicine and agriculture on one hand, and catastrophic destruction of our life-support systems on the other.

In the last two centuries, these tendencies to view nature as insentient or feared and to be controlled and exploited have arguably been reinforced by

---

[4] During my early years in public health, for example, I witnessed HIV/AIDS devastate populations in Africa and smaller groups in the U.S. and elsewhere, and the great fear and suffering it caused before the discovery of the virus and effective prevention methods and treatments. Our desire and moral obligation to prevent and treat these and other diseases does not, I believe, contradict an understanding of the wider and necessary cycle of life and death that we are all part of, without which natural systems cannot exist, and of viruses, bacteria, parasites, and pathogens as part of that cycle, many of which play vital roles in various processes in nature.

biological and evolutionary theories relating to the origins of violence in and toward humans and the wider natural world and on the dominance of the masculine aspect in human societies, described below.

Darwinism Made Me Do It? Biology and Violence

Early theories of "social Darwinism," a term first used by Joseph Fisher in the late 19th century and since applied to an extension of Darwin's theory of evolution to human societies, hinged on the idea that social forms of dominance and competition were part of the "struggle for survival" that governed the natural process of evolution, according to interpretations of Darwin's theory. These theories were attributed to philosophers and scientists such the writer Herbert Spencer, who coined the term "survival of the fittest" in the late 19th century (although his social theories were developed largely before Darwin's theory of evolution). Until recently, a strong emphasis has been placed on aggression, dominance, and competition as the predominant means of ensuring survival fitness—such as fighting among males during mating seasons, the violent defense of territories and food supplies, or the dominant behavior of alpha males among troops of gorillas or herds of musk ox— together with a focus on predator-prey behavior. This view is perhaps epitomized by Richard Dawkins' bestseller *The Selfish Gene*,[5] in which he posits that we are evolutionarily programmed to be selfish to ensure that our genes are passed on. The idea that such behavior in animals can then be extrapolated to human social systems and the degree to which aggression in nature explains or justifies violence, competition and domination among individuals and human groups and toward nature, has been a matter of continuing controversy. There has always been a danger in projecting our own (or our culture's) theories of social behavior (or a desire for simple explanations and solutions to our own complex behaviors) onto other people or species, using patterns in nature to justify such theories. Given the sheer complexity, diversity, and variability in behavior among the millions of species that inhabit the earth, simplistic notions about the connection between survival and domination and aggression are inadequate, as more recent bodies of research have demonstrated.[6]

---

[5] Richard Dawkins, *The Selfish Gene* (Oxford, U.K.: Oxford University Press, 1976).

[6] See, for example, D. Rubenstein and J. Kealey, "Cooperation, Conflict, and the Evolution of Complex Animal Societies," *Nature Education Knowledge* 3 (2010), 78, https://www.nature.com/scitable/knowledge/library/cooperation-conflict-and-the-evolution-of-complex-13236526 ; and Roberto Cazzolla Gatti, "A Conceptual Model of

Recent research by behavioral scientists, primatologists, and biologists—as well as strong moral opposition to such interpretations by religious thinkers, ethicists, and scientists—has demonstrated much deeper complexities in the animal world, where cooperation, love and affection, and altruism are both evident and clearly vital to survival of both groups and the individuals within them; where communal protection, sharing of food or shelter, and care of "weaker" or injured group members is observed; where groups avoid conflict with others by avoiding their territories; and where strong kinship bonds are extended beyond the family. For example, numerous exceptions to generalized behavioral theories abound, even among closely related species (e.g., as the well-known bonobo vs. chimpanzee argument for and against the idea of aggression as a characteristic feature of primate behavior illustrates). Such observations have challenged the emphasis on notions of "fitness" as characterized predominantly by dominance, aggression, strength, and competition. In addition, scientists continue to revise earlier ideas about the degree to which animals, or even some plants, possess forms of sentience, emotions, intelligence, altruism, and the ability to communicate, love, and suffer, leading to the discovery that more living beings may possess these capabilities than previously thought. Perhaps we are no longer quite as sanguine about massive factory farms, or about keeping animals in cramped quarters in zoos, or clear-cutting ancient forests—not only on health, religious, or environmental grounds, but based on the growing realization, as we will explore in forthcoming chapters, that all beings have a measure of sentience as well as intrinsic worth as part of the commonwealth of life.

Violence and Subordination of the Feminine

"The feminine" as a subject among historians, literary scholars, and feminists entered the collective consciousness of millions in the mid 20th century with the writings of Simone de Beauvoir, Marina Warner, and Betty Friedan, among others. After Carl Jung, following earlier theorists, developed the concepts of the anima (or feminine) and animus (or masculine) archetypes that are present (largely unconsciously) in both women and men, though dominant in one or the other, the debate about what constitutes "feminine" and "masculine" characteristics has continued. In various texts, the feminine refers variously to compassion, loving kindness, receptivity, passivity, cooper-

New Hypothesis on the Evolution of Biodiversity," *Biologia* 71 (2016): 343-51. http://www.doi.org/10.1515/biolog-2016-0032.

ation, nurturing, intuition, eros, and the relative lack (compared with the masculine) of such characteristics as aggression, assertiveness, "alpha" behavior, outward activity, egotism, individualism, and rationality ("logos").

Innumerable debates have ensued about the extent to which we agree on labeling these characteristics in this way, and to what extent they are embodied in women or in men. The question of whether they are considered genetically and physiologically determined (the essentialist argument) or socially or culturally constructed (the constructivist argument), or even whether we should think in terms of masculine or feminine aspects in the first place, has also provoked fierce debate.[7] For example, in the 1980s, Carol Gilligan and other researchers identified several characteristics that were more prominent among boys than girls, such as autonomy and outward aggression and conversely, those that were more common among girls than boys, such as empathy, relationality, and contextual thinking.[8] These traits, plus the roles more women than men play in society (carers, nurses, mothers, nurturers of relationships, etc.), have clearly been culturally encouraged from very early ages, as have more self-assertive, competitive, and "tough" or even violent behaviors in boys. The fact that anthropologists and social scientists have repeatedly observed great variations in behavior and social roles among individual and groups of men and boys and women and girls in different societies suggests that such variations are strongly influenced by cultural and social norms and cannot be explained largely by biologically determined differences between the sexes.

The outcome of these arguments, as an aspect of the wider "nature-nurture" debate that has continued for many decades, has obviously profound political and social ramifications. As with the arguments for and against the "social Darwinism" view, there is a clear danger that an overemphasis on biological or genetic determinism can be used to justify a wide range of discriminatory views and policies, as evidenced by the devastating impact of racial and eugenics theories in justifying racial and ethnic oppression, for

---

[7] Gender essentialism and social constructionism have been fiercely debated over the past half century. [See, for example, the widely cited overview by Janis Bolan, "Essentialism, Constructionism, and Feminist Psychology," *Psychology of Women Quarterly* 17 (1993), 5-21, https://doi.org/10.1111/j.1471-6402.1993.tb00673.x.] Whether the feminine aspect is considered socially constructed, biologically determined, or both, the social reality, at least in most Western societies, is that women more typically exhibit characteristics considered "feminine" and men those considered "masculine," and that many social roles are either male- or female-dominated, both historically and to the present day.

[8] Carol Gilligan, *In a Different Voice: Psychological Theory and Women's Development* (Cambridge, MA: Harvard University Press, 1982).

example. Similarly, there is a danger that an overly deterministic view of sex differences can be used to justify the oppression of women by men, and the justification of violence by men. In one important sense, the "nature-nurture" debate has been a kind of red herring that ultimately cannot be resolved, any more than the idea of a mind-body split can be "resolved". First, as new research gives us greater insight into the multiplicity of epigenetic effects and the intimate interaction and feedback between genes, physiology, and environment (upbringing, culture, experiences, social roles, and so on), it is increasingly clear their relative influences cannot be effectively considered as separate, or disentangled. There is no absolute either-or. Second, as genotyping and genetic testing have become increasingly sophisticated and commonplace over the past two decades, it is clear that interpersonal genetic variation exceeds that between groups on many of the genetic markers we can measure. Third, as discussed above, there is abundant evidence of wide cultural variation in cultural and social roles across human groups across historical periods, strongly suggesting that cultural, moral and religious norms and traditions significantly outweigh the influence of biologically determinants of behavior.

Focusing on these unresolvable arguments can also distract from a critical question: To what extent does subordination of the feminine aspect (as so characterized) *in both women and men*—as evidenced by a lack of nurturing, love, cooperation, nonviolence, mutuality, reciprocity, and a sense of the kinship of all beings—contribute to violence not only toward women and men but also toward the wider natural world, as the dominance of the masculine aspects of rationality, competition, aggression and conquest have been institutionalized in capitalism, communism, industrialism, colonialism, militarism, and many forms of religious expression? And to what extent can we prevent or ameliorate violence to each other and the earth by changing our spiritual and moral perspective, including restoring the feminine aspect, i.e., that aspect of our shared humanity in both women and men that has the capacity for love, unity, and communality with all beings?

The Ecofeminist Perspective

Ecofeminism is a heterogeneous movement that contains a diverse range of perspectives linking the modern women's movement with ecological concerns. While definitions of ecofeminism vary, one of the central tenets is that both women and nature have been considered as inferior, object, or "other" in patriarchal societies, and that violence toward and oppression of women is linked with exploitation of the earth. As some writers have put it, the rape of women is linked with the rape of the earth.[9] As both women and nature have similarly been accorded feminine and thus inferior status in patriarchal societies, so too have many of the characteristics that are often associated with the feminine and posed as separate "opposites": reason vs. emotion/intuition, autonomy vs. interconnectedness, objectivity vs. subjectivity, domination/control vs. cooperation, mind vs. body, violence vs. nurturance, agency vs. receptivity. The ecofeminist view emphasizes a nondualistic, nonhierarchical position and, where it takes a spiritual perspective, tends to be more universalist, and more panentheistic, polytheistic, or pantheistic than the monotheism of, say, Christianity. Divinity is seen less as a transcendent entity than as a simultaneously transcendent and immanent, life-giving, loving force embodied in human and natural life. Nature is a "matrix of interconnection." Male and female are restored to an equal and harmonious relationship with each other and with the natural world.

From an ecofeminist perspective, the dominance of the masculine aspect in Western patriarchal societies is a major factor in violence toward women and the exploitation and destruction of the wider natural world. Women have typically been considered "closer to nature" than men, and if nature is viewed as inert, passive, nonsacred, largely insentient, inferior, or as an object to be studied or used for our own purposes, then it can be captured, manipulated, controlled, exploited, and destroyed in much the same way that women and others, e.g., indigenous or subject peoples, have been economically exploited and subjugated, or raped and even murdered, in most societies up to the present day.

Visions of Nature as venerated mother goddess, derived from earlier pre- or non-Christian and indigenous spiritual traditions, and rediscovered and studied by feminist scholars, have been largely eclipsed or rendered seemingly irrelevant in the face of more patriarchal religious traditions.[10] Notwithstand

---

[9] Judith Plant, Introduction to Part One: "Remembering Who We Are: The Meaning of Feminism" in *Healing the Wounds: The Promise of Ecofeminism*, ed. Judith Plant (Philadelphia: New Society Publishers, 1989), 5.

[10] See, for example, Riane Eisler, *The Chalice and the Blade* (New York, Harper and Row, 1988); Marija Gimbutas, *Civilization of the Goddess: The World of Old Europe* (New York: Harper Collins, 1991); Rosemary Radford Ruether, *Goddesses and the Divine Feminine : A Western Religious History* (Berkeley, CA: University of California Press, 2006). Some writers have critiqued the "hierarchical dualisms," lack of egalitarianism, and alienation from nature that characterizes patriarchal societies and have sought to reimagine, though the lens of a Goddess spirituality and the rediscovery and celebration of matrifocal cultures, a

ing evidence of a small number of matrifocal or matristic societies in the past, the vast majority of social groups and nations we know about have been patriarchal in structure. As most traditional religions and the history of scientific and technological endeavors have been dominated by men, so too have human-to-human violence and warmaking. Such violence is reflected in the almost-universal pattern in patriarchal cultures of the subordination of women to men, in which women typically suffer an imbalance of economic and political power and risk direct violence, whether domestic abuse or sexual violence and rape, at the hands of men. Violence toward nature also has largely been the province of men.

To the extent to which men have been acculturated in our Western societies to reject or suppress their feminine aspect, Carl Jung believed that male violence toward women was, at least in part, a projection onto women of the feminine as a rejected or denied part of their own psyches. From an ecofeminist perspective, male fear or hostility toward women, and in particular their ability to produce life, may correlate with a fear or hostility toward "Mother Nature" as life-giver and nurturer. Writers such as Val Plumwood,[11] Susan Griffin,[12] and Rosemary Radford Ruether ground ecofeminism in the understanding that there is a deep connection between the domination and fear of women and the domination of nature. In Greek, Hebrew, and Christian traditions, Ruether argues, women have been identified with the (inferior) body and with nature and have been subject, like nature, to sexual and economic exploitation by men, who are identified with (superior) reason, ideas, spirit, and power. In addition, men have agency while women, like animals and the rest of the natural world, are characterized by passivity as well as inferiority.[13] Ruether identifies two strands within ecofeminism; one approaches the subjugation of women and nature as a social and cultural construction and seeks to "deconstruct" this dualistic patriarchal thinking and to rediscover our commonality as people and in relation to the natural world.[14] A second "es-

---

world where the dualisms male and female, heaven and earth, and transcendence and immanence are reunited in a communal relationship.

[11] Val Plumwood, *Feminism and the Mastery of Nature* (London: Routledge, 1992).

[12] Susan Griffin, *Woman and Nature: The Roaring Inside Her* (London: The Women's Press, 1984). First published in 1978.

[13] Rosemary Radford Ruether, "Ecofeminism and Theology," in *Ecotheology: Voices from South and North*, ed. David Hallman (Maryknoll, NY: World Council of Churches/Orbis Books, 1994), 199-204.

[14] Ruether, "Deep Ecology," 237.

sentialist" strand emphasizes the positive connections between women and nature as nurturers and life-givers.

Some ecofeminists have sought to develop a process view of theology (or thealogy). It emphasizes an embodied view of divinity; immanence of divinity rather than transcendence; and cyclical, dynamic, and interrelational life and evolving and nonhierarchical processes rather than an omniscient, omnipotent, perfected male God ruling over a fixed and immutable universe. Rosemary Radford Ruether and Heather Eaton have sought to develop a specific ecofeminist theology within a Christian framework. While critiquing overly simplistic and one-sided interpretations of Biblical texts as sanctioning the exploitation of women and the earth, they have reinterpreted Hebrew and Christian Biblical texts in terms of their exposition of the covenantal and sacramental relationships to the divine and the creation.[15]

Ruether has critiqued the deep ecology movement for its failure to acknowledge the patriarchal element in both Christian and social oppression of women and nature. She has also emphasized the need to develop a connection within Western ecofeminism between race, class, and poverty and the subjugation of women and the impoverishment of the natural world in patriarchal societies. Ecofeminists in Latin America, Africa, and Asia have developed strong connections, some along the lines of the liberation theology movement in Latin America, between action to reverse the impact of globalization on the poor, where the burden is disproportionately borne by women, and on the agricultural land and forests and water courses, where the bulk of food production is often done by women.[16]

A critical question raised by ecofeminism is the extent to which certain attributes that we associate with masculinity have become unbalanced and overdominant, both in individuals and in the social structures of patriarchy, leading to the levels of violence, aggression, and destructive acts towards each other and the earth that are taking us ever closer to ecocide and collective suicide as the unleashing of nuclear war or climate-induced ecological collapse. More important, the question becomes how this violence, arrogance, and destructiveness can be transmuted and transformed. Jung believed that

---

[15] Heather Eaton, "Ecological-Feminist Theology: Contributions and Challenges," in *Theology for Earth Community*, ed. Dieter Hessel. (Maryknoll, NY: Orbis Books, 1996), 77-92; Rosemary Radford Ruether, *Integrating Feminism, Globalization and World Religions* (Lanham, MD: Rowman and Littlefield Publishing, Inc., 2005); Rosemary Radford Ruether, *Gaia and God: An Ecofeminist Theology of Earth Healing* (San Francisco: Harper, 1989).

[16] Ruether, "Deep Ecology," 229-41.

understanding the psyche was key to collective human survival, which was threatened, in his view, by a lack of understanding of the forces within the psyche that could lead to our extinction. For Jung, the wholeness of the psyche—in which polarities, including the masculine and feminine, are valued, balanced, and given expression—can be realized only through a transformational process of what he called individuation, in which various aspects of the psyche are integrated. As I will explore further in Chapters 5 and 11, many writers, including Jung and other psychologists, feminists, sociologists, and others, have argued that Western societies in particular need to "restore the feminine principle," to reinstate the *balance* between the masculine and feminine aspects of ourselves, both psychospiritually and in their currently distorted and dangerous outward expressions in militarism, scientism, predatory economics, and the exploitation of people and the planet, and thereby transform them.

The Psychology of Apocalyptic Violence: Climate Breakdown and Nuclear War

As explored here, our violence is, in part, a consequence of our hubristic attempt to control, manipulate or conquer other groups of humans and nature, a project that, aided by our brilliant scientific and technological capabilities, is now threatening to destroy us. There also deeper psychospiritual forces at work that may help explain why we are capable of such suicidal violence to each other and the earth and why we seem to be incapable of stopping it. Let's look at these forces further by examining the psychology of ultimate violence to each other and the earth—the intertwined existential threats of nuclear war and climate breakdown.

These deeper dimensions have, in part, to do with our capacity for denial, distancing, and numbing with regard to our destructive capability and its consequences. In part, these tendencies are related to the sheer enormity of our predicament. We appear to be unable to grasp the fact that we are facing an existential crisis; that we can destroy much of human life and many of other life-forms through all-out nuclear war or ecological devastation. Like Frankenstein, through ignorance, willful blindness, hubris or delusion, we have somehow created a monster that we can scarcely understand and cannot seem to control. Yet, as Jung suggested, we know so little about the psychological and spiritual aspects of this fearful capability, and lack the necessary wisdom to temper our cleverness. Despite our breathtaking ability to reach distant planets or to reveal the secrets of the tiniest subatomic particles, we are like children when it comes to understanding the inner psychospiritual landscape of our own minds and hearts.

Robert Jay Lifton, known for his seminal work on the psychological causes and consequences of warfare and mass violence, including Nazism and the use of nuclear weapons, has recently turned his attention to parallels between the moral and psychological impacts of nuclear weapons and climate breakdown. It is worth reflecting in some detail on his analysis, described below, as it can inform our understanding of why we have got to this critical stage in the earth's existence and point to ways we might, as Einstein urged, change our way of thinking and develop new paradigms to live by. Although Lifton focuses more closely on the social impacts of our destructive capabilities, his work also points to the fact (explored in greater depth in Chapter 5), that the very enormity of our predicament creates and is created by a profound sense of separation and distancing from the wider natural world, a sense that has its roots in our traditional religious and scientific worldviews, as described earlier, but which have, arguably, hidden roots in the depths of our psyches.

The "apocalyptic twins" of nuclear war and climate breakdown, as Lifton calls them,[17] demonstrate both the connections between human-to-human and ecological violence and similarities and the differences in their psychological causes and consequences, including the ways we feel we can or cannot control the forces they have unleashed. Perhaps the most dramatic example of destruction during warfare is the effects of the two nuclear bombs dropped on Hiroshima and Nagasaki on August 6 and 9, 1945, not only because they were among the most destructive single actions of the second World War to humans, infrastructure, and the environment, but also because of the unique and unprecedented nature of what they came to represent and presage. The advent of nuclear weapons represented a paradigm shift in thinking in comparison with what were later called "conventional weapons," and their advent gave rise to widespread psychological, moral, and ethical dilemmas that had arguably not existed before.

First, even with the first atomic bombs at Hiroshima and Nagasaki, which released energy equal to 13 and 20 kilotons of TNT, respectively, the idea of radiation fallout that lasted for decades or even hundreds of years raised the

---

[17] Robert Jay Lifton, *The Climate Swerve: Reflections on Mind, Hope, and Survival* (New York: The New Press, 2017), 17 et seq.

moral dilemma of *responsibility to future generations* in a new way. Notably, these early bombs were tiny in comparison with later thermonuclear ("hydrogen" or "H") warheads, which eventually reached as much as 20 megatons. Nuclear weapons became, as Lifton has described it, the first *transgenerational* weapon.[18] Second, perhaps for the first time, as he recounts in his studies of Hiroshima survivors, many feared that *nature itself had been destroyed* by the bomb, perhaps forever (Will the trees ever blossom again? he recalls one survivor asking). Nature would no longer be protection against such weapons, and maybe against other kinds of weapons that could be developed. This fear, a kind of "cosmic uncertainty" as Lifton puts it, continues to haunt both survivors and those who learn about the bombs.[19] Even very young people, in studies conducted at Harvard[20] and elsewhere, reported extreme anxiety about the future, feeling that their lives would be cut short by all-out nuclear war.

Third, the bomb gave rise to highly contradictory sentiments ranging from a kind of hubristic euphoria and awe at what had been created—and the almost godlike power it had given us, even the possibility of a purification and spiritual rebirth (according to some fundamentalists)—to a deep horror that unleashing this monster had made real the possible annihilation of all human life, added to which was the fear that its use was uncontrollable.[21] In this sense, then, the atom bomb opened a Pandora's box, not only for nuclear holocaust but also for *our capacity and willingness to risk our own extinction.* As the writings of several nuclear scientists themselves attest, many were appalled at the actual use of the bomb on human populations and the intention to build up vast arsenals of ever-more-powerful weapons, making Armageddon or Doomsday a real possibility.[22] As Lifton reported many years later, "the

---

[18] Robert Jay Lifton and Greg Mitchell, *Hiroshima in America: A Half Century of Denial* (New York: Avon Books, 1995), 308.

[19] Lifton, *The Climate Swerve*, 8-9.

[20] William Beardslee, Institute of Medicine Steering Committee on the Medical Implications of Nuclear War, "Children's and Adolescents' Perceptions of the Threat of Nuclear War: Implications of Recent Studies," in *The Medical Implications of Nuclear War*, eds. Fred Solomon and Robert Q. Marston (Washington: National Academies Press, 1986), 413-34.

[21] Lifton and Mitchell, *Hiroshima*, 303-5.

[22] It is doubtful whether ecological destruction, even as a "side effect," was uppermost in the minds of the scientists working on the Manhattan Project, President Truman, or the Allied generals, given their immediate priorities, as Lifton and Mitchell describe in *Hiroshima in America*. However, the long-term human health effects of radiation, including environmental contamination, were of significant concern to many.

world's...creative imagination was forever altered by Hiroshima—as much by its larger threat of doom as by its own, immediate horror."[23]

Fourth, Lifton discovered that the bomb gave rise to a condition he named *psychic numbing*,[24] whereby the sheer enormity of the potential destruction, combined with misinformation and secrecy, leads to an inability or unwillingness to feel emotionally connected to what has happened or what might happen. More dangerously, it can give rise to a pervasive and diffuse numbness about *other* forms of violence and suffering.[25] Lifton also describes how people can exhibit what he calls *doubling*, the existence of two near-autonomous halves of the self, whereby a person can be simultaneously kind and loving in some circumstances and yet capable of adapting to or participating in highly destructive and murderous actions and systems.

Fifth, the bomb gave rise to a particularly pernicious form of what Lifton calls *moral inversion*, a kind of Orwellian reversal, exemplified by the urgent need on the part of politicians and military leaders to justify and "find virtue in" the first use in World War II and the subsequent build-up of nuclear weapons, by making the argument that such bombs *save* lives and ensure the preservation of our exceptional *and good* way of life.[26] Such justifications serve both to numb our feelings and our consciences about victims and the destruction of human societies and nature across many generations[27] and to deny, conceal, or lie about the extent of potential or actual destruction to present or future generations.[28] Yet another consequence has been the increasing public awareness that politicians have often lied, denied, or obfuscated in justifying the need for such weapons, and about the likelihood of survival and the dangers of radiation from production sites or fallout, leading to growing distrust of official narratives and of scientists and technologists.[29]

---

[23] Lifton and Mitchell, *Hiroshima*, 342.

[24] Lifton and Mitchell, *Hiroshima*, 337-8.

[25] Lifton and Mitchell, *Hiroshima*, 339.

[26] Lifton and Mitchell, *Hiroshima*, 308-9.

[27] Lifton and Mitchell (*Hiroshima*, 312) cite Joseph Nye (a former assistant Secretary of Defense in the Clinton Administration), from Nye's book *Nuclear Ethics* (New York: Free Press, 1986), who claimed that a "tiny probability" of human extinction doesn't mean that "our generation has no rights to take risks." Lifton notes that Nye claimed that an obligation (to take into account future generations) could "establish a dictatorship" for future generations over the present one. See also Lifton and Mitchell, *Hiroshima*, 337-40.

[28] Lifton and Mitchell, *Hiroshima*, 329-35.

[29] Nowhere, perhaps, has questionable information been more evident than in attempts to reassure citizens of the survivability of a nuclear attack, from the "duck and cover" drills of the 1950s to the "Crisis Relocation Plan" of the early Reagan years to the UK government

Boiling Frogs: Psychological Reponses to Climate Breakdown

Although environmental destruction is rarely discussed as part of the consequences of the production and use of nuclear weapons, with the exception of health hazards from radiation leaks or fallout (with which I am familiar in my own field of research), what is striking is that many responses to the advent of nuclear weapons—hubris, denial and concealment, existential anxiety, psychic numbing, moral inversion, doubling, betrayal, distrust, rage, and grief—can be found in responses to climate breakdown today. There are also other similarities and differences between our responses to nuclear weapons and to climate breakdown. The possibility of nuclear war has diminished in public concern, although it may actually be *more* likely as a consequence of the unfolding global climate crisis. Despite the existence of some 10,000 warheads worldwide (down from a peak of over 60,000 in the late 1980s),[30] no nuclear weapons have (yet) been used since the Trinity test and Hiroshima and Nagasaki bombings in 1945 (notwithstanding accidents and near-misses)—a date occurring before the lifetimes of roughly 90% of the world's current population.[31] However, if even a proportion of the total arsenal is launched (particularly with no certainty as to the extent of escalation), we can expect annihilation and extinction of most of our existing civilizations and incalculable ecological destruction in a matter of minutes. In contrast, climate disruption and looming ecological collapse presents the problem of the slowly boiling frog: It appears to be happening at a slow enough pace to be ignored or denied, partly because we find it hard to grasp exponential acceleration and

---

booklet, distributed to every household, called *Protect and Survive.* The notion that people can protect themselves from nuclear bomb blasts or radiation fallout in a full-scale nuclear attack by hiding under a desk, piling soil on their roofs, or relocating to safe areas has been widely challenged and satirized.

[30] Hans Kristensen and Robert Norris, *Nuclear Notebook: Nuclear Arsenals of the World* (Chicago: Bulletin of Atomic Scientists), https://thebulletin.org/nuclear-notebook-multimedia. The authors also calculated that as of 2013, a cumulative 125,000 warheads had been produced, 97% by the U.S. and the Soviet Union/Russia (after reaching a peak of over 800,000 times the combined force of the Hiroshima and Nagasaki bombs). Fewer warheads now exist, but nuclear arsenals continue to be upgraded and modernized, and more countries now possess them—at least nine at the last count. https://thebulletin.org/2013/september/global-nuclear-weapons-inventories-1945-2013. (The megaton yields of today's warheads are many times those of the first atomic bombs. The relationship between yield and impact depends on various factors, including the design, accuracy of the missile, and where the weapon detonates relative to ground level.)

[31] United Nations Department of Economic and Social Affairs, Population Division, *World Population Prospects: The 2017 Revision, Key Findings and Advance Tables.* Working Paper No. ESA/P/WP/248 (New York: UN, 2017), https://population.un.org/wpp/Publications/Files/WPP2017_KeyFindings.pdf.

feedbacks, partly by means of the psychological mechanisms described above, and in more pernicious ways by climate deniers, pseudoscientists, or technologists' promises of miraculous fixes. This apparent gradualness potentially gives us time (or the illusion of time) to consider mitigation, adaptation, and survival (including the idea of escape to some remote parts of the world, at least for the rich and well-positioned),[32] but it also allows those with corporate and political power to suppress information, to confuse and distort the scientific discourse, and block the transition to sustainable economies and maintain business-as-usual practices and thinking as long as possible.

Notwithstanding certain fundamentalist positions that envisage and welcome "end times" as a way of selective salvation and renewal, what can the moral and psychospiritual response be, that doesn't involve denial or numbing or false optimism? Do we take ecological collapse seriously enough to take measures to prevent or mitigate it in time, and that aren't just more fixes that will fail? Or do we feel, as Lifton documents with respect to nuclear annihilation and the climate crisis, a sense of helpless impotence, despair, and feelings of doom and "futurelessness," as we absorb the unavoidable physics and chemistry of climate disruption so that, as in a speeding car approaching a cliff edge, it turns out it's too late to apply the brakes?

Paradoxically, once we can imagine our collective extinction, we arguably make it a possibility embodied in our technological capacity to bring it about. But at the same time, it is a *failure of imagination* that makes its manifestation more likely—the failure to imagine, first, what we are really risking; and second, a profound *moral* failure of imagination, as if we can readily entertain the notion that mass destruction and ecocide are somehow justified. (For what? Profit? Power? A distorted view of human achievement and progress?) Third, as more people feel like the creator of Frankenstein's monster, apparently helpless in the face of our own creation, it is a failure to imagine that we can still transform the economic, social, and technological systems we alone have created. Last, but I would argue, most critically, it is the extent to which we are suffering from a failure of *spiritual* imagination—that part of ourselves that knows and responds to the power of life, of beauty, of love; that part of us in intimate kinship with all that is; the sacredness of the Self within all things—and thus lack the vision, wisdom, compassion and courage to change

[32] Mark O'Connell, "Why Silicon Valley Billionaires Are Prepping for the Apocalypse in New Zealand," *The Guardian*, February 15, 2018, https://www.theguardian.com/news/2018/feb/15/why-silicon-valley-billionaires-are-prepping-for-the-apocalypse-in-new-zealand.

direction. Like Icarus, we are discovering that we cannot fly too close to the sun—we cannot bend the inescapable laws of nature—yet we seem to be sleepwalking toward catastrophe, trapped between our hubris and our inability to imagine a different future.

Lifton argues that, as in the case of weapons of mass destruction, we must first reach the stage of "formed awareness" before we can act to prevent or avoid climate catastrophe.[33] This means recognizing that using the same familiar economic, technological, and related approaches and corporate thinking that produced them—and that may have worked for us up to a certain point—have become maladaptive. Lifton speaks of the ineffectiveness of "stranded ethics" and "stranded adaptation" in addition to "stranded assets" such as fossil fuels.[34] He points out that, whereas there is always a possibility of abolishing nuclear weapons, however unlikely that may seem for many years,[35] no such option is possible with climate breakdown. Our only choice now is mitigation and adaptation, not abolition, and this requires and can bring about a new form of awareness of our mutual interdependency. Lifton points out a new biological emphasis not on Dawkins's "selfish gene" (described above) but on "species identity" or E.O. Wilson's "evolution for the good of the group," and he argues that such an identity is now necessary for our survival.[36] Although Lifton has little to say about the wider natural world, in my view, a new species identity would mean, more critically, a new awareness of our dependence on each other and nature. Although Lifton doesn't say so, it comes down to *"If we are to survive, you must survive, and if we destroy you, we destroy ourselves,"* and this includes all humanity and all life on Earth.

---

[33] Lifton, *The Climate Swerve*, 137.

[34] Lifton, *The Climate Swerve*, 138.

[35] The movement to abolish nuclear weapons starting in the 1950s took place in an era of ever-escalating tensions and weapons buildups. Physicians for Social Responsibility (PSR) and related groups in the 1970s and beyond recognized that nuclear war represented the single biggest potential threat to public health facing humanity (climate breakdown had yet to become its "apocalyptic twin"). While abolition has yet to be achieved, by the mid-2000s, for perhaps the first time, a UN attempt to negotiate a binding treaty "to prohibit nuclear weapons, leading towards their total elimination" was put forward and adopted in July 2017 by 122 states at a conference attended by a large majority of states and nongovernmental organizations. It awaits ratification. (See United Nations Office for Nuclear Disarmament Affairs, Treaty on the Prohibition of Nuclear Weapons, July 7, 2017, https://www.un.org/disarmament/wmd/nuclear/tpnw/.)

[36] Lifton, *The Climate Swerve*, 150.

In sum, both ecofeminist and psychological analyses point to the need to understand the inner, psychological landscape of violence in order to address the deeper causes and conditions of our violence to each other and the earth. Specifically, the ecofeminist and Jungian perspective speaks to the need to restore what is characterized as the feminine aspect, meaning that part of both men and women that is concerned with seeking harmony, cooperation, nonviolence, nurturing, and caring for each other and the earth. In other words, we need to *integrate and balance* what have been thought of as dualistic, separate, or opposite and competing masculine and feminine aspects. This task mirrors the need for the integration of rationality and emotion, of the human-nature-divine relationship, indeed of spirit and matter itself, due in part to the separation brought about by our dominant scientific and religious worldviews (described in Chapter 3).

However, a critical aspect of the task of overcoming our violence is only indirectly or implicitly addressed by the ecofeminist and psychological perspectives explored above. Most writers pay relatively little explicit attention to the deeper spiritual dimension of our predicament. Some of the great sages and mystics, from the writers of the Vedas to the Buddha, Jesus and beyond, exemplify both a perfection of integration of masculine and feminine aspects in human form and of consciousness raised above dualism, opposition, hierarchy, and separation, and this lies at the heart of the ecological crisis and its healing. It is also the path by which reason and heart, spirit and matter, religions and science, and our violence to each other and the earth, can be reconciled, integrated and transformed. In Part II, I will explore the spiritual dimension of our ecological predicament and how we might ground the task of healing ourselves and the earth. The wisdom that is always available to us in the great traditions also lies in the deepest recesses of our being, and can teach us that the ground of nonviolence and a sustainable life on this earth is a growing realization of our ultimate integrity, wholeness, unity, and reciprocity. It is a realization born of love, the great unifying force, and is the province of man and woman alike.

PART II

PRINCIPLES

The day is not far distant when humanity will realise that biologically it is faced with a choice between suicide and adoration.

—Pierre Teilhard de Chardin

There are a thousand hacking at the branches of evil to one who is striking at the root...

—Henry David Thoreau

There is a principle which is pure, placed in the human mind, which in different places and ages hath had different names.... It is deep and inward, confined to no forms of religion nor excluded from any, where the heart stands in perfect sincerity.

—John Woolman

Pierre Teilhard de Chardin, *The Divine Milieu: An Essay on the Interior Life* (New York: Harper & Row, 2001), 37. https://archive.org/details/TheDivineMilieu/. First published in 1957.

Henry David Thoreau, *Walden, or Living in the Woods* (New York: New American Library Edition, 1963), 56. First published in 1854.

John Woolman, "Considerations on Keeping of Negroes, Part Second," in *The Journal and Major Essays of John Woolman*, ed. Phillips P. Moulton (Richmond, IN: Friends United Press, 1989), 236. First published in 1971.

Chapter 5

Toward a Whole Earth Community: The Spiritual Foundation

I believe in advaita, I believe in the essential unity of man, and, for that matter, of all that lives. Therefore I believe that if one man gains spiritually, the whole world gains with him and if one man fails, the whole world fails to that extent.

—Mahatma Gandhi[1]

...we can say today that man is far too clever to be able to survive without wisdom. ...The exclusion of wisdom from economics, science and technology was something which we could perhaps get away with for a little while, as long as we were relatively unsuccessful; but now that we have become very successful, the problem of spiritual and moral truth moves into the central position.

—E.F. Schumacher[2]

There is not a 'fragment' in all nature, for every relative fragment of one thing is a full harmonious unit in itself.

—John Muir[3]

The ecological crisis is, at its roots, a moral and spiritual crisis. In the absence of a moral and spiritual ground of action in our economies, technologies, and politics, we will not change our way of being in the world sufficiently over the long term to live sustainably together with the wider natural world and within the earth's limits. Based on the now-abundant evidence of increasing global ecological destruction and the unbending reality of living on a finite planet with finite resources, we, particularly those of us who live in

---

[1] M.K. Gandhi, "Not Even Half Mast," *Young India,* Vol. 2 (1924-26), December 4, 1924, 419.

[2] E.F. Schumacher, *Small Is Beautiful: Economics as if People Mattered* (New York: Harper Colophon, 1975), 30. First published in 1973.

[3] John Muir, *A Thousand Mile Walk to the Gulf,* ed. William Frederic Badè (Boston and New York: Houghton Mifflin Company; Cambridge: The Riverside Press, 1916), 164.

material comfort in the wealthiest countries or who have the most wealth and power in the world, must radically transform our ways of thinking and living if humans and the life-forms we depend on are to survive. Yet, despite mounting evidence that our high levels of consumption and wealth have failed to bring the security, wellbeing, or contentment they promised to large numbers of people, many of us in richer countries continue to consume too much, and pollute and destroy too much, to the point where we are close to irreversible global ecological collapse. However, *we clearly have the collective intelligence, knowledge, and technological capacity to live sustainably within the limits imposed by nature*, even at or close to our current and projected population levels. The question becomes, do we have the will and the *wisdom* to do so? And what will guide us?

In the foregoing chapters, I have explored some of the interacting driving forces—including our prevailing models of continuous growth; globalized forms of capitalism that prioritize short-term economic gain over ecological concerns; the destructive aspects of our science and technological capacities; the anthropocentrism that characterizes our most culturally dominant religions; and the dominance of violence, power, and the masculine—and how they have arguably played a part in bringing us to our present predicament. For example, we saw in Chapter 3 how, particularly in the West, via traditional Christianity and the evolution of the Western scientific worldview, we absorbed an essentially dualistic, hierarchical, dominating, and competitive worldview that has profoundly influenced our view of our relationship with whatever we conceive of as the divine and with the wider natural world.

From the abundant evidence of the existential threat posed by the ecological crisis and the risk of nuclear or climate breakdown-induced extinction of much life on Earth, our current scientific-technological, economic, and political approaches to addressing it are clearly failing, and failing spectacularly and tragically. As E.F. Schumacher wrote in the 1970s:

> It is no longer possible to believe that any political or economic reforms, or scientific advance, or technological progress could solve the life-and-death problems of industrial society. They lie too deep, in the soul and heart of every one of us.[4]

Although we will need to use a range of economic, technological, and policy tools to address our predicament, we will need to use them in substantially, often radically, different ways; we cannot use the same approaches that got us

[4] E.F. Schumacher, *Good Work* (New York, Harper and Row, 1979), 36.

into this crisis in the first place. In other words, as Einstein wisely warned, we must change our ways of thinking—and acting—or drift toward unparalleled catastrophe. And this change, as Teilhard de Chardin reminds us, is now becoming a stark choice between what he describes as "suicide and adoration."

To begin to understand the nature of the spiritual and moral transformation that we are called to undertake requires a deeper understanding of our ways of thinking, our paradigms, and our beliefs, which lie at the spiritual roots of the crisis.

Habits of Mind, Habits of Heart: Our Ways of Thinking

We all hold beliefs and attitudes about life, meaning, purpose, right and wrong, and how the world works and why, whether or not we articulate them to ourselves or others. I suggest that we frame our beliefs and attitudes at four levels, which to some extent overlap with one another. The first level is that of pragmatism—for example, I might say I "believe in" practicing nonviolence in certain circumstances because it sometimes works to my or my group's benefit (e.g., when I know I can't beat an opponent). The second, cultural-ethical level is one in which I believe that it is right or wrong to do certain things (commit murder or go to war, for example) based on the culturally accepted mores and ethics of the society or group I live in. At a third level, I might believe that something is right or wrong based on formal religious or scriptural teachings or a position that I accept from a religious authority, or my own interpretation of a religious teaching (e.g., "Thou shalt not kill"). The fourth, or spiritual-mystical level, is one in which I experience an inward (or mystical) realization of a deep truth that convinces me and my conscience of its reality and rightness, whether or not this is reflected in a religious or social-cultural traditions that surround me. In my experience, what we think and believe may come from more than one level (sometimes all four), in ways we may not be fully conscious of. Realizing a truth on a spiritual-mystical level, however, usually (not always) happens only after much reflection, and, like an Aha!, it is more likely to stick in the face of dissent (even penalty or persecution), becoming part of one's unshakeable core be liefs. (Quakers sometimes talk about this deep sense of what's true and right as being "convicted" of the truth, and when called upon to act in concert with that belief at peril of violating their conscience or soul, say "I can do no other.") Most of us, most of the time, however, absorb our ways of thinking and believing osmotically and partly unconsciously from the familial, cultural, economic, social, political, and religious worlds into which we are born or grow up, as described next.

Frames, Contexts, and Paradigms

As individuals, we are influenced from birth by the constant and ongoing interaction of our genes and physiologies with our environment; by our race, gender, and sex; by our parents or parent figures; by our teachers and other authority figures in our early lives; by what we read, see, and learn from the media to which we are exposed, also almost from birth; by the political and social culture, country, and historical period; by significant events in our lives; and (whether we realize it or not) by the wider natural world we inhabit. For example, we have been able to better understand the physical and biological forces that shape our experience of the world (climate, earthquakes, volcanic eruptions, pathogens and so on) and to start to deal with the risks they pose to human life and health only relatively recently in human history. Yet, although we may like to think of ourselves as moderns, who no longer placate the gods or regard plagues as divine punishment, we often cling to superstitions, amulets, rituals, and the like in the face of dangers, disasters, and incurable or mysterious diseases as much as our distant ancestors did in their untamed forests and jungles.

We are both the produced and the producers of our lives as they unfold. We are both rational and irrational and full of conflicting ideas and emotions; semiconscious drives and impulses; and biological instincts inherited from our evolutionary forebears. We are creaturely selves who also have intellectual, moral, and divine qualities—soul or spirit, and the capacity to self-reflect, love, and gaze in wonder at the beauty of the universe. We deal, as humans, with the blessings and angst that are the conditions and contradictory needs of our humanness (fears of mortality, our shame, insecurities, egotism, violence, appetites, and desires) alongside our "better angels": love, forgiveness, courage, compassion, a sense of kinship with all beings, and of justice, beauty, and truth. Depth psychologists such as Carl Jung warned about how little we know about the workings of the psyche, despite the fact that, as he saw it, our unconscious ideas, fears and desires, when repressed, denied, or projected both individually and collectively, are the primary danger for humanity's survival.

Cognitive linguists such as George Lakoff talk of the underlying cognitive "frames" and "central metaphors"[5] by which we conceptualize, understand, and rationalize our world, our moral universe, and our behavior. He describes how powerfully our fundamental ways of thinking or frames influence our beliefs, attitudes, and behaviors, and even our very way of perceiving the world around us. We typically form our moral concepts and values at an early age, and they become part of the almost invisible, even unconscious internal furniture of our minds. These deeply embedded frames may or may not be questioned or revised as we mature. Often, as Lakoff has shown, these concepts are strongly and defensively held, as virtually religious beliefs, and they can be highly resistant to rational argument, facts, and evidence, as if our core selves are under threat. As I would summarize it, *facts tend to bounce off frames*; hence, for example, the denial of climate change, including among those who have no economic or other vested interests in doing so. In his book, *Moral Politics*,[6] Lakoff argued that we need to reframe nature as mother, nurturer, sustainer, provider, and giver of life and as having inherent value, rather than as property, resource, or even adversary, but that to persuade others, rational argument and facts alone are ineffective. We must, he argued, wed truths to values and make them explicit (e.g., through metaphor and story) if our collective consciousness is to change.

On a collective level, each group or society, at any one time and place in history, has a zeitgeist or gestalt of cultural beliefs, mores, and behaviors that forms the wider context of our individual lives and profoundly influences collective behavior. This gestalt is often semitransparent or even invisible to us, like water we swim in, and unless we question its frames or belief systems, we swim along unaware that there are very different ways of thinking and acting in the world. These conditions form the paradigms by which a culture lives at any one time. Periodically, however, as Thomas Kuhn described in his classic *The Structure of Scientific Revolutions*,[7] a *paradigm shift* can occur, defined as "a fundamental change in approach or underlying assumptions" at either an individual or societal level.

---

[5] George Lakoff and Mark Johnson, *Metaphors to Live By* (Chicago: University of Chicago Press, 2003). First published in 1980.

[6] George Lakoff, *Moral Politics: How Liberals and Conservatives Think*, 3rd ed. (Chicago: University of Chicago Press, 2016). First published in 1997.

[7] Thomas Kuhn, *The Structure of Scientific Revolutions: 50th Anniversary Edition* (Chicago: Chicago University Press, 2012). First published in 1962.

Layers of paradigms and frames drive our ecological predicament, some of which we have explored in previous chapters, and some of which we have begun to question as the crisis deepens. Underneath them, at the deepest root level (a level also influenced by "upper level" or outward conditions), lie our most invisible, but arguably most resistant, beliefs about the way things are and *should* be, indeed about the nature of reality itself. Clues as to the nature of these deeper roots can be found in the foregoing analysis of the very predicament itself. The common themes that run through the dominant Western technical, economic, political, and even religious worldviews or frames that have brought us to this predicament are centered on a fundamental paradigm of dualism. As explored in Chapter 3, dualism—particularly, the idea that phenomena consist of two opposing aspects or principles—has philosophical, religious, and scientific origins and aspects. Rather than being a concept of philosophical concern only, dualism and the paradigms that flow from it affect almost every aspect of the way we think, from our anthropocentrism with respect to nature to our fundamental sense of separation and our ideas of hierarchy, domination, and of opposites in opposition. In turn, these ideas foster a culture of competition, either/or, winning or losing, and isolated individualism.

A Sense of Separation

We, particularly in the West, have come to believe—again almost on an unconscious level—that we are *separate*. We separate one individual human from another; one race, gender, or class of humans or nations from another; humans from the wider natural world; the physical and material from the spiritual; subject from object; science from religion; heaven from earth; God from humans; God from other life-forms and the manifest world; and this life from the afterlife. In the psychospiritual realm, we tend to separate the rational from the emotional, the mind from the body, whatever we call our soul or conscience from the emotions and body, the masculine from the feminine. As we saw in Chapter 3, some believe that a transcendent God created the universe and set it in motion, like the "blind watchmaker," to run automatically ever since; or according to pantheism, a divine Force is immanent in life and in the natural world, but not beyond; whereas panentheism holds that God, or a divine source or Force, is both immanent and transcendent, in and beyond the material world. Some believe, as atheists, that no "spiritual" realm exists, although the "material" realm—particularly when considered as the quantum realm of energy, nuclear forces, gravity, waves, quarks, and bosons—is still a plenitude of mystery and undiscovered complexity, as are the forces that govern life itself and that mysterious property of life we call consciousness. In Western cultures, we have tended to regard consciousness as an epiphenomenon of matter, yet, as physicists such as Amit Goswami have postulated, consciousness can be viewed rather as the *ground* of matter, the origin of all things manifest.[8]

In some classic Eastern religions, nothing but the ALL, the One, or That exists, yet it manifests in the ten thousand things that are ultimately indivisible aspects of Brahman, or the One, the Infinite Invisible. Thus Reality is not only the reality of the world of the senses, but rather an aspect of a greater whole, the unity of infinite Consciousness (far beyond our human consciousness) and its infinite forms, of which we are aware of only a fraction. I often think of the image of a tiny ant crawling over a page of Shakespeare's *Hamlet* as I read in my garden—the ant cannot, of course, comprehend the world of physical paper and book, much less the beauty of language, much less again the mind and genius of Shakespeare, yet its world is real, albeit vastly more limited than the human realm. How much might we be like the ant, in this infinite universe?

For centuries, many people, particularly in Western cultures and religious traditions such as Christianity, believed that only humans had been created in the image of God and endowed with divine souls. Indeed, at one time, only certain humans were thought to have souls—not women, or people of color, and certainly not animals, plants, and other life-forms. Animals—even including our primate ancestors—were rarely considered to have emotions or even the capacity to suffer, except at a rudimentary level of physical pain, and certainly were not considered sensate in ways that approached human experience.

Within ourselves, we not only separate the physical body from our mental and spiritual aspects, the rational from the emotional, the masculine from the feminine, the ego from the id, the conscious from the unconscious, but also, most critically, our innermost conscience, or soul, from our outer-facing worldly selves, and our sense of Self (which we could also call our true self, that which is indivisible from all beings, all things, all Truth) from our individualized, ego-bound self. We often experience a sense of conflict between parts of ourselves—we talk of how our consciences, or our deeper instincts

---

[8] Amit Goswami, *The Self-Aware Universe: How Consciousness Creates the Material World* (New York: Jeremy P. Tarcher/Putman, 1995).

or intuitions, wrestle with our fears, our egos, and our desires. At other times, we seem to be asleep at the switch—we have repressed, silenced, or denied the promptings of our inner selves, or our souls, and our hearts; we have stopped listening, or forgotten how to listen, or been so psychologically damaged that we cannot hear the inner voice, which speaks only in the silence of our deepest being.

Distancing

We emphasize our sense of separation by active and passive *distancing*. Distancing occurs in a thousand ways, dividing us within, separating us from each other, and separating us from nature and whatever we conceive of as Spirit. We distance ourselves through our ideas about differences between us (race, class, gender, nationality); through forms of communication—from smartphones, to emails, to online ordering—that often isolate us even as they appear to connect us; through technologies that reduce us to appendages of robotic work practices in which quantity replaces quality and craftsmanship; and through ignorance and prejudice (we don't meet or travel to see or talk to the "other," and we distance ourselves from the moral consequences of racism and discrimination). In addition, we often work in large and complex companies, institutions, or technocracies, in which we are increasingly separated from the consequences of our actions; we eat processed and packaged foods that bear little resemblance to the animals and plants from which they came and we buy products from all over the world, unaware of the impact that our preferences for chocolate or tropical fruit or silk dresses, soft toys or smartphones, or our favorite tourist destinations, may have on distant workers, ecosystems, or wildlife; and we live in larger and larger, more anonymous communities and cities. Nuclear weapons and the many forms of mechanized death and war allow us to dehumanize the "other" by the use of bombs dropped from 30,000 feet or drones controlled from continents thousands of miles away from their targets, so that we never see the agonies of death and destruction; we regard indigenous peoples' lives as somehow less worthy than the lives of those in the "developed" world; and we regard the wider natural world as merely a source of resources and the majority of animals or plants as insentient beings, as fundamentally less than our human selves. Finally, we distance through language. For example, in our use of the terms "natural resources," "ecosystem services," or "natural capital," we subtly set ourselves apart from nature and other living beings and reduce them to objects of instrumental value, rather than consider them as a beloved "community of subjects," as Brian Swimme and Thomas Berry remind us.[9]

One of the practical dangers of distancing is that as our ecological and social "impact distance" has increased, through the globalization of commerce, technologies, and so on, so too has the degree of psychological distancing, thereby amplifying the degree to which we are distanced from the consequences of our ways of living. On a deeper, spiritual level, one of the consequences of distancing is a collective failure of imagination and compassion, response, and responsibility. We fail to see the soul or Light in each of us, the inviolable sanctity of each being, no matter how different we may seem; fail to imagine the connections between every atom, leaf, star, microbe, and form of life in the cosmos; fail to imagine one another's suffering and the suffering of all beings; and fail to imagine that the social constructs, meanings, and explanations of our actions and lives that we learn in our own historical period, culture, and social group are neither final nor universal. We fail to see ourselves as our sisters' and brothers' keepers, responsible in some measure for our actions toward all people. Finally, we often fail to understand the reality of our dependence on, and coresponsibility for, the impact of our actions on all life-forms and the fabric of the earth itself.

Opposition, Hierarchy, Domination, Winning, and Losing

Rather than realizing that all manifestations are aspects of one integrated whole, we (historically more so in the West than the East) often think and act as if they are indeed separate, and not only separate, but occupying two distinct poles, as if dichotomies or binaries (straight or gay, capitalist or communist, individual freedom or collective responsibility, etc.) are in effect the only possibilities, and with little in between. And if at opposite poles, binaries are often considered in *opposition* to one another. And if binaries are in opposition, one must be superior, the other must be inferior; one must be a winner and the other a loser; one must be right and the other wrong; and one must be dominant and the other submissive; in fact, one aspect or position *necessitates* the diminution or exclusion of the other. This leads to ways of thinking that brook no compromise or middle ground or complexity, or that put us in a position of throwing the baby out with the bathwater as we reject something wholesale because of one aspect we disagree with or oppose. (You are

---

[9] Brian Swimme and Thomas Berry, *The Universe Story: From the Primordial Flaring to the Ecozoic Era—A Celebration of the Unfolding of the Cosmos* (San Francisco: HarperSanFrancisco, 1992), 77-9.

either good or evil; or we can have either individual freedom or collective responsibility; or you either love your country or hate it; or capitalism is good, communism bad, and so on.) It is a mark of the power of this thinking pattern that it can oppose the idea of the spiritual or religious life with a political or outwardly active life, an idea that Gandhi, among many others, specifically repudiated. It is also subtly exemplified by the objection that action on the ecological crisis "cannot wait" for us to develop a spiritual or moral ground for action, when in reality, the spiritual and moral dimension *is* the ongoing, emergent, and continuously revealed contemplative ground of outward action, as the root and trunk is to the branches and fruit of a tree. We have, in effect, an embedded idea of "duellism" in our dualism. We are culturally encouraged to believe in winning, in getting to the top of the ladder; in top-down hierarchies and power over others; in good Americans overcoming "evil empires"; and in those with wealth or status or intelligence or good looks being superior to those with none. And, as we saw in Chapter 3 and above, we believe in vertical hierarchies and our anthropocentrism as the natural or religiously ordained order of things, as we justify our domination over both so-called "weaker" and "inferior" peoples and over the wider natural world, in a kind of Promethean quest to control the very elemental forces of nature.

Such paradigms underpin many more subtle social characteristics. For example, as we saw in Chapter 2, we are encouraged to believe, particularly in the U.S. and elsewhere, in achievement, success, the primacy of success and growth, the idea that bigger, more, faster and newer is better, and so on. These paradigms also extends into other, less obvious areas, such as the tendency to practice what I call heroic cures, rather than take preventive measures. This applies to fields such as medicine as well as to ecological sustainability. As many of us in public health are aware, preventive approaches are less persuasive than heroic treatments for disease, spectacular technological advances in artificial organs, or an emergency rescue of a stranded whale on a shoreline, despite typically being less costly and more effective. We cannot so easily see the results of patient, unglamorous work to prevent disease or ecological harms, but riding to the rescue for an outbreak of disease or an oil spill satisfies both the heroic narrative and the media; it is a good story. Thus, as described in Chapter 2, we often focus narrowly on end-of-pipeline fixes rather than on preventive strategies for dealing with ecological damage; on consuming and then recycling and attempting to mop up the plastic on the beach and the oil spills in the oceans rather than reducing what we use; and on refining treatments for cancer rather than preventing carcino-gens from getting into our food supply. It is perhaps a mark of our hubris and impatience, our willful blindness, and our lack of wisdom, at the expense of humility, compassion, patience, and imagination, that we gloss over the fact that we pay a much higher price for our heroic paradigms than we'd like to admit.

Justification

Each of the modes of thinking and acting described above can be either adhered to or countered based on the process of justification. We legitimize our beliefs and actions, even if a part of us recognizes that they can be de-structive, be self-serving, or cause suffering. It is very difficult to question one's own sense of justification, since it seems to be so bound up with our belief in our self-righteousness—the very sense of justice and the rightness of why we do what we do—and thus threatening to one's sense of being a "good person" on a deep level. Nevertheless, by justifying our actions, partic-ularly actions we consider otherwise regrettable, or that have harmful conse-quences for others or nature, we can perpetrate or allow all manner of hor-rors in the world, including wars, ecocide, poverty, and exploitation.

We have many ways to justify actions that cause real or potential harm to others, but two of the most self-deluding are to cloak the venality of our actions in high ideals (or the letter of the law), and to convince ourselves that the ends justify the means. For example, to justify competition, oppression, exploitation, war, or the excessive destruction of nature, we can invoke our families or our group or country, or the noble ideals of individual freedom, while denying freedom to subject peoples, and so on. Or, we justify high levels of profits or avoiding social responsibilities such as taxes or regulations that protect citizenry and the environment on the grounds that we must (legally) maximize profits for our shareholders or else lose our place in the market (this is the way the current economic system operates, after all); we justify high levels of consumption, exploitation, killing, or restricting rights and freedoms on the grounds that it's a dog-eat-dog world, eat or be eaten, or simply the way the world works—rather than tolerance, cooperation and mutuality—or by, for example, a particular interpretation of Darwinian evolu-tion (see Chapter 4) in which primacy of competition and patterns of domina-tion and violence are justified as being biologically destined. We justify eco-logical destruction, negative impacts of technology, or increases in unem-ployment on utilitarian grounds of the (theoretical) greatest good for the greatest number or the necessity of competition (what Marilynne Robinson calls neo-Benthamism[10]); we also justify them, as we saw in Chapter 2, on the grounds of increasing efficiency or convenience, growth, national economic superiority, and ill-defined notions of material "progress"—gods we worship while ignoring the costs to the many nonmaterial, unquantifiable, yet vital cultural, moral, and spiritual aspects of our lives and the earth we depend on.

One of the most pernicious and pervasive justifications is that "the ends justify the means." This notion is used to justify acts from homicide to mass exploitation to state tyranny, war, and genocide. We may use a particular interpretation of scripture to invoke the doctrine of "just war" and the right of self-defense, which often slides into a "God on our side" justification for all manner of wars, colonial expansion, and exploitation.[11] If we brutally colonize or exploit a people or a forest in Africa or elsewhere in order (we say) to (some day) bring modern development or "civilization," or if we say that we must cut down a forest or maximize our profits because we must compete and "win" in business, we are saying that the ends justify the means. As I will explore further in Chapters 6 and 10, we ignore the fact that, as Gandhi and many others have pointed out, the means *are* the ends, since violent means result in violent outcomes, and unjust means give rise to further injustice; and the "ends"—like utopias—recede into an infinite future that never quite arrives. These ideas of justification, often unchallenged and conflated with justice, are all the more potent when driven by fear, prejudice, and ignorance, human characteristics marking each and every one of us in varying degrees. It behooves us to examine our mostly deeply held beliefs and ideas to see if and how what we think of as justice can in fact be questioned as a kind of justification, and if and how our justifications are merely convenient covers for venality, greed, or violence—a deception we practice as much on ourselves as on others.

Lanza del Vasto, a follower of Gandhi and founder of the Ark communities, considers that there are two justices. False justice[12] is "double and con-

[10] Marilynne Robinson, "What Are We Doing Here?," *New York Review of Books,* November 9, 2017, 36. She writes, "Neo-Benthamism stands or falls with our unquestioning subservience to the notion of competition…"

[11] Much more can be said about "just war" doctrine than can be included here, but many have questioned such doctrines, from Richard Niebuhr, despite his brother Reinhold's exposition in defense of the doctrine, to many others who argue for a nonviolent path (see also Chapter 6).

[12] Lanza del Vasto, *Warriors of Peace: Writings on the Techniques of Nonviolence* (New York: Alfred A. Knopf, 1974), 52.

tradictory and…engenders illusions and idols," relying as it does on justifications such as the right of revenge, the idea that good ends justify evil means, and the conviction that justice can be maintained by "fear, compulsion and force."[13] True justice, he writes, on the contrary, is "at one with truth," is both above and within everything, and is synonymous with the God-given order of things.[14] Lanza del Vasto also cautioned that the work of challenging such deeply held ideas such as the justification of violence often involves a lifelong struggle within one's own heart and soul.

How might we reframe these dualistic and hierarchical paradigms so that we might live in a sustainable way with each other and the natural world?

New Paradigms: Reframing our Thinking

Our frames, paradigms, or ways of thinking can be challenged in various ways. The great sages, seers, and prophets and the ancient wisdom traditions tell us of a different reality, a reality that we can intuit as we listen to the still, small voice, the Inner Light, our consciences, or the voice of God, and as we open the eye and heart of the Spirit. Beyond dualism is the One or All, which includes and transcends what Buddhists call the ten thousand things, the manifest and unmanifest world. Two principal truths emerge from this realization: first, that we cannot in fact have one aspect without the other—indeed, we cannot *know* one without the other—and second, that beyond separation and opposition, and domination and hierarchy, lies complementarity, interdependence, reciprocity, synergism, and cooperation. Ultimately, it means that we cannot destroy apparent opposites by elimination, i.e., by trying to destroy the opposite aspect. What appear to be opposites in opposition can be dissolved by a process by which they are *included, transcended, and transformed into new wholes,* much as birth and death are both necessary for each others' existence and included in the one transcendent cycle of life.

These concepts can be recognized in the Taoist "yin-yang" symbol:

---

[13] del Vasto, *Warriors of Peace*, 54.
[14] del Vasto, *Warriors of Peace*, 52.

This ancient symbol indicates the necessary existence, complementarity, and balance of aspects of reality rather than their opposition or domination (birth/death, night/day, masculine/feminine, heaven/earth, reason/emotion, spirit/matter, joy/sorrow, etc.) and their inclusion in one unifying whole. In addition, each aspect contains within it elements of its counterpart. This understanding helps us to grasp that we have often been attempting to separate one side of an indivisible coin from another, as if we could have day without night or birth without death.

We can visualize these concepts using simple diagrams. Our habitual, dualistic paradigm of separate, atomized individuals, species, or entities leads to the idea of opposites in opposition, black and white, either/or thinking. This in turn leads to the idea of win/lose, or a compromise on the spectrum between two polar opposites, visualized thus:

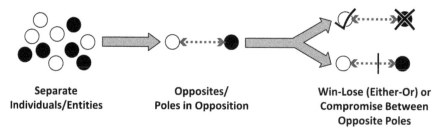

Separate Individuals/Entities | **Opposites/ Poles in Opposition** | **Win-Lose (Either-Or) or Compromise Between Opposite Poles**

Thus, to the extent to which we emphasize atomized individualism and polarized thinking, we tend to see life in terms of zero-sum, competition, and hierarchy. In reality we exist in a web of interdependent connections. This realization creates the possibility of cooperation, complementarity, win-win thinking, and reciprocity. It also opens the possibility of creative synergy, which can emerge when apparent opposites are resolved in a new synthesis, shown below.

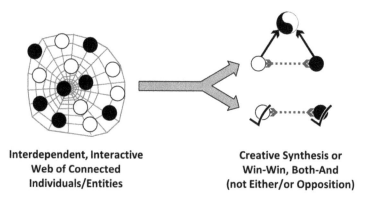

Interdependent, Interactive Web of Connected Individuals/Entities | **Creative Synthesis or Win-Win, Both-And (not Either/or Opposition)**

Similarly, instead of our anthropocentric view of humans as the dominant species in a hierarchical, competitive pyramid of life, we can envisage all beings as fundamentally equal parts of the whole web of interconnected and interdependent life:

Hierarchy of Life   **Web of Life**

Two simple examples illustrate the above points. In many National Parks in the U.S. and Canada, major highways crisscross the parks. In a number of cases, the presence of these highways has reduced the ability of already endangered large mammals (such as bears and bison) to roam freely across their range to feed and breed, and increased the number of traffic accidents, resulting in death and injury to humans and animals. One approach has been to install fences or barriers to deter animals from crossing the roads, but this approach still restricts their range. Recently, however, a creative solution has been adopted of building simple over- and underpasses at places along the routes to provide animal corridors, thereby greatly reducing traffic accidents and animal deaths and fostering the long-term health of the animal populations for minor economic cost. Another example comes from a coastal community in South America where a fishing company used plastic nets, resulting in many deaths of turtles and other marine animals entangled in the nets. After consultation with conservationists and other parties, biodegradable materials are now used for nets. Attention must be paid to ensure the equitable distribution of short-term costs and benefits in these and other examples (as discussed in Chapter 2) and, on a broader scale, the question of balancing e.g., the presence of cars and tourism with conservation must be addressed. Nevertheless, it is possible for the human community and the wider natural world as a whole to benefit directly and indirectly over the longer term in economic, cultural, and spiritual ways. Living in greater harmony with nature is, of course, an overall win-win situation for the human-earth community, while placing certain restrictions on the freedom of some to pursue their individual short-term interests.

Challenging zero-sum or either-or thinking opens the possibility of more inclusive and creative approaches. We find such concepts in Buddhism and other traditions, whereby what appear to be irreconcilable opposites are, as Ken Wilber has emphasized, both transcended and included[15]—and thereby transformed—in a creative synthesis, symbolized by the path of the upper arrow in the diagram above.

As Jung wrote, "becoming conscious reconciles the opposites and thus creates a higher third."[16] This creative synthesis or emergence of the "higher third" does *not* destroy the individual, particular, or constituent parts, any more than the compound salt destroys the constituent elements of sodium or chlorine, but includes them in a new, creative whole. And in our spiritual lives, when we undergo a spiritual process of becoming more conscious of our underlying unity by gradually surrendering our egotistic desires and attachments, we do not lose our ego, or self, but rather it is included and transformed. Nothing is lost, but a new, emergent truth of being, is gained.

On a deeper level, I believe that when the Buddha spoke of a middle way, or Jesus spoke of overcoming evil with love, they did not mean opposing evil with what we call good but rather including and transforming it in an all-powerful love. Cynthia Bourgeault refers to this as the "power (or law) of three," based on her interpretation of the Holy Trinity, and the conscious capacity to reconcile dualistic opposites as unitary consciousness or "the mind of Christ."[17] What this realization also means is that hate cannot overcome or eradicate hate (as we will see when we explore the principles of reciprocity and nonviolence in Chapter 6). Rather, overcoming hate and violence requires the ability to rise in consciousness so that a creative new way (a higher third) can emerge from apparent opposition. Victory or surrender, in this meaning, is a movement not of winning, or of subjugation or giving up, but of reconciliation and transformation. It is, ultimately, an act of love.

Let us examine the implications of the central aspects of these paradigms further with respect to our relationship with each other and the wider natural

---

[15] Ken Wilber, *A Brief History of Everything* (Boston: Shambhala Publications, Inc., 1996), 67.

[16] Carl Jung, Letter to Hélène Kieler, May 14, 1955, in *Letters of C. G. Jung*, Vol. 2, 1951-1961, ed. Gerald Adler with Aniela Jaffe, trans. R.F.C. Hull (London: Routledge and Kegan Paul, 1976), 254.

[17] Cynthia Bourgeault, *The Holy Trinity and the Power of Three* (Boston: Shambhala Publications, Inc., 2013).

world: how, in an interactive, interconnected web of parts, we understand that, rather than separate entities, or polar opposites in opposition, we consist of interdependent and interacting parts that are part of larger wholes, from which creative synergies and new emergent properties can evolve; and second, how all the parts of life—and even what we call "spirit" and "matter"— are inseparable and in constant, dynamically interaction and feedback in a whole earth system that stretches to the farther corners of the cosmos.

Holarchies in Evolution

In the physical world, we can see myriad examples of emergent properties all around us, from simple phenomena like the transformation of a molecule of sodium (a soft and reactive metal) and a molecule of chlorine (a pungent and dangerous gas) to make our common and vital salt; to more complex phenomena like the emergence of living cells that can grow, respond, reproduce, from cellular components such as DNA molecules, mitochondria, and intracellular nutrients; to colored, scented and nectar-laden flowers with specialized petals, stamens and stigma that emerge in a co-evolutionary process from interaction with certain pollinating insects; to the emergence of language and writing from the interaction of individual humans.

The process of inclusion, transcendence, and transformation as integration can also be seen in the creative process of evolution, whether biological or spiritual, in which *holons* (organisms or levels of evolution that are simultaneously both wholes and parts) are both transcended and included in the next level of what Arthur Koestler named a *holarchy*[18] (for example, a cell is included in all organs, which are included in all organisms, all organisms are part of an ecosystem, and so on). Transcendence and holarchy do not imply hierarchy, superiority, or top-down power. Holarchies are evolving, expanding, dynamic, interdependent and integrative, and each level of "wholes" or holons may exhibit emergent properties that are different from those predicted from the sum of its component parts and their individual properties. As described above, the concept also applies to nonphysical aspects of our world, such as the evolving characteristics of societies, or the way in which apparently opposing political positions can be "resolved" by a new, *creative*, "higher third" synthesis that transforms opposing positions by inclusion and

---

[18] Arthur Koestler, "Beyond Atomism and Holism: The Concept of the Holon," in *Beyond Reductionism: New Perspectives on the Life Sciences*, eds. Arthur Koestler and J.R. Smythies (Boston: Beacon Press, 1971), 196-7. See also Arthur Koestler, *The Ghost in the Machine* (New York: Penguin Books, 1990). First published in 1967.

transcendence rather than resulting in win-lose/either-or or a compromise between the two positions.

In my experience, an essential paradox appears to be at work here: *The greater the differentiation, or outward circles of evolution, the greater the possibility and levels of integration.* This applies to both the physical or manifest aspect and the spiritual or consciousness aspect of reality. As one begins to understand more and more of the diversity, complexity, and infinite creative variation of patterns in the universe, so one becomes increasingly aware of the underlying unity and integrity of the whole.[19] As the universe itself has evolved in greater complexity and diversity, so it has evolved in greater consciousness and awareness, and from that emerging awareness can arise the realization, caught in glimpses or in moments of *samadhi* (deep meditation) by ancient and modern mystics and seers, that all this complexity and differentiation, integration and transformation, is profoundly unified and connected, from the deepest subatomic particle to the farthest reaches of the cosmos. What we see in our worldview of nature, then, is not an anthropocentric hierarchy of domination, separation, and competition, although parts and competition exist on one level, but an overarching interdependent web of life, and a dynamic, living holarchical system in which all parts are entwined and mutually interacting, co-arising, and evolving.

The Systems View of Life

Scientists, from physicists to biologists and cosmologists, have begun to understand and model both the intimate *interconnectedness* and *interactive* nature of all parts of the cosmos in ways that are remarkably redolent of the Buddhist view of interconnection and mutual co-arising of all form. The theory of systems, and the systems view of the universe and life, was first developed in the mid-20th century and has found applications in disciplines ranging from physics and biology to economics and sociology. Systems theory also echoes some of the most ancient knowledge systems of the Hindu and Buddhist

---

[19] I first had this experience as a young student of biology, studying mammalian embryology. A single fertilized egg, nourished by the mother's placenta, divides repeatedly; soon, three embryonic tissue types can be differentiated in what otherwise is a ball of cells (endoderm, mesoderm, and ectoderm), each of which is destined to develop into different groups of tissues and organs—for example, the ectoderm gives rise to skin, nerves and certain related tissues. After passing through embryonic stages that all mammals share, differentiation continues until the whole organism develops into one integrated, functioning system to produce otter, ape, or human with its multiple subsystems of organs, tissues, and cells communicating and interacting in concert—all made possible by meat and grain, nut and fruit, sunlight, oxygen, phytoplankton, chlorophyll, and cosmic dust.

traditions in its emphasis on interconnections, interdependency, and dynamic processes acting in a unified whole.

General Systems Theory, first developed by Ludwig van Bertalanffy in the 1940s and '50s, and the systems thinking that applies its principles in different disciplines, states that all parts of a system are interrelated and interdependent, so that a change in one part of the system affects all the other parts; it also states that the whole system is more than the sum of its component parts. In contrast to more reductionist and mechanistic scientific approaches to understanding the world (described in Chapter 3), which historically emphasized breaking things down into their component parts, whether rocks, organisms, genes, molecules, atoms, or quantum particles, systems approaches emphasize dynamic *processes* and *patterns* in attempts to understand organization, relationship, change, context (*gestalt*), and interconnections in whole systems, whether specific human and ecological communities or whole earth systems.[20] These systems are dynamic, evolving, and often self-organizing. This is not to say that the study of component parts, and their quantification and measurement, is unnecessary; on the contrary, it is a vital, necessary, but incomplete part of understanding our physical, social, and ecological realms as holistic, dynamic systems. As such, it has both explanatory power and substantial limitations when considered in isolation, i.e., in the absence of context, patterns, and processes.

Systems are characterized by *nonlinearity*, by the existence of *interactions* and two kinds of *feedback* loops, "reinforcing" loops (so-called "positive" feedbacks) that result in growth or decline and "balancing" loops (so-called "negative" feedbacks) that tend to result in dynamic equilibrium or homeostasis. An example of a reinforcing loop is population growth; an example of a balancing loop is a stable predator-prey relationship in an ecosystem—when predation exceeds the number of available prey, a die-off of predators results, allowing recovery of the population of prey. In actual systems, multiple reinforcing feedback loops interact with multiple balancing loops (so that reinforcing loops do not continue indefinitely), and disequilibrium can be produced by a disruptive change in the system. For example, the hunting of wolves in Yellowstone—the top predators—resulted in a significant increase in elk populations, consequent overgrazing of native vegetation, with cascad-

---

[20] Fritjof Capra and Pier Luigi Luisi, *The Systems View of Life* (Cambridge, UK: Cambridge University Press, 2014), 4.

ing adverse effects on beavers and other species, and eventually prompted the reintroduction of wolves in 1995 by park rangers.[21]

As we saw in the example of the *Limits to Growth* world model developed by Donella Meadows and colleagues (see Chapter 1), researchers applying systems thinking have made full use of computer models to analyze the behavior of complex, nonlinear systems, whether physical, biological, social, or ecological. These models, although they are still abstractions of the systems they model and depend on the validity and reliability of the variables and algorithms that form their inputs, are nevertheless much closer to the actual real-world systems they seek to represent than previous methods. In particular, systems analysis of physical, chemical, and living ecosystems has led to a better understanding of their dynamics and interactions, and what moves them toward and away from balance and equilibrium. Despite such advances, however, there are many processes, interactions and unquantifiable aspects that we clearly don't understand or cannot capture even in the most sophisticated models.[22]

Disrupting the balances, forces, and functions of even the smallest components of ecological systems can have many more far-reaching consequences than we have ever imagined. Physical structures and interconnected systems of life have evolved over millions of years in ways that we still scarcely understand. We need to recognize our ignorance and to question the seductive power of our ability to try to remake the wider natural world "in our own image" according to the anthropocentric pattern and desires we impose on it. Hubris born of our cleverness as we pursue our Promethean project has led us to the brink of catastrophe, and we have yet to see if we have the humility and wisdom to learn from and live with the integrated processes, patterns, processes and systems that have evolved over millennia, and to reevaluate traditional assumptions about what constitutes what we think of matter, spirit, and the nature of the universe.

---

[21] Brodie Farquhar, "Wolf Reintroduction Changes Ecosystem," June 1, 2011, https://www.yellowstonepark.com/things-to-do/wolf-reintroduction-changes-ecosystem.

[22] Donella Meadows was aware that a danger of systems modeling, while very useful if wisely used and interpreted, was that it could be used in reductive, predicative, and simplistic ways that seemed to promise easy answers. In an article in which she listed ways to work or "dance" with systems, she included "Listen to the wisdom of the system," "Celebrate complexity," "Expose your mental models to the open air," "Stay humble. Stay a learner," "Pay attention to what is important, not just what is quantifiable," and, perhaps most significantly, "Hold fast to the goal of goodness." Meadows, "Dancing with Systems," http://donellameadows.org/archives/dancing-with-systems/.

Spirit, Matter and Consciousness as Indivisible

As we have seen in Chapter 3 and above, Western philosophy and religious traditions have posited a dualism between spirit and matter; thus we also see a separation of science (the realm of matter) and religion (the realm of the soul and spirit and God). But in a nondualistic worldview, as the Buddhist sutra has it, "emptiness is form, form is emptiness." The spiritual dimension is not distinct from the material, physical, and biological dimension; rather, one dimension is an *aspect* of the other.[23] As Einstein and others have written, it is as impossible to separate the so-called spiritual and material dimensions as it is to split two sides of a coin. And, as Thomas Berry writes, "There is a spiritual capacity in carbon as there is a carbon component functioning in our highest spiritual experience. If some scientists consider that this is merely a material process, then what they call matter, I call mind, soul, spirit or consciousness."[24] This worldview is also a means by which scientific materialism can be reconciled with spirituality to develop what Ken Wilber and others have called an integral worldview.[25]

Through disciplines like quantum mechanics, the "new physics," system dynamics, chaos theory, and so on, we are becoming aware of dark matter or energetic forces that may affect phenomena at a distance, for example, but we don't know if we have discovered all the laws that govern the workings of the universe, or the totality of subatomic particles, or whether multiple dimensions exist beyond the known physical realm. We know little about the nature of consciousness itself, despite significant advances in neurology and psychology over the past century. Yet, as the traditional scientific worldview evolves, we can discern a growing convergence between the insights and explorations of advanced physics and biology, and what the sages and mystics of Eastern traditions have called the oneness and interrelatedness of reality, in

---

[23] Many scientists acknowledge that we don't really know how to define or explain the phenomenon of consciousness, or what we experience as our religious, ethical, or aesthetic senses, for example, nor do we understand the possible existence of multiple levels (or holons) of supramental consciousness that do not manifest in the material world, at least in ways that humans can currently appreciate. Many mystics allude to infinite levels of consciousness that appear to be inaccessible even to the most evolved spiritual adepts.

[24] Thomas Berry, *The Great Work: Our Way Into the Future* (New York: Bell Tower, 1999), 25.

[25] See, for example, Ken Wilber, *Integral Spirituality: A Startling New Role for Religion in the Modern and Postmodern World* (Boston: Shambhala Publications, Inc., 2003).

ways that presage not a contradiction between science and the spiritual, but an integration.[26]

Sri Aurobindo was a 20th-century Bengali mystic steeped in the ancient Hindu traditions expressed in the Vedas, the *Mahabharata*, *Ramayana*, and related epics and scriptures. He believed that the Absolute, or Spirit, or supreme Consciousness, is unitary and manifests in multiple forms in the material world by a process of involution, involving a diminution of consciousness, from which evolution, or unfolding of that Consciousness, proceeds.[27] Humans are viewed as "transitional" beings, limited in our present level of consciousness but continuing to evolve through levels of being from what he named the physical or vital to the mental and eventually supramental stages of consciousness in a process of inclusion and transcendence. Aurobindo also believed that as we aspire to greater consciousness or awakening, so the unitary Absolute, or supreme Consciousness (which can also be called God, or the divine) reaches down, as it were, to our level of consciousness, in a kind of mutual attraction. Having spent 20 or more years in deep spiritual contemplation, he expounded what he named as the integral yoga, in which he delineates a path of integration and awakening, through the four possible routes of work, knowledge, devotion, or self-perfection.

The concept of involution and evolution of consciousness resembles the views of the theoretical physicist David Bohm, who embraced the concept of reality as an undivided and dynamic whole in which everything is interconnected in a flowing system he named the holomovement, or the ground of matter.[28] He put forward a theory of what he named as the "implicate and explicate order" in the universe to explain the ongoing self-evolution of physical and biological systems in a constant state of "universal flux," unfolding, or becoming, and returning. Bohm suggested—based on his interpretation of the behavior of elementary (subatomic) particles, which exhibit nonlocality, among other properties—that each particle contains information about every

---

[26] See, for example, Fritjof Capra, *The Tao of Physics: An Exploration of the Parallels Between Modern Physics and Eastern Mysticism* 5th ed. (Boston: Shambhala Publications, Inc., 2010). First published in 1975; Danah Zohar, *The Quantum Self: Human Nature and Consciousness Defined by the New Physics* (New York: William Morrow Paperbacks, 1991); George Johnson, *Fire in the Mind: Science, Faith, and the Search for Order* (New York: Vintage Books, 1996); Ken Wilber, *The Marriage of Sense and Soul: Integrating Science and Religion* (New York: Random House, 1998).

[27] Aurobindo Ghose, *The Life Divine* (Pondicherry: The Sri Aurobindo Ashram Press, 2010 edition); see also his *The Integral Yoga: Sri Aurobindo's Teaching and Method of Practice* (1993); Aurobindo Ghose and the Mother, *The Destiny of Man* (1969), from the same Press.

[28] David Bohm, *Wholeness and the Implicate Order* (London: Routledge, 1980).

other part of the whole system and is determined by the pattern of the whole, a principle he likened to a hologram. (In a hologram, every part contains within it the total information of the whole image.)

Bohm also posited that, if consciousness is holographic, then individual consciousness both is transformed by and can transform the unitary collective consciousness of all humans, if they themselves reach a sufficient level of conscious awareness. This concept also resembles the Hindu and Buddhist metaphor of Indra's Net, which has multifaceted jewels at each node that reflect all the other jewels in the net, rather like a dew-covered web shown in the illustration, [29] as a way to describe the cosmic principle of *interconnectedness and dependent origination.*

The Underlying Integrative Principle

The part of our being that many describe as the "soul," that individualized spark of the great divine Fire or All-That-Is, or what Jungian psychologists, along with Buddhists, Hindus, and others think of as the Self, is receptive and responds to what Quakers refer to as the "Inner Light"—whether conceived of as Spirit, God, the Infinite, All-That-Is, Reality, or one's deepest wisdom and awareness. The soul or inner Self is that part of our individual consciousness that is the ground of our conscience, our ethical and moral senses, and our awareness of what many mystics, from the writers of the *Bhagavad Gita* to the Platonists and beyond, believed are the transcendent ideals of truth, beauty, and goodness. To paraphrase the beautiful words of the 18th-century Quaker John Woolman, quoted at the beginning of Part II,

---

[29] Based on an image by Simone Bissi [CC BY-SA 4.0 (https://creativecommons.org/licenses/by-sa/4.0)] from Wikipedia Commons.

"There is a principle which is pure, placed in the human mind…. It is deep and inward, confined to no forms of religion nor excluded from any, where the heart stands in perfect sincerity."[30]

In these senses, the spiritual is the province of every religious believer and none; its nature is what is thought of as secular as well as religious; and it is the province of science and philosophy, from quantum physics to the nature of evolution, as well as of human psychology, morality, religion, and culture. And, as we will see as we explore further, its essential nature is love. Love is not just a feeling or emotion, but rather a force for integrity, for truth, and for transformative power. In its deeper meanings, it is the Great Attractor, the felt bond of unity with all that is, and the force of evolution and life itself. Love is the very force that binds atoms and governs the planets in their orbits, that unites all life. It reconciles apparent opposites, including and transforming them in ever-widening wholes. Love heals our sense of separation, distance, division, and fear-based violence; it is the unifying force that liberates us from the endless dualistic cycle of winning and losing, domination and oppression, and the condition of disharmony. Love knows that everything arises in reciprocity and mutuality and, therefore, that everything is radically equal. It is, as Woolman says, the province of all, the place in the soul's heart where we abide in integrity, inward peace, and wholeness.

Paths to Integration: The Task of the Inner Psychospiritual Realm

What will enable us to heal our sense of separation from each other and the earth, to see and love the reality of our unity with the commonwealth of all life, and to act nonviolently in the world both to each other and the wider natural world? Ultimately, as the inner creates and reflects the outer, and vice versa, the task of integration lies in the psychospiritual realm as well as the outer realm of action. Not only do we suffer from a sense of separation of "self" from "other," but from fragmentation or splitting of our intellect, our emotions, our senses, and our intuitive or spiritual selves. In addition, we attempt to deny or repress our shadow selves—i.e., those aspects of ourselves that we consider shameful, evil, or bad—and we often repress either our masculine or feminine aspects. We are in inner conflict between dis-integrated

---

[30] John Woolman, "Considerations on Keeping Negroes (Part Second)," in *The Journal and Major Essays of John Woolman*, ed. Phillips P. Moulton (Richmond, IN: Friends United Press, 1989), 236. First published in 1971.

aspects of ourselves, even if we are barely conscious of this conflict, and we tend to (unconsciously) project our rejected or shadow selves onto others, where we act them out in the many forms of violence, demonization, distancing, and destruction that we are all only too familiar with.

Carl Jung believed that our capacity for dehumanization, demonization and fear of the "other," together with our technological power over the natural world, was due to the divided nature of the psyche,[31] and that "all division and antagonism" was a manifestation of the dualistic "splitting of opposites."[32] He also felt that one of the primary dangers for the future survival of humanity was the projection of the "shadow"—the denied, repressed, or unwanted aspects of the psyche—onto others, together with the rejection of the anima or feminine aspect, partly as a result of what he argued was an overly "rational" tendency in Christianity to reject or cast out evil. Laurens van der Post recalled that Jung considered that the feminine had been "driven insane" and that this was a key reason for the imbalanced domination of the shadow-driven and violent animus in the world, including the by-then clearly destructive potential of nuclear war,[33] a view shared by a number of ecofeminists over the past 30 or more years, as described in Chapter 4.

Jung believed that, if humanity as a species were to survive, the most important tasks we had to undertake in the realm of the psyche were the mutual withdrawal of projections in order to redeem or integrate the shadow, and the reintegration of the rejected feminine, together with an integration of our reason or intellect with our feelings, instincts and the spiritual dimension of our beings, a process Jung called individuation.[34] Jung himself, who died in 1961, did not (as far as we can tell from his writings and interviews) specifically foresee or comment publicly on the danger of a global ecological crisis, but, having witnessed the emergence of atomic weapons, he warned that without addressing the inner realm of the psyche, humanity was in danger of self-destruction, an analysis as relevant to the dangers of our present ecological predicament as it is to the ongoing reality of nuclear annihilation.[35] (Ways

---

[31] Carl Jung, *The Undiscovered Self* (Boston: Little, Brown and Company, 1957), 85.

[32] Jung, *Undiscovered Self*, 101.

[33] Laurens van der Post, interview with Suzanne Wagner in the documentary *Matter of Heart*, directed by Mark Whitney, (copyright CG Jung Society of Los Angeles, Kino International Films, 1983).

[34] Jung, *Undiscovered Self*, 97, 101-3.

[35] Marie-Louise Von Franz, who worked for decades with Jung, recalls him having had a vision toward the end of his life about the destruction of life on earth: "Jung never thought that we might do better than just possibly sneak round the corner, with not too big a

to integrate the feminine aspect of the psyche are explored further in Chapter 11.)

At a yet-deeper level, as Jung and other psychologists, philosophers and religious traditions such as Buddhism emphasize, we tend to identify the "self" with the ego, or the atomized self, despite experiencing, on an intuitive level, a sense of being a Self, of being an indivisible part of a greater, higher Being or Source, as souls that are like sparks of a single Fire, composed and indivisible from the same Substance as forms in the manifest and unmanifest world.

Arne Naess, the pioneer of deep ecology as a philosophy embracing the unity and intrinsic worth and right to exist of both humans and all life-forms (see Chapters 8 and 9), believed that the *key to ecological restoration is self-realization*; that is, a realization of the essential unity of life and the All that emerges from a deepening and widening of the self.[36] This apparently extraordinary statement seems almost counterintuitive, or even faintly ridiculous, because we are so habituated to our dualistic and individualistic ways of thinking—thinking of ourselves, the "I," as the separate, ego-centered self; of the idea of loving ourselves as if it is separate from loving others; or as if taking care of one's own needs means living in competition with other humans and with nature. Naess, Gandhi, and others, taking the wisdom of the ancient sages into the 20th century and beyond, understood that the dissolution of the boundary between "self" and "other," "subject," and "object" is the bedrock of nonviolence and the essence of the maturation of what Naess called the "ecological self," which he broadly described as "that with which this person identifies."[37]

Integration of each of the aspects described above—mind, heart, body, soul, masculine and feminine, self as other and as greater Self—does not necessarily mean always giving each aspect "equal" or balanced attention, nor does it mean suppressing or losing one aspect in favor of its "opposite." As emphasized above, it means the possibility of including, transcending, and

---

catastrophe…he said 'I see enormous stretches devastated, enormous stretches of the earth, but thank God it's not the whole planet.'…I think that if not more people try to reflect and take back their projections and take the opposites within themselves there will be a total destruction." Marie-Louise Von Franz, interview with Suzanne Wagner, *Matter of Heart*, 1983.

[36] Arne Naess, "Self-realization: An Ecological Approach to Being in the World," *Trumpeter* 4, no. 3(1987), 35-42, http://trumpeter.athabascau.ca/index.php/trumpet/article/view/623.

[37] Arne Naess, "Self-realization," 35.

transforming these aspects, as described with respect to holarchies, emergent properties and creative synergies. For example, I understand wisdom as *intelligence informed by love*; it emerges from the integration of the intellect (or rationality) with the felt sense of our bond of unity with all beings and the intuition of wholeness.

To integrate and thus transform these aspects, we must keep open the eye of reason, but also open the eye of wisdom; keep open the eyes of the body and mind, but also open the eye of spirit. With respect to the emergence of the deeper self, or Self, it often appears that we must "lose" or deny our ego-bound selves. The paradox is that in gradually loosening our ego-driven concepts, ideas, desires, attachments we don't lose ourselves but rather begin to awaken to the ground of our being, where a truth and reality can be glimpsed that is not "ours," though it is within us, but a universal, seamless part of All-That-Is, in which all is contained, including our selves. We discover that it is not our self-generated love, power, wisdom, truth or will that abides within us, but the universal source of truth and wisdom and love that flows through us as it flows through the cosmos. As a tree freely absorbs sunlight, water, nutrients, and water, which flow throughout its roots, trunk, leaves, and fruit, so we gradually absorb the gifts of life and love through the ground of our being and manifest them through myriad acts of compassion and care for all beings in the world. It is the work of a lifetime—or perhaps many lifetimes— to reach the profound inner depths and inner silence where such unity lies, but it is not simply an individual task. It starts with the synergy of daily acts and practice of kindness and care and also the synergy of joining with others in collective efforts, without which the task ahead would be insurmountable.

Neither Jung nor the majority of those involved in psychoanalysis, therapy, or spiritual counseling, would likely underestimate the inner as well as outer tasks facing humanity. Many of us who have faced, or tried to face, our own shadows or demons, or who deal with traumas, mental illness, and the spiritual struggles of our attempts to understand our imperfections, inconsistencies, fears, and flaws and failings, can attest to the enormity of the struggle to grow up psychologically and spiritually and to integrate the damaged, split-off, and fragmented aspects of ourselves, never mind to attempt this on a collective, social level. Indeed, whole shelves of books have been written on this struggle, to which I could add my own story, with its mixture of contradictions, failings, moments of illumination and acceptance and surrender, and (many more) moments of confusion, grief, fear, rage, or despair. In this ongoing journey toward or deepening of spiritual integrity, I have come to understand that, as no actual separation exists between what we think of as the psychological and the spiritual realms, the individual and the collective realms, this process is both a psychological and spiritual path, and it is not "mine" but profoundly and intimately influences and is influenced by the collective realm and the paths of others, probably in ways that I can only dimly imagine.

Despite the apparent impossibility of our condition—my own limitations, the limitations of others, or, we might say, the limited condition that humanity finds itself in at this stage of the evolution of our consciousness—we are obligated to take on the responsibility of our human fate and our impact on the earth. We do not know what the outcome will be, and we do not know what forces might aid us, if we keep faith with the "better angels" of our nature rather than our demons. Most important, among those of us who have undergone (perhaps more than once) a stripping of any religious or spiritual belief or faith that may have sustained us at times, it is possible to come down and rest at the roots in a different way. Whether or not we hold to the view of a transcendent God, it is possible to understand Spirit or the Infinite as the reality, truth, and miracle of Life—life that is a real, pulsating force in evidence all around us—and to fall in love with that Life, to feel the inherent sacredness and reality of that bond of unity, not in any particularly mystical way but simply in the daily interactions we have with our fellow humans, with oak trees, spiders' webs, sparrows, fields of cornflowers, sunrises, a bowl of soup on the table—with the whole, awe-inspiring world we inhabit, whether we live in cities of towering buildings, mud huts on mountains, or tents in deserts.

An experiential truth—therefore believable in our deepest selves—can come from within, and that truth is that, as we are all connected in a cosmic pattern that defies our imagination, we can experience what happens when we love rather than close ourselves in hate and fear, even in the smallest ways. Love, beauty, truth, and life itself are real, and are within and without us; they are the gifts, without condition, for all beings—whether we call them the gifts of life, of Spirit, of Creation, or of God. They are enhanced, multiplied, and reciprocated in all things we are open to. Love, however impossible to believe in as a power that can overcome what we know only too well as the power of violence, hatred, and fear, is real, and it is, ultimately, what can sustain and empower us, as much as water, food and air sustain us in our physical lives, to dwell in greater harmony on our precious Earth. We can finally begin to understand what the great sages and seers, and modern exponents such as Gandhi, Naess, and others emphasized as the process and expression of self-realization, or the truth of being-in-oneness. At its core, self-realization is expressed as love, and love is nonviolent. Thus, nonviolence (ahimsa) is more than a political or tactical or ethical position; it is an expression of love and the truth of the unity and nonduality of all things.

Paths to Integration: Spirit in Action

The inner or psychospiritual dimension can be thought of as the roots giving rise to the branches of the material dimension and thus our actions in the world. The roots of a tree nourish, and are nourished by, its leaves and branches, and by soil, water, minerals, and light. In turn, the tree affects the manifest world, from the life of other trees, which are in constant communication with each other in a dynamic web of interaction[38]; to the great cycles of the elements; to the climate; and even to the planets in their orbits. Similarly, our inward spiritual lives affect and are affected by our outer lives in ever-widening circles of interconnection. Both roots and shoots, the inner and outer dimensions, are part of an integral, complex ecology of reciprocal being, and they require each other to evolve and flourish. In this sense, there is in fact no single "root cause"—as there is no beginning and end to the universe, there is only the intimate, infinite interplay of idea and form, constantly in flux, changing and folding back on itself. While we can see the spiritual dimension as the source or roots of our actions in the world—the source of our motives, our wisdom, our purposes and meaning—they are constantly watered, nourished, and changed by the manifest world we move in. A profound lesson is embedded in the truth of this reciprocity. To put our ethics, morals, and spiritual principles into practice in the world is not only a responsibility but also the way we awaken, the way we learn and develop our inner spiritual understanding. Gandhi saw no separation between the spiritual realm and action in the world; indeed, he insisted that the spiritual life could not and should not exist without social and political expression in the world, as do many Quakers. As William Penn famously put it, "True godliness does not take men out of the world, but enables them to live better in it, and excites their endeavours to mend it..."[39]

---

[38] Peter Wohlleben, *The Hidden Life of Trees: What They Feel, How They Communicate* (Vancouver, Berkeley: Greystone Books, 2018).

[39] William Penn, *No Cross, No Crown* (1669, 1682) 8th ed., corrected (Leeds, UK: Printed by James Lister, 1743), 59. https://archive.org/stream/nocrossnocrown00penn#page/58.

In the same vein, A.T. Ariyaratne, the founder of the Sarvodaya Shram-adana movement, a Buddhist community development movement in Sri Lanka, wrote:

> ...awakening takes place not in isolation but through social, economic and po-litical interaction. Personal awakening is seen as interdependent with the awak-ening of the local community, and both play a part in the awakening of one's nation and the whole world.[40]

To quote Ariyaratne again, "when I struggle to empower the poor, the work becomes the means through which I can attain personal enlighten-ment."[41]

Thus, if we understand the spiritual as being the root of action in the world, then no separation exists between the need for awakening of the spir-itual dimension and the need for scientific, technological, economic, and political approaches to the ecological crisis—rather, *the spiritual, ethical, and moral dimension should inform and be an integral part of these actions in the world.*

In a deep sense, our ecological predicament is a manifestation of a collec-tive sickness in which the spiritual and moral dimension is often separated, distanced, forgotten, or overridden in the messy and corrupt "real" world of competitive economics, politics, and governance. On the other hand, if we believe that the manifest world is illusion, or we act as if the religious life is unconcerned with worldly concerns or a vale of tears from which we (if we are true believers) will finally be swept up (or Raptured) into heaven, then we are not only abdicating from relieving suffering and injustice in the world but also failing to understand that our inward, psychospiritual life both is interde-pendent with our engagement with the world and *calls forth our engagement,* simply because, as the sages and mystics have told us through the ages, *I am Thou and Thou art Me.* My suffering becomes your suffering; my love does not exist except in reciprocity with another's. We learn that we live, in the words of Martin Buber, in an "I-Thou" relationship with all that is in the world around us.[42]

---

[40] Quoted in Shobita Jain, "Public Participation in Development," in *The Economics and Politics of Resettlement in India,* eds. Shobita Jain and Madhu Bala (New Delhi: Dorling Kindersley India Pvt. Ltd., 2006), 65.

[41] A.T. Ariyaratne. "Awakening for All," Interview with A.T. Ariyaratne by Matthew Weiner, *Tricycle,* Winter 2008, https://tricycle.org/magazine/awakening-all/. The princi-ples and practices of the Sarvodaya Shramadana movement are described in detail in Chapter 10.

[42] Martin Buber, *I and Thou,* trans. Walter Kauffman (New York: Charles Scribner's Sons, 1970).

Many people have argued that, as climate breakdown and ecological collapse looms closer than ever, the urgency of our predicament means that we "haven't enough time to wait" for a mass spiritual awakening or indeed any kind of paradigm shift before we act. In my view, while there's no doubt that the closer catastrophe comes, the more likely it is that many options will be foreclosed and that fear will lead to repressive violent panic measures, there are several ways that such arguments can be addressed. First, as described above, the spiritual and moral "awakening" does not *precede* action in the world, it *proceeds reciprocally and synergistically in conjunction with* such action, and as we act, we grow spiritually and morally and we are healed, encouraged, and enlightened by our work. As Joanna Macy, author and founder of the Work that Reconnects Network writes:

> Action on behalf of life transforms. Because the relationship between self and the world is reciprocal, it is not a question of first getting enlightened or saved and then acting. As we work to heal the earth, the earth heals us.[43]

In the same way, as Martin Luther King reminds us, while political, legislative and collective actions cannot by themselves change hearts and minds, they play a vital role in preventing violence, discrimination and destruction in the world.[44]

Second, as we will explore in Part III, we already have sufficient scientific, technological, and economic knowledge and expertise and examples of sustainable practices to *rapidly* change direction, much as the U.S. and other countries did during wartime, to mobilize and convert industries and agriculture, alter our consumer behavior, and create an equitable, just and sustainable economy. What is lacking is an evolving, ongoing shift in our moral and spiritual perspective and ways of thinking, combined with local and regional experiments with new ways of thinking and doing things that can engender shifts in the political will to change at each level. Third, there are numerous historical studies of modern spiritually and morally-grounded movements,

---

[43] Joanna Macy, quoted in *Work that Reconnects Network* newsletter, December 14 2018. See also Joanna Macy's *World as Lover, World as Self: Courage for Global Justice and Ecological Renewal* (Berkeley: Parallax Press, 2007).

[44] As Martin Luther King said in a speech given at the London City Temple on December 7, 1964, in which he spoke of the need for both a change of heart and mind and legislative action if economic and racial justice is to be brought about: "It may be true that the law can't change the heart, but it can restrain the heartless. It may be true that the law can't make a man love me, but it can restrain him from lynching me. And I think that's pretty important also." Transcript from *Democracy Now!* January 21, 2019, https://www.democracynow.org/2019/1/21/mlk_at_90_a_rediscovered_1965.

from Gandhi's satyagraha movement to the civil rights and women's rights movements, peace movements, and poor people's campaigns that demonstrate that, while the trajectories of such movements (and the paradigm shifts they represent) are not linear and while they can appear to fail at any point, they can also suddenly become acceptable, or even "obvious" in what appears to be a sudden tipping point or quantum shift in social views. It is not always clear when and how such a critical mass point is reached, but such shifts do not necessarily require huge numbers of people. Finally, to reiterate a theme woven throughout this book, we have a moral obligation to future human generations, to all life-forms, to whatever we call the Divine Source, the Source of wonder, beauty, and life itself, to do what we are called to do and are capable of doing.

In sum, we can, and must, learn new paradigms and ways of thinking and acting in the world if we are to avoid global ecological catastrophe and conflict. We have seen—or rather reminded ourselves, since these are not new but ancient truths—how both the wisdom of the mystics, sages and seers and our own Inner Guide can help us develop a set of guiding principles to move us toward a more deeply sustainable and loving way of living on this earth. Irrespective of our particular religious or spiritual traditions or none, we can often discern a common path of wisdom and principles rooted in these ancient truths, and learn how to practice what we can call spirit-in-action, or love-in-action, in today's world. In the following chapters, we will explore spiritually grounded responses to the ecological crisis, focusing particularly on the principles underlying Quaker, Gandhian, and Buddhist-inspired approaches to creating and restoring a whole earth community, which share some striking similarities.

Chapter 6

Testimonies and Ecology: A Quaker Perspective

...as the mind was moved on an inward principle to love God as an invisible incomprehensible being, on the same principle it was moved to love him in all the manifestations in the visible world; that as by his breath the flame of life was kindled in all animal and sensitive creatures, to say we love God as unseen and at the same time exercise cruelty toward the least creature moving by his life, or by life derived from him, was a contradiction in itself.

—John Woolman[1]

People being strangers to the covenant of life with God, they eat and drink and make themselves wanton with the creatures...and devouring the creation; and all this in the world, in the pollutions thereof, without God.... [The creatures] being in their covenant, and I being in brought up into the covenant, by which all things are upheld; wherein is unity with the creation.

—George Fox[2]

Quakerism, as it evolved among 17th-century Friends,[3] has been de-scribed both as a mystical and as a prophetic tradition—mystical, in its em-

---

[1] John Woolman, *The Journal and Major Essays of John Woolman*, ed. Phillips P. Moulton (Richmond, IN: Friends United Press, 1989), 28. First published in 1971.

[2] George Fox, *The Journal of George Fox*, ed. John L. Nickalls (Philadelphia: Religious Society of Friends), 2. Fox (1624–1691) was the founder of the Religious Society of Friends (Quakers).

3 Early Friends broke with the 17th-century Protestant church in England, eschewing the use of the Bible and ecclesiastical doctrine and scripture as the primary sources of revela-tion in favor of waiting in silence for the revelation of the Inner Light or Truth. They relied on scripture as a secondary source of guidance and truth—hence the rejection of an ordained clergy and liturgy and the adoption of silent worship together in Meetinghouses, with clerks, members and attenders rather than clergy and congregation. (Today, several distinct branches of the Religious Society of Friends exist worldwide, from "unpro-grammed" Meetings (practicing silent worship with no clergy, set dogma, or creed) to pastored, more biblically focused programmed Meetings, to evangelical Friends. The discussion here largely reflects the practice among unprogrammed Friends in the U.S. and Europe, with which I am most familiar.)

phasis on the central *experiential* practice of attending inwardly to the illumination of the Inner Light,[4] and prophetic in its emphasis on, as one definition has it, on "Spirit-empowered insights, tasks and messages."[5] In another definition, Quakerism is seen as mission-oriented, calling the world to a renewal of faith and expressed in the "prophetic stream" that has flowed through Friends' witness, and that has its roots in the Hebrew prophetic tradition.[6]

For over 350 years, spiritually grounded practices have gradually evolved among Quakers and coalesced into several core "testimonies." Testimonies are grounded in an experiential, rather than strictly doctrinal, faith. They flow from the central belief that, as the founder George Fox first described it, there is "that of God [is] in everyone"[7] (and nowadays, many Friends would add "and everything"). Testimonies constitute ways of *witnessing, living, and acting in the world* both for individuals and for Meetings, not merely ideas or beliefs. Rather than formal statements of ecclesiastical doctrine, creed, belief, precepts, dogma, or spiritual instruction, they are expressions of Friends' evolving experience, both individually and corporately, of the ongoing illumination, guidance, and power given by the Inner Light.[8]

The first, most well-known and enduring testimony is the *peace* testimony. This testimony originated in George Fox's and early Friends' refusal to use "outward weapons" or fight in wars under any conditions, either for the monarch, the state or even, as Fox and others declared, for their religion.[9] As

---

[4] The Inner Light, or the inward guidance and illumination of one's innermost being, whether we call it conscience, the Soul, the Self, the Source, God, or the Divine, is, for Quakers, available to all and does not require the intermediary of a priest or religious authority for either reception or interpretation. (Friends often seek interpretation and understanding of an individual inward leading or illumination by discernment among groups of Friends, or by the Meeting as a whole, however.)

[5] Margery Post Abbott et al., *Historical Dictionary of the Friends (Quakers)* (Lanham, MD and Oxford, UK: The Scarecrow Press, Inc. 2003), 230.

[6] Bill Taber, *The Prophetic Stream*, Pendle Hill Pamphlet No. 256 (Wallingford, PA: Pendle Hill Publications, 1984). See also Lewis Benson, *Prophetic Quakerism* (Philadelphia, PA: Friends Book Store, 1943.)

[7] George Fox, Letter to Friends in the ministry, 1656, in which he writes, "…be patterns, be examples….Then you will come to walk cheerfully over the world, answering that of God in every one…" in Fox, *Journal*, 263.

[8] These experiences are brought together by larger bodies of Friends (called Yearly Meetings) in Books of Discipline, later named Faith and Practice, as a series of corporately discerned advices and guidances for Meetings.

[9] Fox, *Journal*, 64; George Fox et al., "A Declaration from the Harmless and Innocent People of God, called Quakers, Against All Plotters and Fighters in the World…Concerning Wars and Fighting," (London: Wilson, 1660), F1786, http://www.qhpress.org/quakerpages/qwhp/dec1660.htm.

I will explore below, the peace testimony is not only an expression of conscientious objection to war and the advocacy of peacebuilding but also constitutes a fundamental principle and practice of nonviolence to all beings.[10] It is also intimately linked to each of the other Friends' testimonies, nowadays named as *integrity, simplicity, equality, community*,[11] and the most recently evolved testimony, *unity with nature*.

Quakers and Ecological Concerns: A Brief History

The meaning and expression of the testimonies are constantly evolving as Friends are called to meet new challenges, including ecological destruction. This has led to a testimony of unity with nature and earthcare witness. In North America, earthcare witness has been represented at the national level by Quaker Earthcare Witness (QEW, formerly the Friends Committee on Unity with Nature) since 1987,[12] by the studies and publications of the Quaker Institute for the Future,[13] and by the environmental and energy program within the Friends Committee on National Legislation, for example.[14] At the

---

[10] Many books have been written about the Friends' peace testimony. See, for example, Peter Brock, *The Quaker Peace Testimony, 1660-1914* (York, UK: Sessions Book Trust and NY: Syracuse University Press, 1991); Quaker Peace and Social Witness (Britain Yearly Meeting), *Faithful Deeds: A Rough Guide to the Quaker Peace Testimony* (London: Quaker Books, 2002); Sandra Cronk, *Peace Be With You: The Spiritual Basis of the Friends Peace Testimony* (Philadelphia: Tract Association of Friends, 1984).

[11] The testimonies largely owe their origins to ways of living many early Friends were inwardly and corporately led to adopt. These included standing against all wars; treating people equally (including women, Native Americans, and, later, slaves); plain speech, dress, furnishings, and living; honesty in word and deed; and religious freedom of expression for others. These and other community practices (some only rarely practiced today) gradually coalesced into the initial formulations of the testimonies we know today. These (simplicity, peace, integrity, community, equality and now sustainability or stewardship [SPICES]) are relatively new designations, partly based on the work of the eminent Quaker philosopher Howard Brinton in the 1940s and '50s. See Paul Buckley, "The Origin of the SPICES," Talk given at South Central Yearly Meeting, 2012, 2, http://concordfriendsmeeting.org/sites/all/files/documents/241.0496TheOriginOfTheS PICESbyPaulBuckley_bookfold.doc.

[12] Quaker Earthcare Witness, https://www.quakerearthcare.org/. QEW also publishes *Befriending Creation*. Many Yearly and Monthly Meetings have earthcare witness committees and action groups. These bodies are often aligned with QEW or Right Sharing of World Resources (www.rswr.org), an independent Quaker-based nonprofit that works internationally to foster equality and sustainable ways of life.

[13] Quaker Institute for the Future, "Publications and Presentations of QIF and Associates," http://www.quakerinstitute.org/?page_id=5.

[14] Friends Committee on National Legislation, "Environment & Energy: A Faithful and Moral Call to Conscience," https://www.fcnl.org/about/policy/issues/environment-energy.

local and regional levels, many Meetings and individuals participate in ecological concerns, via networks or action groups (such as the Earth Quaker Action Team[15]), and by collaborating with other local organizations.

Friends today speak of living in "right relationship" with each other and the earth, and the seeds of that obligation can be discerned among the earliest writings of the Quaker movement. In the 17th-century England in which Quakerism arose, as in the emerging colonies in America and elsewhere, there was little concern for the wellbeing of wildlife or even domesticated livestock, or for the despoliation and exploitation of the landscape and oceans. Early Quakers' first concerns were focused on establishing the freedom to practice their own nonconforming religious worship and addressing social justice concerns such as slavery and poverty, but from their earliest writings and books of faith and practice, the seeds of a care for all life on earth were evident.

Early Friends saw the natural world as God's creation for our use, as did their Puritan contemporaries. Fox wrote, for example, "He is the living God that clothes the earth with grass and herbs, and causes the trees to grow, and bring forth food for you…. He is to be worshipped who does this."[16] As Virginia Schurman points out, while Fox, in his interpretation of Genesis, also regarded humanity as having dominion or "power and authority" over the earth, it was conditional on following the guidance and wisdom of God and cognizant of the divine order by which all things were in their place and in harmony with divine design.[17] For example, in 1656, George Fox advised Friends to take heed to receive God's wisdom and "how to use the creatures in their places, to the glory of Him that created them."[18]

From the earliest period, Friends did not just express reverence for nature as a gift of creation but also explicitly recognized that nature must not be exploited or defiled as a result of gluttony and greed. If we keep the covenant of life with God, Fox wrote, we will "come to know the hidden unity in the

---

[15] Earth Quaker Action Team, http://www.eqat.org/. Formed in 2009 from members of various Meetings and other supporters, EQAT carries out activism and campaigns in various parts of the U.S.

[16] George Fox, "Epistle 292 (1672)," in Fox, *Works*, Vol. 8, http://esr.earlham.edu/qbi/gfe/e286-300.htm#e292.

[17] Virginia Schurman, "A Quaker Theology of the Stewardship of Creation," *Quaker Religious Thought* 24 (1992): 27-41.

[18] George Fox, "Epistle 128 (1656)," in George Fox, *Works*, Vol. 7 (Philadelphia: Marcus Gould and Isaac Hoppe, 1831), http://esr.earlham.edu/qbi/gfe/e105-130.htm.

Eternal Being."[19] He also warned against destroying nature for future generations: "[L]eave all creatures behind you as you find them, which God hath
given to serve all nations, and generations, and so that you may have food
and raiment, therewith be content."[20] Later, John Woolman (1720–1772)
would echo this view: "I considered that the formation of the earth, the seas,
the islands, bays and rivers, rivers…were all the works of him who is perfect
wisdom and goodness, and as people attend to his heavenly instruction and
put their trust in him, he provides for them in all parts where he gives them a
being."[21] William Penn (1644–1718), the founder of Pennsylvania, considered
that "It would go a great way to caution and direct people in the use of the
world, that they were better studied and known in the Creation of it. For how
could Man find the Confidence to abuse it, while they should see the Great
Creator stare them in the face, in all and every part thereof?"[22] Further, Fox
often made reference to Chapter 26 in Leviticus, in which God promises to
provide rain, fruit, and the increase of the earth, as long as God's law, which
includes allowing the land to lie fallow and not abusing it, is not transgressed.

John Woolman, born in New Jersey in the early 18th century, is perhaps
the most well-known of early Friends with respect to concern for the earth as
well as for his concerns for slavery and the plight of the poor, together with
his contemporary Anthony Benezet (1713–1784), a French Huguenot who
emigrated to Philadelphia in 1731, soon after joining the Quakers. Woolman
writes movingly and eloquently about the natural world as a gift of creation
and thus his love and tenderness for it:

> …as the mind was moved on an inward principle to love God as an invisible
> incomprehensible being, on the same principle it was moved to love him in all
> his manifestations in the visible world; that as by his breath the flame of life was
> kindled in all animal and sensitive creatures, to say that we love God as unseen
> and at the same time exercise cruelty toward the least creature moving by his
> life, or by life derived by him, was a contradiction in itself.[23]

---

[19] Fox, *Journal*, 27-8.

[20] George Fox, "To All Sorts of People in Christendom," (Doctrinals 274, 1667) in Fox,
Works, Vol. 4, 321, https://esr.earlham.edu/dqc/biblio.html.

[21] Woolman, *Journal*, 114.

[22] William Penn, *Some Fruits of Solitude* (1692) (London and Ashford, Kent: Headley Brothers, 1905), 24,
https://archive.org/stream/somefruitssolit00penngoog#page/n0/mode/2up.

[23] Woolman, *Journal*, 28.

Similarly, Benezet famously spoke of a "tender regard to the whole creation,"[24] and exhorted all to show tenderness and compassion to even the
smallest creatures.[25] Benezet wrote that he had formed "a kind of League of
Amity and Peace with the animal Creation, looking upon them as the most
greatful [*sic*], as well as the most reasonable part of God's creatures."[26] He
eschewed eating meat,[27] was reluctant to kill even flies and other insects, and
urged careful and prudent use of the land with attention to waste—a different
stance from a Puritan approach of improving and reforming nature. Benezet,
like Woolman, also objected to the expropriation of land from Native Americans.

Remarkably for their time, both Benezet and Woolman realized that
many of the causes of war, slavery, poverty, inequality and oppression have
the same roots as wanton despoliation of nature, and both have their origins
in greed, wastefulness, the quest for power and domination over others, and
the desire for status, wealth, and possessions, or for what Woolman calls
"superfluities" and "cumber," despite the fact that these often brought suffering and the destruction of human and other life. Benezet lamented that people were "overwhelmed with their own misery and mortality and yet further
labor to increase the wounds of nature and invent new ways of destroying
each other,"[28] and vigorously campaigned against materialism and the "lust"
for wealth, which he saw as connected to poverty, oppression and violence to
all life. Woolman too, warned that "luxury and oppression have the seeds of
war and desolation in them,"[29] and that "…we cannot go into superfluities, or
grasp after wealth in a way contrary to his wisdom, without having connection with some degree of oppression…self exaltation and strife,"[30] and that

<hr />

[24] Anthony Benezet, Letter to David Barclay (1782), quoted in Wilson Armitage, *Anthony Benezet: From the Original Memoir [Roberts Vaux], Revised with Additions* (London: A.W. Ben-nett and Philadelphia: Lippincott and Company, 1859), 13.

[25] Donald Brooks Kelley, "'A Tender Regard to the Whole Creation': Anthony Benezet and the Emergence of an Eighteenth Century Quaker Ecology," *Pennsylvania Magazine of History and Biography* 106 (1982): 69, 74, 77.

[26] Benezet, quoted in Kelley, "'A Tender Regard,'" 76.

[27] Anthony Benezet, Letter to John Smith (1758), quoted in Kelley, "'A Tender Regard,'" 76.

[28] Anthony Benezet, Letter to Israel, John, and James Pemberton (1778), quoted in Kelley, "'A Tender Regard,'" 84.

[29] Woolman, "Considerations on Keeping Negroes (Part Second)," in *Journal*, 228.

[30] Woolman, *Journal*, 120.

the same causes and violent consequences also applied to the natural world. As he writes:

> So great is the hurry in the spirit of this world, that in aiming to do business quickly and to gain wealth the creation at this day doth loudly groan.[31]...
>
> The produce of the earth is a gift from our gracious creator to the inhabitants, and to impoverish the earth now to support outward greatness appears to be an injury to the succeeding age.[32]

It is in this emerging realization of the interconnection of a concern for the rights of all people, whether slaves, Native Americans, women, or the poor, and a concern for the "gift of creation," as Woolman puts it, that we see the ways in which the testimonies are integrated. Therefore, as he so tenderly reminds us, we have a common and reciprocal cause in loving each other and the wider natural world:

> Our gracious Creator cares and provides for all his creatures. His tender mercies are over all his works; and so far as his love influences our minds, so far we become interested in his workmanship and feel a desire to take hold of every opportunity to lessen the distresses of the afflicted and increase the happiness of the creation. Here we have a prospect of one common interest from which our own is inseparable—that to turn all the treasures we possess into the channel of universal love becomes the business of our lives.[33]

In the 18th century and beyond, a considerable number of Quakers took up the study of natural history, both as a scientific endeavor and as an expression of their respect, reverence, and love for God's creation.[34] Benezet, a friend of the naturalist John Bartram, saw no conflict between "true" religion and science, and this view, which we would now call a holistic or integral one, seems to permeate the writings of many of the Quaker scientists both then and now, and has helped inspire my own attempts to integrate the scientific study of nature with a spiritual perspective.

---

[31] Woolman, *Journal*, 183.

[32] John Woolman, *Conversations on the True Harmony of Mankind and How it May Be Promoted*, 1772, ed. and introduced by Sterling Olmsted (Philadelphia: Wider Quaker Fellowship, 1987), 6.

[33] Woolman, "A Plea for the Poor or a Word of Remembrance and Caution to the Rich," in *Journal*, 241.

[34] See, for example, Thomas Slaughter, *The Natures of John and William Bartram: The Pioneering Naturalists, Father and Son, in the Wilderness of Eighteenth Century America* (New York: Vintage Books, 1996), and Geoffrey Cantor, "Quakers and Science," in *The Oxford Handbook of Quaker Studies*, eds. Stephen W. Angell and Ben Pink Dandelion (New York and Oxford, UK: Oxford University Press, 2013), 520-34.

Let's now explore how the Quaker-inspired principles of integrity, nonviolence, simplicity, equality, and community, as integral to a concern for the earth, continue to evolve in today's world, and ways in which Quaker testimonies find parallels in other religious and spiritual wisdom traditions. What follows is a personal interpretation of these testimonies, based on my own experience, experiments and studies over many years, particularly as they apply to ecological and peace concerns. Other Friends' interpretations and practice of the testimonies have also given me fruitful insights, even when my own inner sense of their meaning has differed.

Integrity as Wholeness and Reciprocity

I have come to see integrity and reciprocity as the roots of the Friends' testimonies to peace, simplicity, equality, community, and care for the earth.[35] The testimony of integrity has several layers of meaning. It means truthfulness and honesty in word and deed. It is the search for truth as revealed by the Inner Guide or Light and discerned corporately among Friends in community. It is living outwardly in alignment with one's inner Light or conscience. And, as described in Chapter 5, it has, I believe, a deeper meaning as wholeness, oneness, and unity—and of the inseparability and interdependence of all things. In this understanding, spirit and matter; God, the Source, or All and nature; or what many call heaven and earth are indivisible parts of one whole. From that sense of unity or oneness springs an understanding of community as the interrelatedness, interdependence, and communality of all life; of what constitutes right relationship as peaceful nonviolence and respect for the essential equality of the earth community all beings; and of a sense of spiritual simplicity that obviates the desire for domination and exploitation, material accumulation, power, and status.

These testimonies are inseparable. They work together in a reinforcing synergy. Just as we cannot have peace without justice and equality, and equality without community and a realization of our interdependence and integrity, so we need each of these to move toward a nonviolent, sustainable ecology and economy for all life. As described above, the testimonies are the branches and fruits that in turn feed back into the roots of an inward realization of integrity. We live in a continuous, dynamic, interconnected, reinforcing circle of contemplation and action. To paraphrase the words of the Quaker Caro-

---

[35] Jennie M. Ratcliffe, *Integrity, Ecology and Community: The Motion of Love*, Pendle Hill Pamphlet No. 403 (Wallingford, PA: Pendle Hill Publications, 2009), 7-8.

line Fox,[36] as we live up to the light we are given, more light is given, and as we act in the world, so we are given more strength and wisdom to stay faithful to our leadings.

There are four key truths embedded in the truth of integrity that underpin and inform each of the testimonies, and, as we will see, reflect the universal spiritual principles described in Chapter 5. First, *everything* is interconnected, interdependent, inseparable, and co-creative. Ultimately, no separation exists between spirit and matter, the immanent and transcendent. Second, humans are an integral part of nature, and as such stand neither outside nor against the laws of nature but are subject to them, as are all other beings and physical and nonphysical entities. Third, in the spiritual realm, like creates like. Harmony (whether spiritual, ecological, or social) is achieved not by conquest or winning but by balance, mutuality, complementarity, cooperation, and, as I will describe below, forms of creative reciprocity. Fourth, the heart of integrity is love. At bottom, the realization of unity is the realization of love. Based on the truth of our interdependence, every being and entity is *fundamentally* equal, and, as such, as Buddhism expresses it, deserves love and compassion. Many Eastern traditions believe that all beings, including humans, are continuously evolving in consciousness and awakening to greater and greater levels of awareness of our ultimate unity. We can experience this growing awareness of unity as an expression of the divine in all things, or as a manifestation of the indivisibility of God, or as recognition of our kinship with all beings and the earth. In any of these views, we can respect, care for, and love all the myriad forms of life that make up our world.

Reciprocity in Integrity

We live in a *reciprocal* universe.[37] Reciprocity is at the heart of integrity. The first aspect of reciprocity is the co-arising of everything that exists. When we say we are we are interdependent and interconnected, we are in fact "interbeing," in the words of Thich Nhat Hanh.[38] Buddhists refer to this as mutual co-arising, or "dependent origination," meaning that everything comes into being as a result of and in relation to everything else. "I" become

---

[36] Caroline Fox (1819–1871) wrote in her diary, "I seemed to hear the words articulated in my spirit, Live up to the light thou hast, and more will be granted thee." Quoted in *Quaker Faith and Practice*, 5th ed., Chapter 26.04 (London: Britain Yearly Meeting, 2013).

[37] Ratcliffe, *Integrity*, 8-9.

[38] Thich Nhat Hanh, *Interbeing: Fourteen Guidelines for Engaged Buddhism*, 3rd ed. (Berkeley, CA: Parallax Press, 1987).

"I" because of you and everything else. Thus, all manifestations of forms are ultimately a part of a single Unity that already, always, is evolving and unfolding in reciprocal relationship. Recognizing both the necessity and the limits of understanding parts and mechanisms associated with the traditional scientific method, life scientists, physicists, and others are increasingly emphasizing relational wholes and the "emergent properties" that arise from their evolution (see Chapter 5). This is creative reciprocity, in which systems interact and transform component wholes in a continuous process.

The second aspect of reciprocity follows from the first. It is the reality that what we do to each other and the earth we do to each other and vice versa, and what we do has repercussions throughout the cosmos. As a spiritual principle says, in simple terms, *like creates like*. Many of us recognize that violence generates more violence, whether in the human realm or in nature. Our scriptures tell us that as we do to others, so it will be done to us. But it is often our accumulated *collective* ideas and actions, both historically and currently, that produce like consequences, and these are visited on others collectively, often into the future. Individuals may contribute a fraction or a large measure to those actions at any given time, which then have consequences that affect whole systems in some degree, including, of course, all living beings, both human and other-than-human. One reason we do not recognize the principle is partly because we tend, especially in Western cultures, to think individualistically about the consequences of our actions rather than collectively, partly because individually we may not appear to reap the outward benefits or suffer the consequences of our actions in the short term (and we are easily seduced by short-term thinking and short-term rewards) and partly because we cannot always imagine or foresee the consequences of our actions. Nevertheless, if we recognize that our violence to the earth, as described in Chapter 4, will create a like effect throughout the system, then the idea that we can live by oppositional, win-lose, either-or rules without negative consequences is patently false. The idea of cooperation and mutuality is not simply a moral idea; it is based on understanding the wisdom of reciprocity. When we speak of going with the grain, and ways of working in harmony with nature, and experience what happens when we do, we are witnessing to this aspect of reciprocity.

It is critical to remember that the principle of "like creates like" and "as within, so without" applies equally to the cycle of violence *and* the cycle of nonviolence. In this sense, too, as explored in Chapter 5, *healing and integration within ourselves is central to the healing of the wider natural world, and the healing of nature is also an indivisible part of our inward healing.* These aspects proceed together, interactively, synergistically, and creatively. Thus, the principle of "like creates like" extends to the idea of creative synthesis, or synergy, as we saw in the "higher third" paradigm in Chapter 5. That synergy is possible within us when we can integrate, as far as we are able, our hearts, rational minds, and innermost selves, and create synergies rather than antagonisms between science, the arts, and humanities; between technological progress and our inner wisdom; and between human needs and those of nature. A synergy is also possible when we embrace and integrate the feminine aspect within the masculine in men, and the masculine aspect in women, thereby potentially restoring the balance between them and in ourselves and in society.

A third aspect of reciprocity is that it also imposes *limits.* One of the deep truths embedded in the deceptively simple Taoist symbol of yin and yang (in Chapter 5) is the wisdom that "when the yin reaches its fullest extent, it retreats in favor of the yang" and vice versa. If we try to think and act as if life were a linear progression line, with no effective limits; as if individual freedom means doing exactly what you want as much as you want; and as if more, bigger, faster, and newer is always better, then we eventually come up against the obvious limits of others' needs and of the planet. We also come up against our own limits—which might take the form of burnout, a lack of meaning, illness, permanent dissatisfaction, or spiritual emptiness. Similarly, if we create more and more violence in the human world, then eventually, even if not in the short term, we become victims of that violence, just as when we do violence to the earth we depend on, until ecological collapse destroys our means of life. The cosmic rule is, as the Taoist sages knew, that balance and reciprocity between complementary aspects, not extremes, are necessary for harmony, stability, and peacefulness.

The fourth and most important aspect of reciprocity is love. It is the essential nature and heart of reciprocity.[39] I believe that without the spiritual realization of love, the felt bond of unity, or what John Woolman called "a near sympathy," we cannot fully realize our interconnectedness, or the cosmic truth of our ultimate unity, and we cannot feel deeply responsive to and responsible for each other and all beings. *We cannot so easily destroy that which we come to love, that we recognize as kin, as one with us.* In reciprocity, love creates and attracts love, and all beings are included in it.

---

[39] Ratcliffe, *Integrity*, 11-3.

We might describe the planets as they revolve in their cosmic spheres, to the tiniest subatomic particles as they spin in their atomic orbits, as being made of, being part of, being held by, that Love. This is the "I-Thou" relationship of which Martin Buber speaks,[40] that suffers when others suffer, that knows joy when others know joy, and that seeks not its own advantage at the expense of another. We can be fully human, he writes, only if we are capable of such relationship.

The realization of "I-Thou" is also the realization that *I am because you are.* And every beetle, cornstalk, and drifting plankton; every acorn, rock, swallow and waterfall; and every mouse, leaf, crab, and grain of sand is an integral part of the cosmos and of me, too. Perhaps no one has so lavishly expressed this realization than Walt Whitman, who, in "Song of Myself," writes:

> For [my birth] the nebula cohered to an orb,
> The long slow strata piled to rest it on,
> Vast vegetables gave it sustenance,
> Monstrous sauroids transported it in their mouths and deposited it with care.
> All forces have been steadily employ'd to complete and delight me,
> Now on this spot I stand with my robust soul.[41]

The Principle and Power of Nonviolence

From both Quakerism and other spiritual traditions, and expressed in modern times by Gandhi, King, and many other religious and secular practitioners of nonviolence, we can distill some key and interrelated principles that underpin the practice of nonviolence, whether in the human-to-human realm or in our relationship to nature.

The first principle of nonviolence is this: *It is the active expression of the force and power of truth, love, unity and integrity.* As Arne Naess, the co-founder of the deep ecology movement, wrote, "…the rock-bottom technique for achieving the power of nonviolence is belief in the essential oneness of life." [42] It is the only enduring force and power that is effective in the face of violence and injustice to each other and the earth. Nonviolence is the path by which integ-

---

[40] Martin Buber, *I and Thou*, trans. Walter Kauffman (New York: Charles Scribner's Sons, 1970), 84-5.

[41] Walt Whitman, "Song of Myself," in *Whitman: Poems*, selected by Peter Washington (New York: Alfred Knopf, 1994), 172. First published in Whitman, *Leaves of Grass* (Brooklyn, NY, 1855).

[42] Arne Naess, *Gandhi and Group Conflict: An Exploration of Satyagraha. Theoretical Background* (Oslo: Universitietsforlaget 1974), quoted in David Rothenberg, *Is It Painful to Think? Conversations with Arne Naess* (Minneapolis, MN: Minneapolis University Press, 1993), xix.

rity, wholeness, and harmony are manifest; it is love in action. Deep nonviolence does not require us to deny the existence of violence, nor does it require us to trust or even like those who oppress us or commit violence to others; it does not mean that we practice nonviolence only when we calculate that we will "win," nor that we will always overcome violence in the short term. Nonviolence does ask of us that we place our trust in the spirit of love, and in the truth of the unity of all, and that we do not stand by. Gandhi wrote, "War will only be stopped when the conscience of mankind has become sufficiently elevated to recognize the undisputed supremacy of the Law of Love in all the walks of life."[43] George Fox, in his famous statement to the Commonwealth Commissioners in 1651, spoke of living "in the virtue of that life and power that takes away the occasion for all wars."[44] And in 1682, in his vision for the new colony of Pennsylvania, William Penn wrote, "Force may subdue, but Love gains."[45]

The second principle of nonviolence is this: *Peaceful ends cannot be achieved with violent means.* The means must be consistent with the ends, and indeed the means *will* produce like ends. In other words, the only way to achieve peace and harmony is to use nonviolent means. The Buddhist Dhammapada says, "Hate is not conquered by hate: hate is conquered by love. This is a law eternal."[46] Jesus said, "Love your enemies, do good to them that hate you" (Matthew 5:44). Martin Luther King Jr. wrote, "Darkness cannot drive out darkness; only light can do that. Hate cannot drive out hate; only love can do that. Hate multiplies hate, violence multiplies violence, and toughness multiplies toughness, in a descending spiral of destruction."[47] Gandhi's follower, Lanza del Vasto, wrote, "…violence breeds violence. Whoever thinks he can free himself [by violence] forges his own chains…. Nonviolence is the only, the one and only effective solution, a breaking of the chain, and liberation."[48] We have seen how often the "ends" are used to justify the means in time of war and the fight for social justice and freedom, but as Gandhi pointed out, something cannot give rise to something other than itself any more than an

---

[43] M.K. Gandhi, Letter to Kirby Page, *The Hindu*, November 8, 1926.

[44] Fox, *Journal*, 65.

[45] Penn, *Some Fruits*, 103.

[46] Anon *The Dhammapada: The Path of Perfection*, trans. Juan Mascaro (Harmondsworth, UK: Penguin Books, 1973), 35.

[47] Martin Luther King Jr., "Loving Your Enemies," in *Strength to Love* (Philadelphia: Fortress Press, 1981), 58. First published in 1963.

[48] Lanza del Vasto, *Warriors of Peace: Writings on the Technique of Nonviolence* (New York: Alfred A. Knopf, 1974), 14-5.

acorn cannot give rise to anything but an oak, or, as Jesus said, grapes cannot be gathered from thorns nor figs from thistles.[49]

This principle that the means must be consistent with the ends applies not only to the human realm of conflict and war or civil unrest in the cause of freedom or justice, but also to the very idea of "progress" or "happiness," the end of poverty, and the restoration of a harmonious relationship with the wider natural world. All too often, in service to apparently noble or utopian ends, ends far in the future, or ends so vague that we have lost sight of them, we don't question the desirability of those ends or whether the means are consistent with them. For example, if I design a machine that speeds up production, supposedly with the idea that efficiency will lead to more happiness or leisure, or simply to some vague notion of "progress," even at the cost of livelihoods or the quality of my work life or the environment, I can soon lose sight of whether my machine does in fact improve lives, or happiness, and whether it damages the environment. We make money, but we forget why we are making it; we improve longevity, but we don't know how to live more contentedly in the present; we acquire power, and more and more stuff, but we forget what the purpose is. And we are so used to the idea that more is good, or efficiency is good, that we justify logging huge forests, fishing oceans and lakes to extinction, flying around the world to ever more exotic locations, making bigger and more efficient bombs and guns, and robotizing and automating factory production, as if these were automatically means to some end called happiness or meaning, success, security, pleasure or comfort. As we saw in Chapter 5, justification of such violent means allows us to ignore or rationalize the reality that they cannot lead to peaceful ends and the expression of the primary values of truth, goodness, and beauty; of living in love; or being in tune with the Infinite, All-That-Is.

The third principle is this: *Those who commit violence to others or the earth also commit violence to themselves, and those who act nonviolently bring inward peace and nonviolence to themselves.* Again, the underlying principle of like creating like is applied here to the inner and outer faces of nonviolence. On one important level, though, we clearly must consider this principle from a collective point of view. This principle does *not* mean that an individual who is personally nonviolent will necessarily avoid outward suffering and violence. From our personal and collective experience, this is not so. In conflicts and wars, famines and floods, many people, animals, and other beings are caught up in the

---

[49] Gospel of Matthew, Chapter 7:16 (KJV).

violence whether or not they contributed directly to it, whether we are referring to warfighting, ecological destruction, or any other violence.

Many Quakers, Gandhi, King, Dorothy Day, and countless others have been willing to sacrifice their personal freedom and even their lives to fight nonviolently for the causes of justice, peace, and liberty. Indeed, Gandhi insisted that his followers must have the willingness and courage to do so, if nonviolence was to be the truth power that could overcome violence and oppression. While persecution, material suffering, and even death have been the fate of many who follow this path, we tend to overlook the inward freedom that arises from living a life in alignment with one's deepest convictions, and trusting that in the long run it will overcome violence and disharmony. As many practitioners have testified, acting nonviolently both arises from and leads to inward peace and a sense of integrity. If we act with compassion, care, and mindfulness, we are opening our own hearts to love, relieving ourselves of the suffering of guilt and anguish, and coming into a greater sense of inward unity, whereby we do not need to project or suppress the "shadow" parts of ourselves, a form of repression that, as we have seen, can lead to explosions of rage and violence.

Further, *nonviolence is not "selfless" or sacrificial, in the usual senses of the words.* Rather than sacrificing power, wealth, or status, our very survival depends on living harmoniously within the commonwealth of life. The earth has the abundant capacity to give us the gifts of life, beauty, and joy, without the need for violent and competitive rapaciousness. And more than that, living lightly and nonviolently gives us, if we are wise, the possibility of greater inner peace and equanimity. Finally, as nonviolence and reciprocity mean cultivating a deeper connection and openness to love, this enlivens us and yields a greater depth of being and sense of belonging. Ultimately, nonviolence is the realization of the truth of our unity, in which the "self" is seen to be part of the whole Self, the wider natural world, and the All.

It is difficult to see these principles as real when we are thinking about human conflict, or when we are fearful of scarcity or the forces of nature that we cannot control. As many teachers of nonviolence have emphasized repeatedly, acknowledging the truth that violence and war are not the answer is only the first step to practicing nonviolence; their roots in fear and anger are rarely overcome by reason and ethical conviction alone. As I will explore further in Chapter 11, it requires training and practice in nonviolent techniques, for months, years, or decades, before rage and fear can be subdued in the face of our desire to lash out, seek revenge, or resist by counter-violent means. Gandhi, King, Badshah Khan, Dorothy Day, many Quakers and others realized that the desire to fight back against rampant injustice or to protect that which we love must not be denied but rather can be converted into the courage to resist nonviolently if called. Gandhi, for example, realized that the courage required for nonviolent resistance greatly exceeded the courage to fight and resist violently, and that it was possible only when grounded in both spiritual conviction and constant practice. But, like George Fox and others, he also realized that such courage was a manifestation of the force and power of truth and love, and that this power is within each of us.

The Richness of Simplicity

Simplicity has both material and spiritual dimensions. Material poverty and deprivation cause clear suffering and call for the alleviation of the causes and conditions of the vast inequality that exists within and across countries as a moral imperative and as a necessary component of addressing the ecological crisis (see below, and Chapters 1, 8 and 10). For those of us who are fortunate enough to have plenty of material goods and services, however, (and leaving aside personal reasons why we might want to simplify our lives), greater material simplicity can become an integral part of treading more lightly on the earth, based on the realization, as described in Chapter 1, that our overconsumption all too often comes at the expense of conflict, exploited workers, poisoned waters, or exterminated wildlife. We may be aware of the ecological impact of our consumption, or even that (as described in Chapter 2) it doesn't necessarily bring us continued satisfaction. Nevertheless, material simplification can often appear to be a giving up of things or activities, even when we might feel trapped in a seemingly endless cycle of overwork, the need for more money, and the stresses of a consumer lifestyle. It is difficult to imagine that, paradoxically, we might gain a different and more deep-rooted richness and freedom of a life lived with a greater sense of sufficiency and a greater sense of peacefulness and harmony with nature and one's inner and outer lives.

Outer simplicity is both a path to and an expression of an inward, spiritual simplicity. As John Woolman, who gave up parts of his modest merchant and tailoring business, wrote:

> My mind through the power of Truth was in a good degree weaned from the desire of outward greatness, and I was learning to be content with real conveniences that were not costly, so that a way of life free from much entanglements appeared best for me, though the income was small.... I saw that where the

heart was set on greatness, success in business did not satisfy the craving, but that in common with an increase in wealth the desire of wealth increased.[50]

What does inward simplicity consist of? It is ultimately an aspect and expression of unity, of wholeness, of integrity. Thomas Kelly writes, "Simplification comes when we 'center down,' when life is lived with singleness of eye."[51] And Elaine Prevallet says, simplicity is an "undivided heart."[52] To me, this "singleness of eye" is not about renouncing the world or our material existence, in the form of a spiritually focused asceticism, as if they are sinful or wanton; *it is about relinquishing everything that obscures our realization of the truth of interrelationship and unity of all things.* Simplicity helps us free ourselves from what Buddhist wisdom recognizes as the prison of our desire and our attachments, whether they are ego-driven, are fear-driven, or take the form of physical or mental addictions; it is about realizing the inevitability of impermanence and change, and how the seasons of birth and death, growth and decay, and joy and sorrow are inseparable one from the other. Paradoxically, by hallowing and loving life and its ever-changing nature, we can gradually let go of our clinging and our desire for power or status and the permanence of things, achievements, or experiences. Then, as we deepen our inner simplicity, we begin to find ourselves open to receiving the limitless gifts of life and love.

Second, the single eye is about the alignment or congruence of the inner and the outer selves. It is a condition not of double-mindedness or division or opposition, or of a split between a spiritual aspiration and worldly attachment; it is a condition in which there is unity, integrity, and reciprocity. The way of simplicity is one of reconciliation, or unification, and the "purifying way of love."[53] What is so difficult for many of us to grasp is that simplicity also can be a liberation, not just for those of us who sense the craziness and addictiveness of having too much stuff, too many commitments, and too little time to breathe but also for those of us who are often overcome by our opposite fear of scarcity and lack. Gradually we can be freed of relentless desire, dissatisfaction, and a sense of insufficiency, freer to enjoy the simple yet abundant gift of life, and freer to love. We discover what we really need, what

---

[50] Woolman, *Journal*, 35.

[51] Thomas Kelly, *Testament of Devotion* (New York: HarperCollins Publishers, Inc., 1992), 42. First published in 1941.

[52] Elaine Prevallet, *Reflections on Simplicity*, Pendle Hill Pamphlet No. 244 (Wallingford, PA: Pendle Hill Publications, 1982), 9.

[53] Prevallet, *Reflections*, 22.

really matters, what really opens our hearts, and what gives us peace. At bottom, the practice of inward and outward simplicity enables us to experience the unity of our being with all things and to know what really sustains us.

Right Relationship in Equality and Community

The spiritual ground of equality and community, like that of nonviolence and simplicity, is also rooted in integrity as the recognition of our fundamental interdependence and reverence for all things in the web of life. Recognizing our fundamental human equality is the recognition that we are part of a global human community. Understanding the reality of our dependence on and fundamental right to exist of other life-forms is the recognition that we are all integral parts of the commonwealth of life and a single earth community. What binds the commons together is the collective realization of this fundamental equality. The lexicon of equality and community is integration, cooperation, reciprocity, and right relationship, not separation, zero-sum competition, hierarchy, domination, and opposition.

Equality does not mean sameness; in fact, it celebrates the infinite variation and diversity of life and the different roles each part plays in the whole fabric of life. Similarly, community does not mean a loss of individuality or cooperation that never includes competition. A reciprocal relationship does not eschew competition, difference, or individual freedom of action but subsumes them within limits, within the greater cooperative whole of a community. In our political systems, we have at times opted for extreme versions of collectivism on the one hand, where the needs of the individual were strongly subordinated to the (apparent) good of the whole, with enormous costs in human lives and individual freedoms. On the other hand, extreme versions of individualism have incurred enormous costs in collective freedoms. (Ironically, of course, in the world of political power, both extreme types of systems become subordinated to oligarchic or dictatorial power of a tiny minority, whether through direct political authoritarianism, the corrupting influence of money and power, or both.) In our social systems, we need a balance between individual freedom and collective responsibility to the community. We cannot live entirely independently of each other any more than we can live without the wider natural world. The desire to do so, to be "an island," is often born of a childish yearning for untrammeled freedom from responsibility and restraint, from the impatient driver who's frustrated by the traffic lights and speed limits governing the flow of traffic in town to the heads of some of the largest transnational corporations who aim to maximize profits but avoid all social responsibility for the social and ecological impacts of their operations.

Accepting our place in community is another way of recognizing reciprocity and limits, and of the fundamental rights accorded to each member. And, as with nonviolence, we come to recognize yet another paradox: Reciprocity means we can't exploit or break the rules of our community without consequences for each member, just as we can't break the laws of physics and chemistry in nature without consequences. As described in Part I, we all too frequently see abuses of the commons by a small minority, and what often strains and breaks communities and nations, causing conflict, is the unequal distribution of the costs and benefits of the consumption of goods and services, as well as political subjugation and ideological divisions. As we will explore in Part III, one of the ways in which equality and community coherence can be maintained is by keeping things at a human scale, smaller and more localized, and to reduce the distancing effect (described in Chapter 5) that we experience when we don't know or care about each other or the natural world. As many of us are aware, there are numerous practical challenges involved in working or living in community. In addition to maintaining the balance between individual freedom and the needs of the whole, there needs to be a balance between, on the one hand, keeping a community small enough to maintain sufficient communication, participation and reciprocity, and, on the other, responding to the wider human community, up to and including the national and international level. The same applies to our relationship both with our local ecology and the wider earth community. Since we now live in globalized economies and are affecting the earth on a planetary scale, often at great distances, this challenge is arguably greater than at any time in human history.

In sum, the Quaker testimonies, as they continue to evolve, are equally applicable to the ecological crisis as to the more "traditional" concerns of social justice and peace. Each of the testimonies rests on the underlying universal truth of the unity and sacredness of life, human and other-than-human, and on the power of truth, love and life, expressed as nonviolence, unity and justice and a care for all living beings. In this way, they are aligned with the same principles that guide Gandhians, Buddhists and others who seek a peaceable earth restored. The testimonies are indivisible and interdependent: integrity, wholeness and reciprocity—the realization of oneness—are at the roots, and nonviolence, simplicity, equality and community are the branches, which give rise to spirit-led action that returns in an unbroken, reinforcing cycle to nourish the roots. In practice, as we will see in Part III, this means that we cannot practice peace without practicing justice to both each other and the wider natural world, and we cannot build a sustainable world without equality, nonviolence, and, as described here and in Chapter 5, a recognition that we are all interdependent members of both the human community and the whole earth community.

Chapter 7

Other Religious Responses to the Ecological Crisis

God's creation is, for every Christian, an essential way of living faithfully in Christ's world that will necessitate personal study of, attention to and engagement with emerging and new environmental concerns that are persistent, acute, and pressing.

—Presbyterian Church (USA)[1]

The urgent challenge is now to continue our work...to overcome the grave menace of climate change, taking into account firstly the care and protection of the earth as well as of the poorest and more vulnerable communities and countries.... As faith based communities we reiterate our determination to support you in our common efforts to offer security, prosperity and dignity to the life of men, women and children around the world, caring also for all the wonders of God's good Creation, sustaining the treasure of life.

—World Council of Churches[2]

Every world religion and wisdom tradition has expressed a view of the relationship between God, Spirit, or the Infinite All; humanity; and the wider natural world, whether through written holy books, doctrine, teachings and parables, oral traditions, or living examples. As explored in Chapters 3 and 5, different religious traditions, from Christianity, Judaism, Buddhism, Islam,

---

[1] Presbyterian Church (USA), "On Lifting Up the Call to Restore the Creation," statement approved by the 210th Presbyterian Church (USA) General Assembly, 2010, Office of the General Assembly of the Presbyterian Church (USA), Louisville, KY, https://presbyterian.typepad.com/files/call-to-restore-creation.pdf.

[2] World Council of Churches, "No More Delays–Life on Earth Is in Peril," statement to the High-Level Ministerial Segment of the 16th Session of the United Nations Framework Convention on Climate Change (UNFCCC) Conference of Parties (COP 16), Cancun, Mexico, December 16, 2010, https://www.oikoumene.org/en/resources/documents/wcc-programmes/justice-diakonia-and-responsibility-for-creation/climate-change-water/statement-to-cop16-un-climate-conference-cancun.

Hinduism, Taoism, Confucianism, and Jainism to indigenous traditions, have viewed this relationship in multiple ways: from a Creator God, who created humanity in God's image with dominion over the earth, to Brahman or the one underlying Reality, the Infinite, or All-That-Is, whereby humanity and nature are parts of a nondual cosmos, and where every particle of the cosmos is endowed with Spirit and is sacred. None of these traditions is monolithic, and interpretations of their inherited scriptures and traditions have varied widely both within different subgroups and individuals and from one historical period to another, but various dominant strands in these traditions—ranging from a cosmology that emphasizes a dualistic, hierarchical, and anthropocentric worldview to a largely nondualistic worldview or a pantheistic nature spirituality—have influenced their responses to the ecological crisis today.

In previous chapters, I have argued that to restore right relationship with the whole earth community, i.e., *all* forms of life on our interconnected and interdependent Earth, we must more fully understand the principles of integrity and reciprocity, expressed as nonviolence, simplicity, equality, and justice, and a commitment to our collective responsibility for the commonwealth of life. This understanding will allow us to restore and build the spiritual foundations for a life-enhancing deep ecology, a deep economy, and a deep peace. To do this, we cannot be concerned solely about preserving nature for our own uses, and we also cannot ignore or contribute to injustice, inequality, violence, and conflict, whether among us or to the wider natural world. How have various religious traditions, particularly Christian denominations, responded to our present ecological predicament and to what extent have they included ecological and human justice, nonviolence, and equality as integral parts of their response, all of which I believe we must integrate if we are to restore right relationship with the whole earth community? Let us explore some of these responses.

Christian Responses

How have Christian denominations responded to the ecological crisis? I will consider three overlapping areas of concern: first, the churches' positions regarding of the relationship of God and humanity to the natural world; second, the question of overconsumption, justice, and inequality in relation to sustainability; and third, the questions of violence and militarism as they relate to ecological sustainability. In the majority of Christian denominational responses, we find most emphasis on the first area; increasing evidence of concern regarding the second, leading to the emergence of ecological justice and environmental ethics as distinct disciplines and movements; and comparatively little on the third.

Until the 1970s, most Christian theologians and ethicists were still primarily concerned with issues of war, racial and economic justice, and human rights rather than ecological concerns. Comparatively little attention was paid to their interconnections and to questions of sustainability and our relationship and responsibility to the earth. We have had, as Mary Evelyn Tucker puts it, "ethical systems for homicide and suicide but not for biocide..."[3] Over the past 40 years, individual theologians and ecumenical bodies have begun to wrestle with the ethics of a Christian response and their responsibility to the wider natural world.[4] Out of this struggle a new ethics has emerged that challenges theologians, Tucker argues, to move beyond theocentric and anthropocentric theologies towards "anthropocosmic" theologies that integrate the divine, human, and earth.[5]

Reflecting the wide range of denominations within Christianity, there has been a similarly wide range of responses to the ecological and climate crisis. As Cherryl Hunt of the University of Exeter points out, for example,[6] some Christians, particularly in evangelical denominations with an eschatological worldview, interpret biblical texts (such as Peter 3:10 and other apocalyptic prophesies in Revelation and elsewhere), to mean that the earth is going to be destroyed—or renewed and transformed—by God's will and design, not our own, that we may be living in the end times now, and that we either should not or cannot interfere with God's plan. However, the majority of the major Christian denominational and ecumenical bodies have issued corporate statements over the past 30 or so years on the ecological crisis that call for humanity to care responsibly for the earth.

In 1979, the World Council of Churches adopted a formal position on "justice, participation and sustainability," based on a consultation on Church

---

[3] Mary Evelyn Tucker, "The Role of Religions in Forming an Environmental Ethics," in *Theology for Earth Community*, ed. Dieter Hessel (Maryknoll, NY: Orbis Books, 1996), 144.

[4] Janet Parker and Roberta Richards, "Christian Ethics and the Environmental Challenge," in *Theology for Earth Community*, 113-31.

[5] Tucker, "Role of Religions," 147.

[6] Cherryl Hunt, "Beyond Stewardship," online syllabus, University of Exeter (U.K.) Department of Theology, https://humanities.exeter.ac.uk/theology/research/projects/beyondstewardship/. See also David G. Horrell, *The Bible and the Environment: Towards a Critical Ecological Biblical Theology* (London: Routledge, 2014).

and Society in Bucharest in 1974. The consultation comprised scientists, theologians, and economists, including some of those involved in the *Limits to Growth* report of the Club of Rome (see Chapter 1) in which the concept of sustainability was introduced. It was renamed the "Justice, Peace and the Integrity of Creation" initiative in 1983.[7] The JPIC conferences and documents that followed focused on the need to redefine and understand anew three areas of ethical concern: first, the orthodox theology of creation; second, the complex relationships and tensions between justice, peace, and the economy; and third, the integrity of creation in a global context, i.e., including the voices of people from poorer countries and from indigenous cultures, and the notion that these are interconnected, rather than competing, concerns.

Other Western denominations followed with their own denominational statements, reflecting similar concerns.[8] In addition, the National Council of Churches in the U.S. instituted an Eco-justice Working Group,[9] as did the North American Coalition on Religion and Ecology[10] and the interfaith National Religious Partnership for the Environment.[11]

The global Catholic Church began to express its concern for nature publicly in 1971, when Pope Paul VI referred to the risk that humans could cause ecological devastation and in turn become victims of this destruction.[12] This was followed in 1979 by Pope John Paul II's first encyclical, which warned

---

[7] D. Premain Niles, "Justice, Peace and the Integrity of Creation," November 2003, http://www.wcc-coe.org/wcc/who/dictionary-article11.html.

[8] See, for example, Presbyterian Eco-Justice Task Force, *Keeping and Healing the Creation* (Louisville, KY: Presbyterian Church USA, 1989); Evangelical Lutheran Church Environmental Task Force, *Caring for Creation: Vision, Hope and Justice* (Minneapolis: Evangelical Lutheran Church in America, 1993); US Catholic Bishops, "Renewing the Earth: An Invitation to Reflection and Action on Environment in Light of Catholic Teaching," *Origins* 21 (1991): 425-32, http://www.usccb.org/issues-and-action/human-life-and-dignity/environment/renewing-the-earth.cfm.; United Church of Canada, *One Earth Community: Ethical Principles for Environment and Development* (Toronto: United Church of Canada, 1992).

[9] National Council of Churches (U.S.), Eco-justice Working Group, http://nccecojustice.org.

[10] The US network, based in Washington DC, is part of the International Consortium on Religion and Ecology.

[11] National Religious Partnership for the Environment (U.S.), http://www.nrpe.org/. For a comprehensive list of religious organizations concerned with the environment, see, for example, the *Encyclopedia of Religion and Ecology*, 1st ed., ed. Bron Taylor (New York: Bloomsbury Academic, 2005).

[12] Pope Paul VI, "Octogesima Adveniens," Apostolic letter to Cardinal Maurice Roy, Vatican, May 14, 1971, para 21, at http://w2.vatican.va/content/paul-vi/en/apost_letters/documents/hf_p-vi_apl_19710514_octogesima-adveniens.html.

about the dangers of not seeing meaning in nature other than what it provides for our use and consumption[13]; a warning that Pope Benedict XVI later echoed. In 1990, Pope John Paul II also emphasized the threat to peace represented by environmental destruction in his speech "The Ecological Crisis: A Common Responsibility" on the World Day of Peace.[14] By the time we reach Pope Francis's 2015 widely publicized papal encyclical entitled "Laudato Si'," the Church shows a deepening position of repentance and humility and a growing emphasis on the connections between poverty, injustice, and violence to each other and the earth.[15] Pope Francis's encyclical opens with the words of his namesake, St. Francis of Assisi, from the "Canticle of the Creatures": "Praise be to you, my Lord, through our Sister, Mother Earth, who sustains and governs us, and produces various fruit with coloured flowers and herbs."[16] Pope Francis says that Sister Earth now "cries out" to us because of the harm we have inflicted on her. Drawing the connection between our inner violence and the damage we have done to life, he writes:

> …we have come to see ourselves as her lords and masters, entitled to plunder her at will…. The violence present in our hearts…is also reflected in the sickness evident in the soil, in the water, in the air, and in all forms of life.[17]

What is most striking is Pope Francis's clear emphasis on our equality and unity with nature, sharing Francis of Assisi's experience that "*every creature was a sister, united to him by bonds of affection* [my emphasis]."[18] As important, he goes on to speak of how Francis of Assisi "shows us just how inseparable is the bond between concern for nature, justice for the poor, commitment to society and interior peace,"[19] a claim that echoes one of the central themes explored throughout these chapters, that we must address the interconnections

---

[13] Pope John Paul II, "Redemptor Hominis," Encyclical letter given at Rome at St. Peter's Basilica, March 4, 1979, at http://w2.vatican.va/content/john-paul-ii/en/encyclicals/documents/hf_jp-ii_enc_04031979_redemptor-hominis.html.

[14] Pope John Paul II, "Peace with God the Creator, Peace with All of Creation," Message for the Celebration of the World Day of Peace, January 1, 1990, http://w2.vatican.va/content/john-paul-ii/en/messages/peace/documents/hf_jp-ii_mes_19891208_xxiii-world-day-for-peace.html.

[15] Pope Francis, "Laudato Si,': Care for Our Common Home," Encyclical letter given at Rome at St. Peter's Basilica, May 24, 2015, http://w2.vatican.va/content/francesco/en/encyclicals/documents/papa-francesco_20150524_enciclica-laudato-si.html.

[16] Pope Francis, "Laudato Si'," para 2.

[17] Pope Francis, "Laudato Si'," para 2.

[18] Pope Francis, "Laudato Si'," para 11.

[19] Pope Francis, "Laudato Si'," para 10.

between violence, domination, overconsumption, inequality, and injustice, and our underlying sense of separation, if we are to address the roots of the ecological crisis. Thus, perhaps for the first time from a traditional Christian denomination, Pope Francis specifically calls for a more equal relationship between ourselves and nature, born of a sense of awe and wonder for the natural world. For, as he writes, "if we no longer speak the language of fraternity and beauty in our relationship to the world, our attitude will be that of masters, consumers, ruthless exploiters, unable to set limits on their immediate needs."[20]

The Concept of Earth Stewardship

The majority of mainstream denominations have called for us to be "stewards" or "trustees" of the earth or creation. Humanity is, according to their interpretations of the Bible, exhorted to care for creation and is answerable to God for our treatment of other creatures, while retaining our special status in relation to God as the only beings created in God's image. For example, in 1990, the Presbyterian Church (USA), one of the first denominations to speak to concerns about the environment in the U.S., issued a "Call to Restore Creation," which declared, "Earthkeeping today means insisting on *sustainability* [their emphasis]—the ongoing capacity of natural and social systems to thrive together—which requires human beings to practice responsible stewardship after the model of servanthood that we have in Jesus."[21] The General Assembly reaffirmed that call on the 20th anniversary of that declaration, calling on the Church to renew its commitment to "earthkeeping, justice, and to community."[22] Similarly, in 1991, the Board of Social Responsibility of the General Synod of the Church of England on Stewardship published a statement that included the following:

> We all share and depend on the same world with its finite and often non-renewable resources. Christians believe that this world belongs to God by creation, redemption and sustenance, and that he has entrusted it to humankind, made in his image and responsible to him; we are in the position of stewards,

[20] Pope Francis, "Laudato Si'," para 11.

[21] Presbyterian Church USA, *Restoring Creation for Ecology and Justice, A Report Adopted by the 202nd Assembly of the Presbyterian Church USA* (1990) (Office of the General Assembly of the Presbyterian Church USA, Louisville, Kentucky, 1990), 117, https://www.presbyterianmission.org/wp-content/uploads/restoring-creation-for-ecologyjustice.pdf.

[22] Presbyterian Church, "On Lifting Up the Call," 2010.

tenants, curators or guardians, whether or not we acknowledge this responsibility.[23]

This statement makes clear that the responsibilities of stewardship imply
"caring management, not selfish exploitation" and require "justice, truthfulness, sensitivity, and compassion."

A somewhat similar evolution of responses to the ecological crisis can be
traced in modern Jewish writings. As with most Christian denominations,
writings on the ecological predicament by Jewish theologians and scholars
began to appear in the early 1970s, reconsidering the human relationship and
responsibility to nature in the light of both traditional and new interpretations
of the Hebrew scriptures.[24] A number of Jewish scholars and denominations
emphasize the celebration of the tree of life (*etz chaim*) as both a central spiritual metaphor in Judaism (exemplified by the celebration of the holiday of
Tu B'Shvat)[25] and as a recognition of God's gift of life and our responsibility
to be "keepers" and "guardians" of the earth as part of our obligation to care
for and repair the world (*tikkun olam*). While there have been many historical
interpretations of the role and responsibility of humans in relationship with
nature, it is evident that, as in Christianity, a commitment to caring for the
earth, together with more unifying and reverent view of nature, and incorpo-
rating in some cases Kabbalistic, Hasidic or other mystical views, have
emerged with increasingly urgency among various denominations within
Judaism in recent decades.[26]

With respect to Islamic interpretations of our relationship and responsibilities to the natural world, Muslims are instructed to care for the natural
world in both the Qu'ran and Hadith, as in the scriptural teachings and in-
structions found in Judaism and Christianity. Allah is the Creator and owner
of the earth and everything that moves upon it, and nature is seen as divine
gift of Allah's generosity and abundance, as well as a "cosmic Book" from

---

[23] General Synod of the Church of England, *Christians and the Environment: A Report of the Board of Social Responsibility on Stewardship* (London: General Synod of the Church of England, July 1991).

[24] See, for example, Hava Tirosh Samuelson, ed., *Judaism and Ecology* (Cambridge, MA:
Harvard University Press, 2002), and discussion in Chapter 3.

[25] Ari Elon, Naomi Mara Hyman, and Arthur Waskow, eds., *Trees, Earth, and Torah: A Tu B'Shvat Anthology* (Philadelphia: The Jewish Publication Society, 2000).

[26] See, for example, the various Union of Reformed Judaism Resolutions on the environment from 1965 to 2017, at the Religious Action Center of Reform Judaism's "Position of
the Reform Movement on the Environment," https://rac.org/position-reform-
movement-environment.

which humans learn about the divine order.[27] The Qur'an exhorts humanity to consume the produce of the earth in moderation and in their season: "Eat of [the produce of the land] when they bear fruit and pay their dues on the day of their harvest, and do not be profligate."[28] Humanity, according to Khalid and other scholars, is appointed "vice-regent" on Earth, i.e., in the role of steward or trustee, a role that imposes a moral responsibility for keeping the natural order, as long as humans submit to the divine will and order. Khalid points out that Islamic jurisprudence sets out complex rules for the conservation of water, land, the establishment of protected lands and the protection of wildlife, although many have fallen into disuse in recent times.[29]

The Iranian-American scholar Seyyed Hossein Nasr writes that Islamic responses to the ecological crisis have been relatively muted until recently, in part, in his view, because environmental destruction has been seen by many Muslims as a consequence of and a primary responsibility of the development of a secularized Western science and technology and of the West's domination of global commerce and ecological exploitation.[30] Since the 1960s, Nasr has written probably more than any other scholar of Islam on the ecological crisis and the need for Muslims to engage in both a new evaluation of traditional Islamic teachings on the human-earth relationship and ways to address the global ecological crisis in today's world.[31] (Nasr also points out, however, that while Islam is deeply embedded in a cosmic worldview that includes all of nature, making it "easier to develop an authentic environmental philosophy," the governments of Islamic countries are, in his view, primarily concerned with economic progress and thus "strongly oppose" consideration of environmental issues.)[32]

---

[27] Munjed M. Muhad, "Islamic Environmental Stewardship: Nature and Science in the Light of Islamic Philosophy," *Union Seminary Quarterly Review* 63 (2010): 147.

[28] Qur'an 6:142, quoted by Fazlun M. Khalid, "Islam and the Environment," in *The Encyclopedia of Global Environment Change, Vol. 5: Social and Economic Dimensions of Global Environmental Change*, ed. Peter Timmerman (Chichester, U.K.: John Wiley and Sons, Ltd., 2002), 333.

[29] Khalid, "Islam and the Environment," 332, 337.

[30] Seyyed Hossein Nasr, "Islam, The Contemporary Islamic World, and the Environmental Crisis," in *Earthcare: An Anthology of Environmental Ethics*, eds. David Clowney and Patricia Mosto (Lanham, MD: Rowman and Littlefield Publishers, Inc., 2009), 82-3.

[31] See, for example, Seyyed Hossein Nasr, *The Encounter of Man and Nature: The Spiritual Crisis of Modern Man* (London: Allen and Unwin, 1968); and *Religion and the Order of Nature* (New York: Oxford University Press, 1996).

[32] Seyyed Hossein Nasr, radio interview with Paul Kennedy on "Ideas," August 15, 2015, Canadian Broadcasting Company, https://www.cbc.ca/radio/ideas/islam-and-the-environment-1.2914131.

Beyond Stewardship?

In the role of steward, humanity arguably remains in the position of a special relationship with God, given the earth in trust to fulfill what has been described historically by Christian theologians and scholars from Augustine to Calvin and beyond as the role of "husband" or "caretaker," "tenant," "guardian," "viceroy," "bailiff," or, latterly, "earthkeeper" or "cocreator," but still with the implication that the earth is ours to use, albeit with care and responsibility. Dieter Hessel, for example, while holding the view that nature is intrinsically valuable and has the right to exist irrespective of its instrumental value to humans (a view that corresponds with a deep ecology perspective, described further in Chapters 8 and 9), has argued that we must take the role of "household manager" with respect to nature, as part of his articulation of an environmental ethics.

Hessel focuses on the concept of grounding such an ethics in the concept of *appropriateness or right relations* in the relation of humans to the wider natural world, a concept that he associates in the 20th century with Reinhold Niebuhr and his exponent James Gustafson. Hessel tells us that "Gustafson asked and answered the basic ethical question, What is God enabling and requiring us, as participants in the pattern and processes of interdependent life, to be and do?, and then answers it: We are to relate to all others in a manner appropriate to their relation to God."[33] He goes on to emphasize God's role not only as creator but as the *continuing sustainer* of all creatures: The wellbeing of all creatures *matters to God and affects God*; they have intrinsic value and right to enjoy their existence irrespective of their instrumental value to humanity (a view that can be found in the first two chapters of Genesis); and the whole earth community, including humanity, is intimately interconnected. In all, he argues that we are to grant other life-forms the freedom to exist and to understand the need for a harmonious participatory relationship with them by restraining our use of them. Hessel also emphasizes the promises and expectations contained in the "covenant ethics" (made explicit in passages in Exodus, Deuteronomy, and Leviticus) that call for the "humane management" of creatures. Nevertheless, in this relationship, he argues, "Humans are accountable for the wellbeing of all. The primary human vocation is to care for creation with love that seeks justice, consistent with the

---

[33] Dieter Hessel, "Now that Animals Can Be Genetically Engineered: Biotechnology in Theological-Ethical Perspective," in *Ecotheology: Voices from South and North*, ed. David Hallman (Maryknoll, NY: World Council of Churches/Orbis Books, 1994), 286.

divine purpose....The normative human role is that of earthkeeper or household manager (*oikonomos*), to be exercised with loving intent and humility."[34]

But does the concept of stewardship or earthkeeping go far enough to challenge our assumption that we have God-given dominion over the earth and thus can continue to use it for our own purposes? Or does this role sound all too much like the "benevolent" but paternalistic slaveholder or aristocratic landowner, or the patriarchal master of women, still holding the assumption of superiority and rights and assuaging that injustice by benevolent but autocratic dispensation of that power? And does it frame stewardship only in terms of human health and wellbeing, albeit with concern for ecological justice for those who suffer most from the impacts of the climate crisis and environmental hazards? In other words, does it maintain, rather than challenge, an essentially anthropocentric and hierarchical view of our relationship to God and nature, and fail to include all living beings within the sphere of equal moral concern?

Suzanne Finch quotes a Quaker thus: "Even to be stewards of the planet is still to be in authority, to be separate from, different to, and that is not how I see God's—the creative power of the universe's—creation."[35] For some religionists and, as will be discussed in Chapters 8 and 9, many ecofeminists and deep ecologists, the concept of stewardship maintains an instrumental view of nature and a fundamentally dominant relationship with the natural world. It is one thing to be sensitive and responsible to the wider natural world; it is another to consider ourselves responsible for the natural world in the sense of being God's chosen species and "keeper" of other life-forms. However, some writers and theologians have argued that, since humans *do* interact with and manipulate nature, at least in some degree (unless we attempt a return to pre-agrarian societies), something closer to a responsible stewardship model (such as practiced by Benedictine monasteries, for example) is necessary as well as preferable to the current exploitative and inequitable relationship we currently have with nature, and reflects more accurately the reality of our inescapably dominant presence on Earth.

Process theology, developed by John Cobb Jr., Charles Birch, David Griffin, and others,[36] emphasizes, in part, the relationality and continuity of

[34] Hessel, "Animals Can Be Genetically Engineered," 289.

[35] Suzanne Finch, *A Quaker Testimony to the Earth?* Bridport Preparatory Meeting for the Quaker Bookshop (London: Friends House, 2000), 47SS.

[36] John B. Cobb Jr. and David Griffin, *Process Theology: An Introductory Exposition* (Louisville, KY: Westminster John Knox Press, 1996).

phenomena, and posits a difference in degree rather than kind between nature, humanity, and the rest of the natural world. This theology emphasizes more strongly the immanence of the divine than does orthodox "post-Kantian" theology, and divine power acting through rather than over the natural world; however, it does not share with pure pantheism the view that God is nature alone. John Cobb Jr. argues that, while finding much common cause between process theology and deep ecology, deep ecologists, in his view, differ from process theologians in the degree to which they emphasize the fact that the fate of the earth does lie in the hands of humankind.[37] He sees acknowledgement of this reality as an act of responsible concern for the rest of the natural world rather than a continuation of a position of dominance, and he reads a danger in a deep ecology perspective that could encourage a withdrawal of human involvement in nature and thereby lead to an abandonment of this responsibility.

Cobb points out that, while both schools of thought grant both humankind and other life-forms a sacredness and intrinsic value, and in this sense sees them as kin, process theologians insist that, while all life is sacred, and while "God's spirit" is within each creature, only God is divine. In this view, neither humans nor other creatures share the divinity of the creator. Further, as well as being idolatrous from a theistic standpoint, the emphasis on the sacredness of all creatures carries a danger of attributing *absolute* value to all creation. This view can theoretically lead to the impossibility of making choices between one life-form and another, choices that, in fact, must be made continuously by humans and other species, Cobb argues. A refusal to grant differential value to different life-forms, on the grounds that such gradations infer a hierarchy of domination, is one that process theologians such as Cobb reject, on the grounds that other life-forms *do* differ in the complexity and depth of their experience. In earlier writing, Cobb argued that, for him, the concept of intrinsic value hinges upon *feeling*. He posits the view that "while everything has instrumental value, only feeling is the locus of intrinsic value,"[38] and argues that experiences of living organisms that involve greater breadth and intensity can be assumed to involve more feeling. This gradation

[37] John B. Cobb Jr., "Protestant Theology and Deep Ecology," in *Deep Ecology and World Religions: New Essays on Sacred Grounds*, eds. David Landis Barnhill and Roger s. Gottlieb (Albany, NY: State University of New York Press, 2001), 213-27.

[38] John B. Cobb Jr., "Ecology, Ethics and Theology," in *Valuing the Earth: Economics, Ecology, Ethics*, eds. Herman Daly and Kenneth Townsend (Cambridge, MA: Massachusetts Institute of Technology Press, 1993), 212.

of the capacity for experience and feeling provides, for Cobb, the basis in any ethical system of values for a necessary ranking of the intrinsic value of living organisms. Such a ranking, in Cobb's view, is a necessity to avoid the otherwise unworkable conclusion that, at its extreme, microbes count for as much as a human being. Such a view, he argues, does not ignore the fact that vertebrates and mammals, for example, depend on invertebrates and microbes for their existence, or that diversity has value for whole ecosystems, or that all life-forms exist ontologically in relationship to each other and are interdependent.

However, we are still left with the problem of according other life-forms primarily instrumental value to humans by providing the means by which we live and enjoy our existence. To what extent should we sacrifice other species for the sake of our own good, even if such good were to be widely and equitably distributed among many? If we take the instrumental view, we will (theoretically) stop sacrificing other species only when such action has a net negative impact on our own wellbeing. If we accord intrinsic value to other living beings, we still somehow have to effect a balance between human needs and value on the one hand and the value of other organisms on the other, but at least we will be doing so on an ethical rather than on a strictly instrumental basis. And, as Cobb further points out, the recognition that we do indeed owe our very lives to the web of all life, existing as it does only in relation to the atmosphere, geosphere, and hydrosphere, may engender in us the ethical sense of an obligation to serve the earth. Such considerations, however, pertain to an ethics of humanism. Arguably, none fully addresses the theological question of whether or how we attribute value to other species and the earth (or cosmos) based on a belief that all things and beings are an incarnation or expression of God or the divine Source, or are imbued with a soul.

Ecojustice: Cry of the Earth, Cry of the Poor

Several Christian denominations and individual theologians have turned their attention to environmental justice, or ecojustice, which encompasses a range of concerns. These include consideration of the rights of and justice towards the natural world and the specific intersection of human and ecological justice. Dieter Hessel speaks of ecojustice as pertaining to all areas that have "dynamic intersection between ecological integrity and social justice."[39]

---

[39] Dieter Hessel, "Introduction: Why This Field Guide?" in *Theology for Earth Community*, 14.

He also says, "Eco-justice occurs wherever human beings receive enough sustenance and build enough community to love harmoniously with God, to achieve equity among humans, and to appreciate the rest of creation for its own sake and not simply as useful to humans."[40] Some ecojustice thinkers and ecumenical bodies have attempted to locate the earth and our relationship to it as the *foundation* for other concerns, rather than simply as a concern of equal merit with, for example, racial or economic justice.[41]

A significant criticism of some of the theologically grounded thinking on ecojustice and environmental ethics to date is that the emphasis has been on how to transform the theological tradition on which a new ethics can be grounded rather than on the social and political action needed to bring about such transformation in the world, or on the abundant evidence, described in Chapter 1, that ecological destruction disproportionately affects indigenous peoples, the poor, people of color, and women, both within and across countries (see discussion below). As Rosemary Radford Ruether warns:

> ...we must be wary of new forms of privatized intrapsychic activity, divorced from the social systems of power. *We must see the work of eco-justice and the work of spirituality as interrelated* [my emphasis], the inner and outer aspects of one process of conversion and transformation.[42]

Arguably, mainstream Christian denominations have placed relatively little emphasis historically on social and political action to address overconsumption and destruction of the natural world, and its intersection with human justice. Until recently, critiques of ecological injustice have often come more from a secular and political base or from liberation theology and other "nontraditional" perspectives rather than a traditionally grounded (and predominantly North American or European) theological base. However, individual clergy, some coming from a liberation theology perspective, for example, have emphasized the clear social disparities in who bears the burden of environmental degradation, hazards, and pollution as a function of poverty and lack of political power both within communities and across countries as globalization has made an impact. Those who pay the highest price for environmental devastation (as described in Chapter 1) also generally contribute the least to overconsumption and devastation. As a Costa Rican priest asked at the first meeting of the [Episcopal] Bishop's Environmental Stewardship

---

[40] Hessel, "Introduction," 12.

[41] Parker and Richards, "Christian Ethics," 123.

[42] Rosemary Radford Ruether, *Gaia and God: An Ecofeminist Theology of Earth Healing* (San Francisco: Harper, 1989), 4.

Team, "for whose grandchildren are [North Americans] saving the earth?"[43] Leonardo Boff, the Brazilian liberation theologian, famously talks of the "cry of the earth, cry of the poor."[44] Janet Parker and Roberta Richards argue that the approaches of liberation theology, ecofeminist theology, and Native American theology are proving to be more fruitful in this regard than a more traditional denominational or ecumenical approach, by emphasizing social action based on historical conditions ahead of theological traditions and positions.[45] An example is ecowomanist writings, which point out not only the relationship between exploitation of the earth and of black women's bodies and the relationship between race and disproportionate exposure to environmental waste and degradation, but also the central contribution of women of color to the environmental justice movement.[46]

Despite—or because of—such critiques from within and outside denominations, the connection between the way we treat the earth and each other is slowly being recognized by more denominational and ecumenical bodies, as is the articulation of the disproportionate impact that the destruction of the earth and scarcity of vital resources have on the poor and, in some areas, of the connection between war, violence, and environmental devastation. The evolving position of Catholic Church (described above) provides one example of how these connections are being recognized. Among other denominations, the ecojustice working groups of the World Council of Churches, Presbyterian Church, and Lutheran Church, among others, emphasize the interconnection of social justice, racism, and ecological concerns.

The experience of the World Council of Churches' efforts also illustrates the immense difficulties in both articulating the relationship between these areas and emerging from years of discussion with a practical agenda that links justice in political and economic structures, the liberation and grassroots struggles of the poor, militarism, science and technology, and cultural identity, all within an ecumenical framework. The faltering and disbanding after four years of its initial program for a "Just, Participatory and Sustainable Society," launched in 1975, and the early struggles of their JPIC program to pick up

---

[43] Quoted in Carla Berkedal, "Spirituality and Sustainability," in *Sustainable Development: The Challenge of Transition*, eds. Jurgen Schmandt and C.H. Ward (Cambridge, UK: Cambridge University Press, 2000), 107.

[44] Leonardo Boff, *Cry of the Earth, Cry of the Poor*, trans. Phillip Berryman (Maryknoll, NY: Orbis Books, 1997).

[45] Parker and Richards, "Christian Ethics," 117.

[46] See, for example, Melanie L. Harris, ed., *Ecowomanism: African American Women and Earth-Honoring Faiths* (Maryknoll, NY: Orbis Books, 2017).

and move forward on the JPSS's central concerns, testify to the challenges these efforts have presented.[47]

Nevertheless, activist interfaith and interdenominational movements have begun to emerge that do not sit within one or other tradition but embrace secular and other religious traditions within their midst, and that emphasize the need to address poverty, racism, economic discrimination, militarism, and ecological destruction as interrelated concerns. Among the most notable is the new Poor People's Campaign, emerging from the original movement of that name led by Martin Luther King Jr. The campaign is codirected by The Reverend Dr. William J. Barber II, a Protestant minister of the Disciples of Christ, board member of the National Association for the Advancement of Colored People (NAACP), former president of the North Carolina NAACP chapter and founder of the nonprofit Repairers of the Breach, and by The Reverend Dr. Liz Theoharis, a Presbyterian minister and codirector of the Kairos Center for Religions, Rights, and Social Justice. The campaign is "committed to lifting up and deepening the leadership of those most affected by systemic racism, poverty, the war economy, and ecological devastation,"[48] and seeks to build an activist "fusion politics" that joins people of different faiths and denominations (or none) to address these intersecting concerns.

The "Greening of World Religions"—Old and New Wisdoms

What can we learn from other religious traditions in terms of their responses to the current ecological crisis? There has been a significant increase in the number of books, conferences, and dialogs on the relationship between ecology and religion, part of a process called the "greening of world religions."[49] Many of the world's religions are included in the debate, most notably in a landmark conference series and resulting books on World Religions and Ecology published by the Center for the Study of World Religions at Harvard Divinity School.[50] Mary Evelyn Tucker, one of the founders of the

---

[47] Wesley Granberg-Michaelson, "An Ethics for Sustainability," *Ecumenical Review* 43 (1991): 120-30, https://doi.org/10.1111/j.1758-6623.1991.tb02682.x.

[48] "Fundamental Principles," Poor People's Campaign: A National Call for Moral Revival, https://www.poorpeoplescampaign.org/fundamental-principles/.

[49] Rosemary Radford Ruether, *Integrating Ecofeminism: Globalization and World Religions* (Lanham, MD: Rowman and Littlefield Publishing Inc., 2005), 45 et seq.

[50] The *Religions of the World and Ecology* series, edited by Mary Evelyn Tucker and John Grim, is published by the Harvard University Center for the Study of World Religions and

Yale Forum on Religion and Ecology, and co-editor of the book series, argues that an interreligious dialogue may help inform the theological response to the ecological crisis from different traditions, provided each tradition is open to the perspectives of others and willing to engage in a "vulnerable dialogue" that presupposes openness, tolerance and a "willingness to be transformed."[51] While a detailed exploration of these traditions is beyond the scope of this chapter, most of them—whether originating in the Abrahamic traditions of Judaism, Christianity and Islam; in eastern traditions of Hinduism, Jainism, Buddhism, Confucianism, Taoism, and the older Shinto tradition; or within the many indigenous traditions of the world—articulate both a sacred relationship with and a deep awe and respect for the wider natural world.

Almost all Asian traditions, for example, articulate forms of nonviolence to nature, which takes various forms of expression.[52] Hinduism not only has many gods in the form of animals, plants, mountains, and sacred rivers like the Ganges but also eschews the killing of certain animals, notably the cow, while strict practitioners in the Jain tradition seek to practice nonviolence to all living beings, including birds, insects, and so on, practicing veganism, and even avoiding stepping on or inhaling insects and other creatures as they go about their daily lives.

As with Christianity, the relevance and practice of religious traditions of a particular country or culture in modern times are by no means necessarily consistent with the founding principles of these religions. Rosemary Radford Ruether, for example, has argued that the track records of countries that view nature as sacred or divine, or as permeated by the divine, are no more impressive in terms of ecological protection than those that envisage God as a transcendent creator,[53] but given the complex and interacting factors that determine relations with and behavior towards the natural world, together with the difficulties inherent in assessing reasons for ecological protection or the lack of it (particularly the level of industrial and technological development and the commitment of political leaders, for example), it would be difficult—and

---

distributed by Harvard University Press. The series includes volumes on Christianity, Buddhism, Confucianism, Daoism, Hinduism, Indigenous Traditions, Islam, Jainism, Judaism, and Shinto, among others, published between 1997 and 2004. See http://fore.yale.edu/publications/books/cswr/.

[51] Tucker, "Role of Religions," 143-52 (quote on 146-7).

[52] See for example, Christopher Key Chapple, *Nonviolence to Animals, Earth and Self in Asian Traditions* (Albany, NY: State University of New York Press, 1993).

[53] Ruether, *Integrating Ecofeminism*, 79.

unwise—to come to any generalized conclusions. For example, we could point to the worldviews of indigenous religions and their relatively minor impact on the natural environment and argue that, rather than being due to their view of the sacredness of all beings, it is rather a result of the lack of technological development in past centuries followed by their domination by other cultures over the past several hundred years. However, many indigenous peoples have held on to a deeply reverential view of our relationship with nature, and a number of indigenous people and those in so-called "developing" countries have also refused certain kinds of violent modern technological development precisely because of a different worldview of the relation between humans and the wider natural world[54] (see also Chapters 9 and 10).

In many countries, religious traditions that have identifiable naturecentric theologies or traditions (such as Taoism, Shintoism, or Jainism; some of the indigenous traditions; and, to some extent, Buddhism and Confucianism) have been marginalized or supplanted either by other religious forms or by the secularization of the society. The forces of modernization, and more recently the globalization of Western cultural patterns, have, temporarily at least, arguably suppressed the expression of these traditional religious forms, albeit with some notable exceptions. In Asia, particularly in India and China, the accelerating pace of modern development resembles, at least on the surface, a pattern of growth and development—with high levels of industrialization and an emphasis on advanced technology and capitalistic economic structures—typical of countries with Western religious traditions, despite having very different native religious traditions.

Many religious traditions embrace adherents who pursue eremitic and monastic ways of life as well as adherents who work in the world from within their denominations and places of worship. Taoism, for example, which places significant emphasis on the harmonious relationship of humans with nature, advocates withdrawal from society to cultivate this relationship, and values the solitary way of life. Confucianism, on the other hand, which also emphasizes harmony between heaven, earth, and humanity upon which a harmonious society depends, stresses the active participation in social and political roles by humane and spiritually adept teachers and government officials.[55] For Quakers, as we saw in Chapter 6, living according to the Inner

---

[54] See, for example, Jace Weaver, ed., *Defending Mother Earth: Native American Perspectives on Environmental Justice* (Maryknoll, NY: Orbis Books, 1996); Winona LaDuke, *All Our Relations: Native Struggles for Land and Life* (Boston: South End Press, 1999).

[55] Tucker, "Role of Religions," 149-50.

Light and the testimonies means, as early Friends put it, being patterns and examples in the world, and endeavoring to act in the world to prevent and heal suffering, or in other words, putting love into action. These examples emphasize that there is no either-or or only one effective or right way to live or practice in harmony with the wider natural world. Meister Eckhart, St. Francis, Brother Lawrence, Thomas Merton, and others lived in monastic orders or even as solitary mystics yet lifted up enduring visions of nonviolence, and of unity with nature, that have inspired me and many others.

In sum, as we experience our present ecological predicament, the dilemma illustrated by the differing views of the various faith traditions and denominations reviewed here raises some of the central ethical challenges explored in greater depth in the following chapter and in Part III, including: Does the concept of "earth stewardship" as the formal position of many faith communities go far enough to protect and heal our relationship with the wider natural world? To what extent can we practice a nonviolent relationship with the wider natural world and still remain active participants in whatever modern society and economy we find ourselves in? Must we withdraw from society to live in harmony with nature? How can we living in accordance with the principles and ways of being explored in Chapters 5 and 6 and our spiritual obligation to participate in acts of *tikkun olam*, that is, to help "heal the world?"

Chapter 8

Principles of Deep Ecology, Economy, and Peace: An Integral Approach

The ecological age fosters the deep awareness of the sacred presence within each reality of the universe.... The ecological age seeks to establish and maintain this subjective identity, this authenticity at the heart of every being.... Only such a comprehensive vision can produce the commitment required to stop the world of exploitation, of manipulation, of violence so intense that it threatens to destroy not only the human city, but also the planet itself.

—Thomas Berry[1]

The outward harmony that we desire between our economy and the world depends finally upon an inward harmony between our own hearts and the originating spirit that is the life of all creatures, a spirit as near to us as our flesh and yet forever beyond the measures of this obsessively measuring age.

—Wendell Berry[2]

Self-interest and self-preservation demand complete non-violence, co-operation and submission, to the ways of nature if we are to maintain permanency by non-interference with and by not short-circuiting the cycle of life.

—J.C. Kumarappa[3]

To explore the principles and practice of an integrated deep ecology, economy, and peace in the age of ecological crisis, I will draw primarily on the perspectives of several philosophical and spiritually grounded ecological movements of which I have had personal experience. Although developed at different periods and among different religious and spiritual traditions, they have many common roots, connections, and practices. In addition to the

---

[1] Thomas Berry, *The Dream of the Earth* (San Francisco: Sierra Club Books, 1990), 46. First published in 1988.

[2] Wendell Berry, "In Distrust of Movements," in *In the Presence of Fear: Three Essays for a Changed World* (Great Barrington, MA: The Orion Society, 2001), 35-44.

[3] J.C. Kumarappa, *The Economics of Permanence: A Quest for a Social Order Based on Non-violence* (Varanasi, India: Sarva Seva Sangh Prakashan, 1948), 9. First published in 1945.

Quaker perspective described in Chapter 6, they include the deep ecology movement based on the ecosophy of the Norwegian philosopher Arne Naess; the work of Thomas Berry and others, based on Berry's vision of an Ecozoic era; the life and work of Gandhi, based on Hindu and Jain traditions but expressed in practical ways in his Constructive Programs in early 20th-century India and by Gandhians today; and the work of A.T. Ariyaratne in Sri Lanka and E. F. Schumacher and others in the West who were influenced by Gandhi's work and legacy.

Remarkable similarities exist, for example, between the Gandhian principles of *advaita* (the truth of being and nonviolence), *satyagraha* (truth force or soul force), *swadeshi* (self-reliance and equality in community), and *sarvodaya* (the welfare of all) and Quaker testimonies, as each is part of a unified system and rooted in the same undergirding principles. Similarly, the practices that arise from them are interlinked. Thus, working for more egalitarian and less consumer-oriented economies within and between countries can lessen some of the drivers of conflict and insecurity; working to prevent war can increase material and food security and protect other life-forms; and, at the root, understanding and experiencing a felt bond of unity with all life, and the unity of what we call spirit and matter, or God and nature, however tentatively and fragmentarily, can lead us away from destruction and in the direction of an equitable and peaceable world and an earth restored.

As we saw in the discussion of religious and spiritual (in particular Christian) approaches to the relationship between humans and the wider natural world (Chapters 3 and 7), nature can be viewed in many ways—as created by a single transcendent Deity (or Gods) for our own use and pleasure, as sacred (imbued with spirit or soul) or as nonsacred, as subject to our dominion and control, or in interdependent relation to us—and this informs how we view our responses to and responsibility toward nature. Where a secular or religious community falls on this spectrum depends on differences in religious or spiritual worldviews (or their absence) as well as on technological, demographic, and cultural shifts. As described in Chapter 2, sustainability is often defined primarily in economic terms, as we consider the costs and benefits of ways we can conserve "resources" and "ecosystem services" and deal with "externalities" such as pollution. And while an increasing number of Christian denominations in the West have espoused stewardship views of creation to foster more sustainable ways of living (Chapter 7), the needs of present and future (human) generations are often cited as a primary rationale. From a deep ecology perspective, however, we are still placing humans in the position of privilege, domination, and control, of considering only human and economic needs, with nature having no intrinsic rights as we think of them for humans. At the same time, we tend to ignore the reality of our absolute dependency on the natural world.

Deep ecologists argue, along with many indigenous peoples, that there is a subtle but vital difference between regarding nature as the sacred creation of God as a gift to humanity solely for our use and regarding it as sacred and having inherent worth. One of the central aims of a deep ecology perspective is to find ways we might live in a *reciprocal*, not competing, relationship with the wider natural world, respecting the principle that all life has fundamental value. However, as we will explore further below, a deep ecology approach does *not* mean putting the needs of other life-forms above all human needs, nor is it an argument against any instrumental use of nature—Gandhi, for example, did not see a conflict between a spiritual regard for the sacredness of nature and the use of nature for essential needs, if done with wisdom, nonviolence and respect for the right of all life to its existence. This perspective means addressing the thorny questions of what constitutes material sufficiency in a economically globalized world, and what really sustains us materially, culturally, and spiritually, if we are to live more harmoniously and peaceably with each other and the wider natural world.

While recognizing the challenges of putting the ideal of a deep ecology perspective into practice and in equitable ways (as we will explore below and in Chapter 9), a deep ecology approach seeks to revere life, to realize our oneness with the web of life, to understand, respect and nourish the fragile balances that constitute nature, and to restrain ourselves from overconsumption, willful destruction, and the thoughtless exploitation of nature, i.e., to minimize our impact on nature while providing for the essential needs of all people. We do this not merely because we are good stewards and know we need to conserve resources for our own future needs but also because we experience the wider natural world as an integral and interconnected part of who we are, a part of what we love and cherish, and because we regard all life-forms as having intrinsic value. We can arrive at a view that is consonant with a deep ecology perspective from what many would call a "secular" moral and ethical or philosophical standpoint as well as a specifically religious standpoint. For example, in the declaration of the Earth Charter,[4] a global

---

[4] The Earth Charter emerged out of meetings between members of the Club of Rome and the UN Commission on Environment and Development in 1987; following six years of worldwide consultations, it was launched in 2000. http://earthcharter.org/. See Chapter 1.

initiative started in 1987 and comprising a wide range of nongovernmental organizations and movements, including UNESCO and related agencies, is the statement, "Recognize that all beings are interdependent and every form of life has value regardless of its worth to human beings," a position that aligns closely with the deep ecology perspective first articulated by the philosopher Arne Naess, described here.

Arne Naess and Ecosophy

If we read Arne Naess, the pioneer of the long-range deep ecology movement, we should perhaps first reframe the question "What is deep ecology?" as "What is ecosophy?"—a term he proposed for the broader philosophy in which deep ecology principles were grounded. Naess's ecosophy, or ecological philosophy (as briefly described in Chapter 5), which he described as being deeply influenced by Spinozan and Gandhian thought, is the understanding of the ecological self as Self.[5] We gradually awaken to the realization of the unity of all things and of oneself as an integral part of this whole—an indivisible part of the gestalt, or network of connections, of life. Ecosophy has metaphysical underpinnings but, as Naess stressed, is also entirely compatible with a scientific ecological perspective. Naess defined it, in part, thus:

> By an ecosophy I mean a philosophy of ecological harmony or equilibrium. A philosophy as a kind of sofia (or) wisdom, is openly normative, it contains both norms, rules, postulates, value priority announcements and hypotheses concerning the state of affairs in our universe. Wisdom is policy wisdom, prescription, not only scientific description and prediction...."[6]

For Naess, in contrast to most philosophical traditions focusing exclusively on the human condition, ecosophy embraces the investigation of human-nature relationships with the goal of developing ecological wisdom or ecological values. As Naess emphasized, this involves an ongoing process of exploration and can accomodate diverse values and aims.

Within the context of ecosophy, Naess, George Sessions, and others, starting in the early 1970s, developed the philosophical foundation of what Naess called the *long-range deep ecology movement*, also articulated in later writings

---

[5] Arne Naess, "Self-realization: An Ecological Approach to Being in the World," *Trumpeter* 4, no. 3 (1987), 35-42, http://trumpeter.athabascau.ca/index.php/trumpet/article/view/623.

[6] Arne Naess, "The Shallow and the Deep, Long-Range Ecology Movement: A Summary," in *The Deep Ecology Movement: An Introductory Anthology*, eds. Alan Drengson and Yuichi Inoue (Berkeley, CA: North Atlantic Publishers, 1995), 8.

by Warwick Fox, Bill Devall, Alan Drengson, and Michael Tobias, among others.[7] Naess contrasted the deep ecology movement with what he referred to in some writings as the "shallow" ecology movement (an arguably unfortunate label that potentially implied that these movements were in conflict with one another), which referred to the relative depth of the foundational principles on which the movements were based. Naess delineated four levels of ecological thinking or philosophical inquiry and their resultant policies and actions.[8] In his scheme, practices and policies evolve upwards from principles, rather than from top-down power structures.

Eight principles are articulated in the deep ecology platform, centered on the proposition that all life has intrinsic, rather than simply instrumental, value. In other words, humans should not be considered the only species of importance, with exclusive rights to control, exploit, or destroy nature. These principles, as modified by Naess and Sessions in 1984, are as follows:

1. "The well-being and flourishing of human and nonhuman life on Earth have value in themselves (synonyms: inherent worth, intrinsic value, inherent value). These values are independent of the usefulness of the nonhuman world for human purposes.

2. Richness and diversity of life forms contribute to the realization of these values [and to the flourishing of human and nonhuman life on earth[9]] and are also values in themselves.

3. Humans have no right to reduce this richness and diversity except to satisfy vital needs.

4. Present human interference with the nonhuman world is excessive, and the situation is rapidly worsening.

5. The flourishing of human life and cultures is compatible with a substantial decrease of the human population. The flourishing of nonhuman life requires such a decrease.

---

[7] See, for example: Arne Naess, *Ecology, Community, and Lifestyle: Outline of an Ecosophy*, trans. and revised by David Rothenberg (Cambridge, UK: Cambridge University Press, 1989); Arne Naess, *The Ecology of Wisdom: Writings by Arne Naess*, eds. Alan Drengson and Bill Devall (Berkeley, CA: Counterpoint Press, 2008); Bill Devall and Warwick Fox, *Toward a Transpersonal Ecology: Developing New Foundations for Environmentalism* (Albany, NY: State University of New York Press, 1995); George Sessions, ed., *Deep Ecology for the 21st Century* (Boston: Shambhala Publications, Inc., 1995); Bill Devall and George Sessions, *Deep Ecology: Living as if Nature Mattered* (Layton, UT: Gibbs Smith Publishers, 1985); Michael Tobias, *Deep Ecology* (San Marcos, CA: Avant Books, 1988).

[8] Naess refers to Level I as "Ultimate Premises" (e.g. Taoism, Christianity, ecosophy); Level II, as "Platform Principles Movement" (e.g., peace and social justice movements); Level III, as "Policies"; and Level IV, as "Practical Actions."

[9] Naess, "Basics of the Deep Ecology Movement" in *Ecology of Wisdom*, 111.

6. Policies must therefore be changed. The changes in policies affect basic economic, technological structures. The resulting state of affairs will be deeply different from the present.

7. The ideological change is mainly that of appreciating life quality (dwelling in situations of inherent worth) rather than adhering to an increasingly higher standard of living. There will be a profound awareness of the difference between big and great.

8. Those who subscribe to the foregoing points have an obligation directly or indirectly to participate in the attempt to implement the necessary changes."[10]

Life's "equal right to live and blossom," as Naess put it, goes beyond the concept of conserving what we refer to as natural resources or ecosystem services. And restricting human destruction of other life-forms (and the soils, water, and air on which they depend) to "satisfying vital needs" arguably goes beyond the concept of earth stewardship, which, as we saw in Chapter 7, characterizes the position taken by some, if not most religious denominations and some environmental ethicists. However, neither Naess nor other advocates of deep ecology regard their position as in fundamental contradiction to Christian or other ethical practices if each seeks to protect and nourish life, whether or not nature has economic or instrumental value for humans. As described above, Gandhi also emphasized in his writing and work that no necessary or fundamental contradiction or opposition need exist between what has intrinsic value and what has instrumental value to humans. Further, the more we come to realize how integrated our life-support ecosystems are, as we have seen, the more the division begins to dissolve between the parts of nature we consider economically useful to humans and those that are not.

Naess continued to evolve his views about what he had earlier described as "biospherical egalitarianism," which he later replaced with the idea of life-forms' intrinsic "right to live and blossom," for example. According to correspondence quoted by John Clark, an author in the deep ecology movement,[11] Naess recognized that the idea could easily be misconstrued—to imply that humans were equal to insects, for example, and we should not kill animals under any circumstances—rather than viewing the moral dilemma in more complex and nuanced ways. Naess also came to agree that greater emphasis

---

[10] Foundation for Deep Ecology, "The Deep Ecology Platform," http://www.deepecology.org/platform.htm.

[11] John Clark, "A Dialogue with Arne Naess on Social Ecology and Deep Ecology," *Trumpeter* 26, no. 2 (2010), 24, http://trumpeter.athabascau.ca/index.php/trumpet/article/view/1176/1527.

should be placed in Principle 6 on the need to deter social domination of one person or group over another, for example.[12]

Some critics of a deep ecology approach have argued that this platform is elitist, or even that it borders on what some call ecofascism and the pitting of other species' needs *against* those of humans. Some have objected to the idea implied in the fifth principle that human populations should be decreased, a proposition that is fraught with serious ethical dangers (see Chapter 2 and below). Others have argued that even deep ecologists are acting from an anthropocentric viewpoint, demanding of others that they value nonhuman life, when this is just as much a human-centered value system as one that prioritizes human life. Still others have taken extreme approaches (such as some Earth First! proponents) that appear to prioritize nature over human needs, leading to clashes over whether indigenous people should continue traditional practices of small-scale hunting and fishing, for example.

A particularly vitriolic attack came from Murray Bookchin, one of the most prominent founders of the social ecology movement. As described by John Clark,[13] while originally taking an approach that was largely considered complementary rather than oppositional to deep ecology, Bookchin began to take an increasingly antagonistic and even demonizing position against it. In a widely published article,[14] he accused Naess and other deep ecologists of taking the view that humans had overpopulated the world and even were a cancer on the planet, and of being willing to consider letting millions of people in the developed world die of starvation, for instance. He drew a direct analogy between what he referred to as the "eco-brutalism" of deep ecology and the horrors of Nazism and Hitler's intention to purge the world of "undesirable" populations, leading to racial cleansing, eugenic policies, and mass death. This in turn provoked a strong riposte from leading deep ecologists such as Clark, who argued that their views were deeply misrepresented in Bookchin's critique.

The problem with the either-or character of some arguments for and against a deep ecology approach is that most deep ecologists are quite aware of the complexity of determining the vital needs of humans, and are emphatically not equating the concept of the intrinsic value of all life with the idea

---

[12] Clark, "Dialogue with Arne Naess," 33.

[13] Clark, "Dialogue with Arne Naess," 21-4 et seq.

[14] Murray Bookchin, "Social Ecology versus Deep Ecology: A Challenge for the Ecology Movement," *Green Perspectives, Newsletter of the Green Program Project*, nos. 4-5, Summer 1987.

that humans should not kill or use any animal or even much plant life.[15] Nor is a deep ecology position pitting Earth's needs against human needs. Rather it sees *all humans as an integral part of the whole earth community and having the right to take our place in that community.* Part of the ongoing process of exploration that moving from Naess's Level I to Level IV (see above) involves is a constant dialogue, working out how to integrate the principle that all life has inherent value with the principle of satisfying human needs for an adequate means to live, along with the means to flourish spiritually, psychologically, and culturally. We necessarily have an impact on the wider natural world to live and thrive, as must all other animals or plants in some degree, but the challenge is to minimize our impact in ways that are both equitable within human communities and respectful of all life-forms. Part of this evolutionary process is to learn practical ways of "treading more lightly" on the earth, whether in agriculture or other spheres (which will be explored in Part III), and, as we have seen, grounding those ways in integrity, reciprocity, nonviolence and equality.

Gandhian Influences on Naess's Deep Ecology

Gandhi's life work and philosophy predate the modern environmental movement and the deep ecology movement, yet the essential elements of a deep ecology perspective are implicit in his practice of *satyagraha* or nonviolent resistance and in the *sarvodaya* (wellbeing of all) movement or Constructive Program that he and his followers developed in the 1920s. Gandhi insisted on minimizing human impacts on the wider natural world by practicing nonviolence, simplicity in one's material life, the development of a local economy using local food and other materials, and the wise use of technology. As explored in Chapters 5 and 7, the spiritual ground that informed both Gandhi's nonviolent philosophy and his beliefs about how humans should regard the wider natural world can be found in the Hindu and Jain traditions of *advaita,* or nonduality, the truth or reality of the oneness and unity of all life with *brahman,* the ground of reality; and *ahimsa,* the practice of nonviolence to all beings, which Gandhi understood as the removal of the desire to do harm.

---

[15] Having spent my career in environmental epidemiological research and public health, I would not be willing to argue that pathogens (parasites, ticks, bacteria, etc.) should not be destroyed if a person's health is at stake, for example. At the same time, the widespread use of many herbicides and insecticides, for example, can be argued against because their use can destroy multiple other life-forms that are vital for healthy ecologies and, indirectly, our wellbeing (bees are an example) and where far less destructive alternatives exist and can be applied. Similarly, there are strong ecological arguments for vegetarianism, or veganism, but not as absolute prohibitions in all cases. The ethical issues are complex and require openness, humility, and dialog.

Jainism, the religious tradition practiced by Gandhi's mother, holds that, as Christopher Chapple describes it, "all aspects of physical reality are imbued with multitudes of life" or "the livingness of all things."[16] Gandhi also held that violence (*himsa*) against a living being was a form of violence against oneself and an impenetrable barrier to self-realization. This philosophy strongly influenced Naess's view of the centrality of nonviolence in the practice of a deep ecology, based on his view that "Gandhi made manifest the internal relation between self-realization, non-violence and what sometimes has been called biospherical egalitarianism."[17]

Among Jain adherents, killing any animal and the needless destruction of nature should be avoided. Hence we see practices ranging from fasting, vegetarianism, and minimizing material consumption through a simple lifestyle among lay practitioners, to wearing masks to avoid swallowing flying insects and sweeping the floor to avoid stepping on small animals among its stricter adherents. Hinduism also takes the view that all life is one unity,[18] which informs its adherents' nonviolent relationships with nature from the Brahmanic period around 600 BCE onward, including vegetarianism (although ritual sacrifice and meat-eating were permitted in some circumstances).[19] Gandhi believed that "we should feel a more living bond between ourselves and the rest of the animal world"[20] and that "we [should] recognize that animals had rights, no less than man."[21] He also believed that the worship of the cow "takes the human beyond his species.... Man, through the cow, is enjoined to realise his oneness with all that lives."[22] (In Gandhi's ashram, killing venomous snakes or other potentially dangerous animals was strongly discouraged, and anecdotes about snakes being ignored, or picked up with tongs and deposited outside, apparently without incident, were widespread.)

---

[16] Christopher Key Chapple, *Nonviolence to Animals, Earth, and Self in Asian Traditions* (Albany, NY: State University of New York Press, 1993), 9; also see *Jainism and Ecology*, ed. Christopher Key Chapple (Cambridge, MA: Harvard University Press, 2002).

[17] Naess, "Self-realization," 39.

[18] See, for example, *Hinduism and Ecology*, eds. Mary Evelyn Tucker and Christopher Key Chapple (Cambridge, MA: Harvard University Press, 2000).

[19] Christopher Key Chapple, *Nonviolence to Animals*, 15-6.

[20] M.K. Gandhi, "Our Brethren the Trees," *Young India*, December 5, 1921, quoted in Thomas Weber, *Gandhi as Disciple and Mentor* (Cambridge, UK: Cambridge University Press, 2004).

[21] M.K. Gandhi, "Harijans and Pigs," *Harijan* April 13, 1935, quoted in Weber, *Gandhi*, 2004.

[22] M.K. Gandhi, "Hinduism," *Young India*, October 6, 1921, quoted in Weber, *Gandhi*, 2004.

Thomas Berry and the Great Work

In *The Dream of the Earth*, published in 1988, Thomas Berry—a former Catholic priest, a cultural historian, and an ecotheologian—first articulated, after a lifetime of reflection and exploration, his vision of what he called the story of the universe and the emergence of a whole earth community from a new point of view: a dynamic, evolving and ever-developing reality that is not only "out there" to be studied by our cosmologists and scientists but also perceived and experienced in new ways by us humans as part of this miraculous, evolving process. As Berry describes it, "*We need to see ourselves as integral with this emerging process,* [my emphasis] as that being in whom the universe reflects on and celebrates itself."[23] His book is also a lament for our sense of alienation and separation from the wider natural world, as I have been exploring in this book, and for the loss of the wisdom of how to live more integrally and harmoniously with nature, respecting the autonomy of other creatures to live.

Berry sensed that modern, technologically oriented human societies have lost a sense of place in the great cosmic story of unfolding and our place as a part of a whole earth community, and as such have lost a deeper sense of meaning, belonging, and possibility. Apocryphal visions replace visions of hope and possibility; a sense of disintegration is evidenced by social and cultural breakdown and alienation from the wider natural world. Berry's gift, however, in this and subsequent writings, was to articulate a new vision of cosmic unfolding and the place of the earth, humans and other life-forms in what he called this "larger sacred community." With the cosmologist Brian Swimme, he wrote a new story of the universe[24] as a way to reframe and reconnect us with "healing cosmologies" that "call for a sensitivity and affectivity to the larger pattern of life and death in the natural world,"[25] and to introduce a vision of a new "Ecozoic" era,[26] an emerging ecological age in which humans will finally learn to live as an integral part of a mutually benefi-

---

[23] Berry, *Dream of the Earth*, 81.

[24] Brian Swimme and Thomas Berry, *The Universe Story: From the Primordial Flaring Forth to the Ecozoic Era—A Celebration of the Unfolding of the Cosmos* (San Francisco: HarperSanFrancisco, 1992).

[25] Thomas Berry: Biography, "Universe Story," http://thomasberry.org/life-and-thought/about-thomas-berry/a-universe-story.

[26] "[t]he emerging period of life following the Cenozoic, and characterized, at a basic level, by its mutually enhancing human-Earth relations. The word derives from the scientific tradition that divides the Phanerozoic eon into the Paleozoic, Mesozoic, and Cenozoic eras." Glossary, *The Universe Story*.

cial and flourishing earth community. To repeat Berry's quote from the beginning of this chapter, "The ecological age fosters the deep awareness of the sacred presence within each reality of the universe."[27] We and every other living being, and the soils, waters, and air that support us, are all indivisible parts of this commonwealth of life.

This vision was carried forward in Berry's classic *The Great Work*,[28] in which he described the work required to manifest this new Ecozoic era. For Berry, this work rests on what he called the fourfold wisdom:

> …we might reflect that a fourfold wisdom is available to guide us into the future: the wisdom of indigenous peoples, the wisdom of women, the wisdom of the classical traditions, and the wisdom of science.[29]

Why these four pillars, and how might they support the emergence of a new age? What is instructive about Berry's vision is that it comprehends the value of what have been considered as vastly different, and in fact oppositional, ways of thinking and being—from the ways of indigenous peoples and women to the Hindu sages and Greek classicists to the work of the most advanced sciences—and from largely ignored or silenced wisdoms to (presently) dominant and highly valued sources of wisdoms. Here again, as in the thread that has woven through the exploration in this book, the central theme is one of integration, of restoring and bringing back into balance and presence, wisdoms that have been dominated, subjugated, or lost, so as to survive and thrive in creative harmony with the whole earth community.

As Berry writes, despite the enormous survival challenges faced by indigenous peoples in the past four centuries or more, some of their wisdom has survived too, to be passed down, usually orally, by elders, shamans, and other keepers of tradition, ritual, and story. We, that is, cultures that have decimated indigenous cultures and peoples and devalued the significance of their wisdom, are belatedly waking up to the fact that we can learn from these traditions to find ways back to that vital wisdom. Second, as described in Chapters 3 and 4, the silenced wisdom of the feminine aspect must be reintegrated to balance rationality with intuition, subjectivity with objectivity, and our feeling and intuitive aspects with the intellect and senses. He also calls upon us to (re)discover the wisdoms enshrined in the great classical world traditions of

---

[27] Berry, *Dream of the Earth*, 46.

[28] Thomas Berry, *The Great Work: Our Way to the Future* (New York: Bell Tower, 1999). Berry's vision and work is carried forward by the Center for Ecozoic Studies (https://www.ecozoicstudies.org) among other organizations.

[29] Berry, *The Great Work*, 176.

religion and philosophy—from the Hindu, Taoist, and Buddhist traditions to the strands of Greek, Roman, Jewish, Muslim, and Christian traditions of Western civilizations—and to integrate these with the emerging and ever-deeper discoveries of our scientific era—from the world that Kepler, Descartes, Newton, Darwin, and others could see to the present "quantum world" of subatomic particles, gravitational fields, consciousness studies, and the ongoing search for a "unifying vision" of the ever-changing, emergent universe (see Chapter 5).

Berry also recognized the need to integrate a deep psychospiritual perspective with the work of science and technology. In other words, the Universe story is as much a spiritual story as it is a scientific cosmology. In an echo of the deep ecology philosophy of Naess and others, this transformation calls for an *experiential* sense of our connection with nature, a spiritual realization of the self as Self, as much as an intellectual-rational-scientific explanation of our ecological connectedness. Second, he draws on both Asian, particularly Buddhist, spiritual traditions and on a transformative Christian spirituality as inspiration for the spiritual ground of our emergent relationship with the earth. As with Lynn White's critique of traditional Christianity's view of nature[30] (discussed in Chapter 3), Berry also characterized traditional Christian spirituality as one that, along with positive aspects, enshrined a view of the divine as strictly transcendent, of only humans rather than nature as possessing a divine spirit, and of an eternal destiny beyond the earthly realm, as promised in the human-God covenant.[31] As described in Chapter 3, this form of spirituality, along with the Cartesian view of a split between inanimate matter and mind or spirit, coalesced to produce the worldview of nature and the universe as inanimate objects. As Berry so eloquently puts it, the central commitment of the Ecozoic era is to "the natural world as revelatory, to the earth community as our primary loyalty, and to the progress of the community in its integrity."[32]

---

[30] Lynn White Jr., "The Historical Roots of the Ecological Crisis," *Science* 155 (1967): 1203-7.

[31] Berry, *Dream of the Earth*, 113-4.

[32] Berry, *Dream of the Earth*, 82.

Awakening to Unity: The Experience of Deep Ecology

The ancient classical religions, and the sages, seers, and prophets throughout the ages have been telling us the eternal story in many forms: The world is one, a whole, a unity, and not only the world, but ourselves—we are not merely individuals, isolated in our individualism, but we are an integral, indivisible part of All-That-Is. In Hinduism, for example, the Atman is the eternal Spirit or soul within us that is, in the words of the Chandogya Upanishad, "beyond age and death," one with *brahman*, the ultimate Reality beyond all forms. We may even believe this in an abstract way, but it usually requires many years of inner work and reflection to even begin to glimpse the deepest truth of our ultimate unity and the implications of that truth, whether we describe it as self-realization; or seeing that of God in everything; or awakening to the One or All That Is; or simply the reality of our interdependence on everything as far as we can imagine. Gandhi spent decades engaged in what he called his experiments with Truth, and after many years began to see the unity of all things—and that, for him, Truth (or Reality) was God, that Truth was also love, and that nonviolence to all beings was the expression of that love.

The critical question becomes: If we are capable of awakening to this reality, even in small measure, will it move us in the direction of ecological sanity? As described in Chapters 1 and 2, we in richer countries have so far largely failed to respond adequately to the weight of scientific evidence, the environmental movement's campaigns, or the moral, dutiful exhortations of environmental ethicists, particularly at the corporate and governmental level. I believe that if we can glimpse what is in reality a sense of identification with All-That-Is, we can develop the capacity to experience a felt bond of unity that we can truly call love, and at the same time, love helps us to identify with All-That-Is. And more: If we experience love, in its deepest sense of compassion, identification, kinship, and coresponsibility, as part of our expanded selves, with no ultimate boundary or distinction between "self" and "other," we will begin to experience a taste of liberation, of joy, of sufficiency, and fulfillment, all of which we tend to lack in our isolation and thus seek to replace with power, wealth, and accumulation of ever more stuff, achievements, status, and excitements. The idea of self-realization sounds as if it belongs only in the rarified and intellectually abstract realm of philosophers and religious mystics, but in reality it is absolutely the realm of concrete everyday experience, whenever we feel joy at seeing a sparrow on the bush in the park, rescue a struggling turtle caught in fishing net on the beach, plant seeds in our backyard, talk with our political representatives about clean energy, or help establish a community garden. Acts of love and connection start with simple, daily, local acts among the people, animals, and plants with which we share our immediate communities and landscapes. Whether or not we take part in more widespread action, if our sense of kinship and love guides us toward care, nonviolence, and coresponsibility, it radiates out into a web of infinite connection, of mutually reinforcing circles, in ways we may never have imagined.

But I also believe that, given our present condition, we must remind ourselves that we are all, at some level, deeply afraid and insecure, and that our psychological and material insecurities and fears are as much drivers of our predicament as our desires or our failures to connect with others and the natural world. That is, for me, a central reason why compassion and tenderness for our condition are an integral part of a deep ecology approach to our predicament, and why building a deep economy and a nonviolent world are vital and integral parts of working synergistically toward a sustainable ecology for all life.

Thus, a deep ecology perspective is born not only out of a philosophical, scientific, or even religious or spiritual worldview but also out of deep *experience*, a point that Arne Naess often emphasized. And this experience is not confined to mystics, or poets, or people who spend a lot of time on remote mountains, as Naess did. It is emphatically something that can arise spontaneously in a flash or insight or after deep thought, in a laboratory or on a wild mountaintop, in a backyard or a city park, in the silence of a Quaker Meeting or a quiet walk in a forest. It is the response of the soul's heart that every person shares, the principle that is, to repeat the words John Woolman wrote two centuries ago, "confined to no forms of religion nor excluded from any."[33] Sometimes the philosophical intellect, the rational mind, is a barrier to this awareness, which in truth is utterly simple and yet encompasses what Taoists and other Eastern traditions refer to as the ten thousand things—the infinite multiplicity of forms in the manifest world. It is becoming aware of an ever-widening set of relationships or connections between things, the *gestalt*, the patterns that connect, and of seeing how all things fit together in

[33] John Woolman, "Considerations on Keeping Negroes (Part Second)," in *The Journal and Major Essays of John Woolman*, ed. Phillips P. Moulton (Richmond, IN: Friends United Press, 1989), 236. First published in 1971.

one interpenetrating whole—Thich Nhat Hanh's interbeing.[34] At that moment, what I have described as a felt bond of unity or kinship with all beings often occurs, not (or only) as a romantic or sentimental form of love, but as something deeper and more primordial, as if we suddenly have jumped to a new level of consciousness about our place among things, life, and the cosmos, and the places of all other things that belong in that vastness.

Naess emphasized that the development of the ecological self and ecosophy depended on connecting such experiences with values, aims, and action in the world. Crucially, he also held to the view that if a person does have a deep experience of the reality of one's ultimate unity with all beings and the earth, perhaps even if this only happens as a rare realization (what we might call an Aha! moment nowadays), this is more deeply persuasive and transformative than an intellectual-rational or scientific argument or a strictly moral argument about how our lives depend on our environment, or how we *ought* to take care of nature because our scriptures tell us "thou shalt not kill," for example.

My own experience is that once one has caught, however tentatively, even a glimpse of the felt bond of unity with all life and its infinite interdependence, beauty, and wonder, it is like tasting the Truth of Being, or the truth of the unity of Reality and knowing it for the first time. I came to understand that *we do not live by bread alone, but bread is sacred too, and there is no separation.* This realization is no longer theoretical. The Buddha's teaching that everything is mutually co-arising, or the Taoist's poem about finding oneself in all beings, the Hindu vision of Indra's Net, the Sisters and Brothers that St. Francis saw in every planet and living being, the eloquent writings of John Woolman, and the mystical insights at the heart of Quaker worship, all start to make sense. And in that tender sense of unity is the first awakening of love, and in that love, the emerging, unshakeable knowledge that all life is a miracle, all life is my life, all suffering and joy is my suffering and joy, and what I do to any being, I ultimately do to myself.

This direct experience of the unity of life can be found among the traditions of many indigenous peoples, which were often in peril of being lost until more recent revivals and the restoration of their wisdom teachings. It can also be found in the works of some of our most well-known writers, poets, and naturalists, from Emerson to Thoreau, from John Muir to Aldo

---

[34] Thich Nhat Hanh, *Interbeing: Fourteen Guidelines for Engaged Buddhism*, 3rd ed. (Berkeley, CA: Parallax Press, 1987).

Leopold to Thomas Berry, and from Wendell Berry to Barry Lopez, Terry Tempest Williams, Mary Oliver, Annie Dillard, and many others. One of the most eloquent exponents of this realization was Aldo Leopold, employed initially in the 1920s as a wildlife manager in Wisconsin, and who readily adopted the prevailing assumption that extermination of wolves was justified on behalf of human needs. His experiences, including that of watching a wolf die, reoriented Leopold's thinking, as he described in his classic *A Sand County Almanac*.[35] His gift was to ground his understanding in both his thinking and his actual experience, and he bequeathed an account that has become a foundational text for the field of environmental ethics in the 60-plus years since his death. Leopold realized that we are, as he put it, plain members of the biotic community. He summed up his experience with his well-known dictum "A thing is right when it tends to preserve the integrity, stability and beauty of the biotic community. It is wrong when it tends otherwise,"[36] and argued that regarding nature as an adversary to be conquered, or as a resource only if its use is economically valuable, was a limited and ultimately self-defeating view, assuming, as it does, that "the economic parts of the biotic clock will function without the uneconomic parts."[37] It is worth quoting at some length Leopold's exposition of what he named a "land ethic." He writes, "We can be ethical only in relation to something we can see, feel, understand, love or otherwise have faith in."[38] In the light of that sensibility, a sense of being a member of a single earth community can arise:

> An ethic, ecologically, is a limitation on freedom in the struggle for existence. An ethic, philosophically, is a differentiation between social and anti-social conduct…. The thing has its origin in the tendency of interdependent individuals or groups to evolve modes of cooperation. The ecologist calls these symbioses…. There is as yet no ethic dealing with man's relation to the land and to the animals and plants which grow upon it…. The land relation is still strictly economic, entailing privileges but not obligations…. The extension of ethics… is…an evolutionary possibility and an ecological necessity…. The land ethic simply enlarges the community to include soils, water, plants, or animals, or collectively: the land…. In short, a land ethic changes Homo sapiens from conqueror of the land-community to plain member and citizen of it.[39]

---

[35] Aldo Leopold, *A Sand County Almanac, and Sketches Here and There* (New York: Oxford University Press, 1968). First published in 1949.

[36] Leopold, *A Sand County Almanac*, 224.

[37] Leopold, *A Sand County Almanac*, 214.

[38] Leopold, *A Sand County Almanac*, 214.

[39] Leopold, *A Sand County Almanac*, 202-4.

Integrating Deep Ecology, Deep Economy, and Deep Peace

In Chapter 6, I described how the Quaker testimonies are of a piece; each gives rise to and is influenced by each of the others, with integrity—the underlying unity of the whole earth community from humans to the wider natural world, bound together in love—as the root that is nourished by and nourishes the branches and fruits of nonviolence, simplicity, equality, and community. They are, in Buddhist terms, mutually interdependent and co-arising. In the same way, a deep ecology perspective both gives rise to and is supported by what we can call a deep economy perspective, and each gives rise to and is supported by the inner and outer practice of what we can call deep peace, which includes nonviolence toward all life, and the rocks, soils, rivers, oceans, and air that support life. A deep ecology and economy perspective integrates a fundamental concern for the intrinsic right of all life-forms to their lives with a corresponding concern for the rights of all humanity, both present and into the future; to meet the essential needs of life, which include not only material but also cultural, esthetic, and spiritual needs; and to live equitably in security and peace with each other. Ultimately, each path or aspect is indivisible, as we explored in Chapters 5 and 6. As Gandhi wrote:

> ...[the] exclusive search for physical and economic wellbeing prosecuted in disregard of morality is contrary to divine law...all [economic and other] activities should be centered in the search for Truth, and...that Truth can only be sought through ahimsa, or nonviolence, which at its core is harmony, kinship, justice, and love. Truth and nonviolence are as inseparable as the two sides of a coin.[40]

What then, might we consider as underlying principles of an integrated deep ecology, economy, and peace?

- A deep ecology and economy should be equitable, just, nonviolent, and sustainable, i.e., in a reciprocal and integral relationship to each other and the wider natural world. While the taking of life and alteration of the land, oceans, air, and water is inevitable, human activity should minimize such interference compatible with providing for essential needs and maintaining sustainable life.

- Every member of a community has the right to adequate food, clean water, sanitation, housing, clothing, healthcare provision, education, cultural and spiritual needs, and dignified work. These needs should be provided for first, before other wants, and every individual member has the right

---

[40] M.K. Gandhi, *Sarvodaya (The Welfare of All)*, ed. Bharatan Kumarappa (Ahmedabad, India: Navajivan Publishing House, 1954), 7.

to participate equally democratically in the governance of their community and beyond.

- The intrinsic right of humans and other life-forms to a peaceful and secure life is honored, and violence to and the economic exploitation of people and other life-forms is eschewed.

These fundamental, spiritually grounded principles should also underpin the way we apply our science and technologies in the service of a deep ecology, economy and peace. E.F. Schumacher, who pioneered the concept of appropriate technology, understood the principles underlying it as an integral part of a nonviolent, equitable, deep economy, as did Gandhi in his Constructive Program. According to these principles, an appropriate technology must serve the essential needs of the local then wider community in which it is applied, while minimizing long-term damage to local ecologies and economies and integrating as much as possible indigenous practices, labor and traditional knowledge and resources. (The aims and practice of appropriate technology are discussed further in Chapter 10.)

Of course, translating principles into practice is far from simple when what is called for is a radical transformation of the way many of us live if we are to avoid ecological catastrophe. To seek to put into practice deep ecology, deep economy, and deep peace requires that we learn ways to wage, not war, but nonviolence; that we seek sufficiency and deeper equality and thus deeper security in our societies; that we understand ourselves to be integral members of our whole earth community; and seek to live in cooperation with each other and in alignment with nature. Given how embedded the ways of thinking and acting in the world are that have got us into the existential predicament we are now facing, we have no easy paths or answers as to how we can put such principles into practice. As emphasized in Part I, it is now abundantly clear that the pursuit of economic growth, consumer capitalism, and the exploitation of nature, particularly by the richer countries of the world, have brought us to the brink of ecological collapse, but if we are to live within our ecological means on a global level we must address the vast inequalities in material wellbeing within and between countries, and learn—or re-learn—ways to live fulfilling, nonviolent, spiritually and culturally prosperous and materially sufficient lives in greater harmony with the wider natural world. We must "make the path by walking," as the saying goes, and continually evolve and revise our thinking—and practices—as we go. Nor can we practice outwardly without practicing inwardly, and this is particularly true of the practice of inward peace and nonviolence toward all beings.

In sum, despite the enormity of our predicament, we can (re)discover radically different and life-enhancing principles, paradigms and ways of thinking and being in the world, grounded in our classical spiritual traditions, indigenous wisdoms, and the mystical and prophetic teachings of the great sages and mystics. Such paradigm shifts, named by Joanna Macy, David Korten and others as the Great Turning, and the Great Work by Thomas Berry, are being integrated into our 21st century world, using and transforming each of the interconnected spheres of ecology, science, technology, economics, politics, and peacemaking, and enlivening a new, radical, yet ancient spirituality. As I will describe in Part III, multiple examples already exist of ways these principles are being put into practice, involving people who are walking paths of deep ecology, economy, and peace, making tracks to follow while treading lightly on the earth.

PART III

PRACTICE

What matters is to discover if there is such as thing as a nonviolent economy, free of all forms of pressure and closed to all forms of unfairness;...whether there is such a thing as nonviolent justice;...such things as nonviolent farming, nonviolent medicine, nonviolent psychiatry, nonviolent diet. And to begin with, what matters is to make sure that all violence...has been weeded out of our religious life.

—Lanza del Vasto

Instead of the anxious, illusory pursuit of more money and possessions, people need to think about pursuing joyful, grateful and fulfilling lives in right relationship with life's commonwealth.

—Peter Brown and Geoffrey Garver

The world faces not a preordained future, but a choice.

—Donella Meadows

Lanza del Vasto, *Warriors of Peace: Writings on the Technique of Nonviolence* (New York: Alfred A. Knopf, Inc., 1974), 49.

Peter G. Brown and Geoffrey Garver, *Right Relationship: Building a Whole Earth Economy* (San Francisco: Berrett-Koehler Publishers, Inc., 2009), 168.

Donella Meadows, Jorgen Randers, and Dennis Meadows, *Limits to Growth: The 30-Year Update* (White River Junction, VT: Chelsea Green Publishing Company, 2004), 283.

Chapter 9

The Practice of Deep Ecology

... we are beginning to move from democracy to biocracy, to the participation of the larger life community in our human decision-making processes.

—Thomas Berry[1]

Appreciate all life forms rather than merely those considered beautiful, remarkable, or narrowly useful.... Never use [them] merely as means. Remain conscious of their intrinsic value and dignity, even when using them as resources.

—Arne Naess[2]

The deep ecology perspective raises many thorny ethical, moral, and practical questions. As explored in foregoing chapters, we have reached that turning point in our collective evolution where we must discover what really sustains us. How much is "enough"? What are our essential needs? How do we provide for human needs now and into the future equitably and justly, so that costs are not borne disproportionately by some groups of humans and other life-forms while the benefits accrue mainly to others? How do we, perhaps for the first time in our modern era, reconcile our needs for survival and culture with the right of other life-forms to their existence and live as an integral part of the whole earth community, in reciprocal rather than oppositional relationship to other living beings? In other words, how do we actually practice "right relationship" with the earth?

The practice of deep ecology is intimately intertwined with how we practice our human economies, our science and technology, and our governance, and all of these, as we explored in Part II, are underpinned by how we discern and practice spiritual and moral principles, exemplified by the Quaker principles of integrity, nonviolence, simplicity, equality, justice and community in

---

[1] Thomas Berry, *The Dream of the Earth* (San Francisco: Sierra Club Books, 1990), xii.
[2] Arne Naess, "Lifestyle Trends Within the Deep Ecology Movement," in *The Ecology of Wisdom, Writings by Arne Naess*, eds. Alan Drengson and Bill Devall (Berkeley: Counterpoint Press, 2008), 141.

the whole earth community. *In other words, we can only practice a deep ecology if we practice a deep and just economy and nonviolence to each other and all life, and vice versa,* both on a small, local scale and on a global scale. To give a single example at one end of the scale, attempts to patent life-forms such as seeds or the potentially commercial properties of native plants in India and elsewhere represent a new and possibly dangerous development in what has always been a struggle to maintain lands, oceans, rivers, and the life-forms that inhabit them as part of the commons. These developments call for a deeper ecological and economic approach to concepts of ownership, property, profit, and right relationship with the earth. On a global scale, as we saw in Chapter 1, the world continues to spend trillions of dollars each year on armaments and conflicts, involving incalculable human and ecological destruction, while climate breakdown presents the single greatest global risk to life and security the world has ever faced. Again, we cannot develop a deeper ecological and economic approach without addressing the need to challenge our priorities, and to channel these massive funds, technologies and energies into life-preserving and enhancing, rather than life-destroying, programs on both national and international levels.

In this and the following chapters, we will explore the questions, How might we practice a deep nonviolent ecology, via our science and technology and economies, in our direct relationship with earth systems as it applies to land and waterways use, agriculture, food and water consumption, and the conservation and restoration of life-forms and habitats? And how can we practice a deep and just ecology and economy that allows for human needs to flourish in *reciprocity* with each other and the wider natural world—a peaceable world where we seek a just and sustainable distribution of food, water, shelter, healthcare, and other human needs and a wider responsibility for restoring ecological devastation, the impacts of which have been borne disproportionately by the poor and by countless other life-forms?

Conscientious Protection—Conserving the Commonwealth of Life

As described in Chapter 1, there is an urgent need to protect life in the oceans, rivers, and land from further ecological devastation. While the focus today is primarily on ensuring "sustainable resources" for burgeoning human populations into the future, a wide range of conservation movements has emerged around the world, dating back centuries in some cases. In America, for example, the idea of preserving wilderness gradually took hold from the 19th century on, inspired by visionaries such as John Muir and embodied in organizations like the Sierra Club, the Conservation Society, and many others. Muir's vision, which helped lead to the establishment of the first National Parks in the U.S., was partly to allow for the human enjoyment of nature but also to help preserve wilderness and other life-forms for their own sakes. All life—human and other-than-human—has been the beneficiary of these protected areas in these magnificent parks, along with a multitude of regional and local parks, small though these may be compared with developed land, and despite the ongoing pressures of agricultural, mining and logging interests and urban development, which threaten to encroach on even those small areas designated for conservation and protection.

Of course, debate has always followed development of parks and other preserves and sanctuaries: Who benefits? The people? Which people? Tourists, indigenous people, private owners, or corporations? Wildlife? Both? As populations and tourism have grown, the tension between human interests and the needs of wildlife has become more evident. Can we have reciprocity rather than competition? In a few countries, some designated wilderness areas have been protected from most human intrusion,[3] while others have attempted both to manage the impact of increasing numbers of visitors without excluding them from such areas and to resist the pressure to sell off or lease such areas to mining, ranching and other private interests. Muir's calculus was primarily one of wisdom, not of economics; of morals, not money; and was the foundation of every attempt he made to preserve now and into the future our sacred and communal home, of which he realized we humans are but a small part. Inevitably, economic considerations became and still are a significant part of the calculus, and it's impossible to say whether they weigh more heavily now than they did, say, a century ago. However, if we read the history of the struggle to establish the national parks, as with other conservation efforts, it was the need to preserve landscapes and wildlife *for their own sake* that inspired the efforts of Muir and countless others to fight for their creation and preservation, and enabled them to persuade Theodore and Franklin D. Roosevelt and other members of government to support the necessary legislation. Such efforts demonstrate that a spiritually and ethically grounded

---

[3] For example, the International Union for Conservation of Nature (IUCN) has designated the approximately 66-square-mile Swiss National Park and the Engadin valley as a "strict nature reserve," meaning that human activity is highly regulated and many areas are off-limits to people.

principle of protecting wildlife and habitats for their own sake can be translated successfully into practical action at the local, regional, and national levels, in contrast to the dominance of policies that commodify and monetize
nature and make decisions heavily biased in favor of short-term economic
interests.

Nevertheless, the ongoing tension between the needs of humans and of
other life-forms is evident in the work of many of today's conservation organizations. Thousands of individuals and organizations worldwide have been
dedicated to the conservation of lands, plants, and animals that are threatened
with extinction irrespective of their economic uses. The massive and unprecedented loss of populations and whole species witnessed over the past 40
years (see Chapter 1) has drawn attention to the causes of these threats, from
the loss of insect species due to climate change, pesticide use and habitat loss,
to the loss of orangutan habitats in Indonesia to make way for palm oil plantations, to widespread poaching of elephant and rhino tusks for ornaments, to
"harvesting" pangolin scales for medicinal uses, and so on. Organizations
such as the World Wildlife Fund (WWF) and the International Union for
Conservation of Nature (IUCN) work to designate and protect threatened
areas and ecosystems and, at least in principle, to protect the rights of indigenous peoples to their traditional lands and practices. They have published a
series of principles and guidelines to underpin their programs, and in them we
can see attempts to resolve the tension between what appear to be conflicting
demands of protecting wildlife, the rights of indigenous peoples, and the
forces of "development." The guidelines they have drawn up justify the value
of protected areas primarily in economic terms,[4] as biodiversity resources or
recreational benefits, with relatively little language to suggest an ethical obligation to protect wildlife and undisturbed habitats. While on one level, such
efforts to protect vulnerable areas and species are laudable and have met with
success; on another, they maintain a primarily anthropocentric framework
that seeks to evaluate the *economic* benefits of biodiversity and conservation in
terms of human needs such as "cultural resources." On yet another level, the
IUCN and other bodies recognize that a strictly economic approach is insufficient to guarantee the protection of biodiversity, and call for government
regulation to ensure such action as a "public service."

---

[4] World Commission on Protected Areas, *Economic Values of Protected Areas: Guidelines for Protected Area Managers*, ed. Adrian Phillips (Gland, Switzerland, and Cambridge, U.K.: IUCN, 1998), https://www.iucn.org/downloads/pag_002.pdf.

Where indigenous peoples' ways of living are concerned, these challenges must be worked out with the participation and empowerment of such communities, which has often been lacking. For example, in one of its guidelines, the IUCN states as a guiding principle that:

> Agreements drawn up between conservation institutions, including protected area management agencies, and indigenous and other traditional peoples for the establishment and management of protected areas affecting their lands, territories, waters, coastal seas and other resources should be based on full respect for the rights of indigenous and other traditional peoples to traditional, sustainable use of their lands, territories, waters, coastal seas and other resources. At the same time, such agreements should be based on the recognition by indigenous and other traditional peoples of their responsibility to conserve biodiversity, ecological integrity and natural resources harboured in those protected areas.[5]

The case studies presented in their document illustrate some of the challenges and problems involved, including cases where the indigenous peoples were not sufficiently consulted about decisions to declare areas they lived in as protected areas, raising thorny questions about the degree to which outside agencies exert power over indigenous ways of life, which people are responsible for the ecological destruction that drives the need to protect certain areas, and who benefits from such protection, aside from considering the threats to wildlife.

Sanctuaries: Places to Connect with Nature

As the rate of global urbanization and technological intrusion in our lives has accelerated, more and more people are distanced from the wider natural world, and from the essential time, silence, and solitude in nature that, to me, are as vital for my body and spirit as are clean air, fresh water, and nourishing food. While some of us were fortunate enough to be raised in or close to the countryside, or by rivers or oceans, and at a time when it was safe to allow children to roam freely on foot or bicycle across hills and dales, this is no longer the case for more and more children; the experience of the wild and learning about nature's beauty and ways are often confined to a classroom or a screen rather than the outdoor world. To counteract this trend, many thousands of nature preserves and sanctuaries, farms, parks, and educational and recreational centers allow children and adults to experience and learn about

---

[5] World Commission on Protected Areas, *Indigenous and Traditional Peoples and Protected Areas: Principles, Guidelines and Case Studies*, ed. Javier Beltrán (Gland, Switzerland and Cambridge UK: IUCN, 2000), x,
https://www.portalces.org/sites/default/files/migrated/docs/879.pdf.

their local ecology, to spend time outdoors and perhaps in wilderness, and to observe and touch and learn about animal and plants that are infrequently found within dense urban areas. Equally, urban-based centers provide walks and talks to discover the hidden life-forms that share our urban environments.[6]

Equitable Land Ownership and Use

We tend to hear of land-reform movements in poorer rather than richer countries, but, as discussed in Chapter 2, who owns the land (and what lies on and below it) in all countries is as central an issue to the establishment of sustainable economies as who owns property and businesses. The principle of private ownership of land, water, mineral rights, forests, vegetation, and other "natural resources" has been almost sacrosanct in the U.S. and many other countries, together with the assumption that owners have exclusive rights to do whatever they want with the land unless prevented by litigation or regulation (which has frequently been unsuccessful due to a bias in favor of owners' rights). Even the preservation of the relatively tiny fragments of land that remain as ancient "commons,"[7] i.e., land traditionally owned by the parish or community for the shared use of the community for grazing, wood-collecting, mowing, growing food, or recreation, has typically been bitterly fought over. Nevertheless, land-reform movements have always existed and have become more prominent as ecological and population pressures have increased.

For example, in the late 1960s, Robert Swann (the founder of the E.F. Schumacher Society, now the Schumacher Center for a New Economics) and colleagues Ralph Borsodi and Erick Hansch launched the International Independence Institute, to provide training and technical assistance for rural development, basing their concept on the Gandhian-inspired Bhoodan-

---

[6] For example, in my own corner of North Carolina, a short distance from several cities, the 165-acre Timberlake Earth Sanctuary is an example of a preserve "where people come to be inspired, to renew their spirits, and to remember who they are as a part of One Earth community." (https://www.timberlakeearthsanctuary.com/.) Owner Carolyn Toben has for decades preserved the woods, waterways, and old farm buildings within the preserve, and offers educational programs including indigenous wisdom traditions and Thomas Berry's teachings, retreats, and meditational walks on miles of woodland and lakeside trails. The Triangle Land Conservancy (https://www.triangleland.org/) and many other not-for-profit organizations also maintain preserves and offer agricultural conservation and educational programs within walking, cycling or driving reach of the three of the largest cities in the Piedmont region of the state.

[7] In the U.K., for example, common land now constitutes only 4.8% of the land mass of England, Wales, Scotland, and Northern Ireland.

Gramdan land gift and reform movement of Vinoba Bhave and others in India.[8] Changing the name to the Institute for Community Economics shortly after, they began to apply the concept of community land trusts to urban as well as rural areas, and to promote community ownership and control of land, housing, and public service resources.[9] ICE has provided over $44 million in financing for land trusts, limited-equity cooperatives, and nonprofit afforda-ble-housing cooperatives since its founding, and this effort led to the found-ing of the Community Investment Fund and the Social Investment Bank. The U.S. now has approximately 250 community land trusts, with a number in partnership with local municipalities.[10]

Agroecology: Nonviolent Farming

Agriculture, forestry, and other land uses combined contribute in the region of 25% of global greenhouse gas (GHG) emissions, with food produc-tion constituting the largest part of that percentage,[11] much of it from inten-sive modern farming methods and meat production, resulting in widespread deforestation, soil erosion, and overuse of chemical fertilizers and pesticides (see Chapter 1). The emerging field of agroecology is a form of agriculture that first, integrates conservation and protection of the ecology and wildlife, the long-term sustainability and nonviolent production of food in ways that are optimal for local and regional physical conditions, and active *restoration* and regeneration of damaged soils, water, landscapes, and wildlife. Second, it aims to provide a sustainable livelihood for local populations. Third, it aims to be a nonviolent way of providing for other essential uses of plants or ani-mals, such as reeds and palms for shelter, or flax, wool, or cotton for cloth-ing. The successful implementation of agroecology requires an in-depth

[8] For a brief description of Vinoba Bhave's movement, see Subhash Mehta, "Bhoodan-Gramdan Movement—50 Years: A Review," http://www.mkgandhi-sarvodaya.org/bhoodan.htm. Also see Lanza del Vasto, *Gandhi to Vinoba: The New Pilgrim-age* (London: Rider and Company, 1956).

[9] Institute for Community Economics, https://community-wealth.org/content/institute-community-economics. See also: International Independence Institute, *The Community Land Trust: A Guide to a New Model of Land Tenure in America* (Cambridge, MA: Center for Com-munity Economic Development, 1972); Institute for Community Economics, *The Commu-nity Land Trust Handbook* (Emmaus, PA: Rodale Press, 1972).

[10] John Emmeus Davis, *The Community Land Trust Reader*, ed. John Emmeus Davis (Cam-bridge, MA: Lincoln Institute of Land Policy, 2010), preface.

[11] Gabriel Blanco et al., "Drivers, Trends and Mitigation," in *Climate Change 2014: Mitigation of Climate Change. Contribution of Working Group III to the Fifth Assessment Report of the Intergov-ernmental Panel on Climate Change*, eds. Ottmar Edenhofer et al. (Cambridge, U.K.: Cam-bridge University Press, 2014), https://www.ipcc.ch/report/ar5/wg3/.

knowledge of local and regional natural ecologies, which in turn relies on the traditional and current knowledge of the indigenous or local people. If blended skillfully with careful scientific investigation and appropriate technological innovations, it can, in a symbiotic process, help improve areas of poor ecological conservation or limited food, water, and sanitation provision without violating the principles of nonviolence to the earth, self-reliance and local control of the economy, providing for essential needs of the community first, and ensuring the dignity and employment of local labor.

Some communities, mostly in poorer countries, have managed to maintain traditional methods of sustainable (or sustenance) farming that suit the climate, geography, and soil of the region; use limited machines and technology; and have a low impact on soils, water and other life-forms. In other cases, farmers and communities are adopting or reviving agroecology methods after a period of nonsustainable "development" or the takeover of traditional agriculture, often with the consent of state and local governments, by large agricultural corporations. Some communities are also developing new holistic practices that produce sufficient food with minimal impact on soils, water, and wildlife.

Gandhian-inspired Agroecology

In 2007, I visited a farm in India that had adopted a Gandhian-inspired agroecology approach, at the Friends Rural Center at Rasulia, near Hoshangabad in Madhya Pradesh. The center was started by Quakers in the 1930s and continues to be run in association with Friends. Marjorie Sykes, who personally knew and worked with Gandhi, joined and periodically ran the center from 1956 on, and was inspired by Gandhi's nonviolent methods of working.[12] Partap Aggarwal, a volunteer with Marjorie Sykes, had previously asked her help in returning to farming methods without pesticides and chemical fertilizers and in becoming self-reliant in food, clothing, shelter, and other essential goods. In 1979, he and 15 or so households took on this experiment at Rasulia, along with appropriate technologies such as solar ovens. Aggarwal was also inspired by the "natural farming" methods developed by Japanese scientist and farmer Masanobu Fukuoka, who visited the Center in 1988. Aggarwal adopted Fukuoka's approach, renaming it *rishi kheti*, or "agriculture of the gods." (Fukuoka's methods are described in detail below.) The

---

[12] Martha Dart, *Marjorie Sykes, Quaker Gandhian* (Syracuse, NY: Syracuse University Press, 1993).

Friends Center and the work of the farm continue,[13] albeit on land fast being surrounded by development and an increasing local population. They are still experimenting with nonviolent and sustainable farming and appropriate technology methods, such as biosand water filtration,[14] also used by Friends' projects in Burundi (see Chapter 10).

How did Gandhi, better known for his nonviolent movement to achieve Indian independence, inspire nonviolent farming and modern agroecology methods? Although he lived well before the present ecological crisis, his principles of the unity of all life and of nonviolence to all beings (described in Chapter 5)—as applied to agrarian life in traditional Indian villages—apply equally to our industrialized agriculture and food consumption. Gandhi advocated vegetarianism and the non-harming of life not only in his ashrams but also in his less well-known but equally important Constructive Program for the development of self-reliant "village republics" (also see Chapters 8 and 10). These communities were grounded in the principles of nonviolence, voluntary simplicity and subsidiarity, the equal and just participation and care of the human community, and protection of all life. They prioritized the sustainable and local production of food for essential needs, focusing on growing vegetables and staples such as beans, rice, and sorghum. The Constructive Program model has inspired several present-day agrarian experiments. For example, the Brahma Vidya Mandir, an intentional community for women in Paunar, Maharashtra, established by Gandhi follower Vinoba Bhave, has experimented since 1959 with Gandhian-inspired farming, growing a diversity of crops using traditional methods on a small scale, with "low-input" technologies and minimal or no chemical inputs.[15] This community has also led to the founding of two other farms in India; each embodies a communal spiritual practice, nonviolence, working by consensus, and self-reliance.

---

[13] Quakers in the World, "Friends Rural Centre, Rasulia, India," http://www.quakersintheworld.org/quakers-in-action/361/Friends-Rural-Centre-Rasulia-India.

[14] Shreya Pareek, "A Simple Technology that Can Solve India's Clean #Water Problem in Just Rs.3,000," *The Better India,* September 15, 2014, https://www.thebetterindia.com/13532/biosand-filters-providing-clean-drinking-water-remotest-areas-india/.

[15] A. Whitney Sanford, "Gandhi's Agrarian Legacy: Practicing Food, Justice and Sustainability in India," *Journal for the Study of Religion, Nature and Culture* 7 (2013), 65-87, http://dx.doi.org/10.1558/jsrnc.v7i1.65.

Vandana Shiva is a scientist, environmental activist, and co-founder of Navdanya—a Gandhian-inspired, nongovernmental organization (NGO) based in India and dedicated to preserving biodiversity, organic farming, seed and food sovereignty, fair trade, and the rights of farmers.[16] She has written widely since the early 1980s on ecological issues, particularly as they relate to women and agrarian communities in the poorer countries of the world. As Shiva and others have described, the ecological challenges in poorer countries largely concern the interrelated developments of a takeover of land and agricultural practices by large or multinational agribusinesses combined with the loss of traditional farming methods and local control of land, food production, and water supplies. This has meant not only a loss of food, seed, and land sovereignty but also the introduction of costly and polluting modern machinery, pesticides, and chemical fertilizers, which increase the indebtedness of farmers while causing damage to local ecosystems. In many respects, these developments are the antithesis of the deep ecology and deep economy principles developed by Gandhi, Naess, and others, as described in Chapter 8. The incursion of industrialized agriculture has been substantial in many parts of rural India, and it is unclear to what extent local farmers are and will be economically able to practice the most appropriate mixes of new and traditional farming methods and technologies to feed their communities and India's increasingly urban population.[17]

Shiva and others have also documented attempts by agribusinesses and others to patent life-forms or chemical properties of organisms for profit, including seeds, plants with traditional medicinal properties, and so on. Some of these attempts have been successfully prevented in court cases, while others have not. A full discussion of this complex ethical and legal area of dispute is beyond the scope of this discussion, but in law, the line separating "naturally occurring" organisms and life-forms—not considered legally patentable—and those that could be patentable either by genetic modification or isolation in a laboratory, for example, and thereby claimed as "human inventions," has become increasingly blurred under pressure from medical, pharmaceutical, biotechnology, agribusiness, and other interests, and has profound social, ethical, and ecological implications.[18]

---

[16] Navdanya, http://www.navdanya.org/site/.

[17] Vandana Shiva, *Who Really Feeds the World? The Failures of Agribusiness and the Promise of Agroecology* (Berkeley, CA: North Atlantic Books, 2016).

[18] As of the early 2000s, six agribusinesses owned 900 patents on varieties of the five major staple food crops. See, for example, R. Charnas, Council for Responsible Genetics, "No

Shiva describes numerous programs, from locally inspired to government-supported, that combine resistance to agribusiness with the preservation and restoration of nonviolent, appropriate agriculture and technology and the right sharing of food and water.[19] These projects eschew the use of chemical pesticides and fertilizers, both because of the damage to native plants, insects, microorganisms and soils and because of the unsupportable cost to and health effects on local communities, including an epidemic of suicides among indebted farmers. The goals of these programs include increasing biodiversity, the conservation and use of indigenous seeds and plant varieties (rather than e.g., genetically modified or patented seed varieties), reliance on low-input technologies, and support for small farms.

Women play a critical role in agriculture in poorer countries, much of it unpaid and with little control over land and property ownership. According to the UN's Food and Agriculture Organization,[20] women constitute some 43% of the global agricultural labor force, but this aggregate figure obscures large variations across countries. Overall, the labor burden of rural women exceeds that of men, including collecting fuel and water and cooking, as well as having the primary responsibility for the care of children. Several projects in poorer countries are led by women, combining ecological conservation, agroecology, and women's empowerment and income generation. As Shiva points out, "because the division of labor has left the sustenance economy largely in women's hands, women generate, sustain, and regenerate life."[21] For example, in addition to the well-known Chipko movement in India (described further in Chapter 10), the Green Belt Movement in Kenya, founded by Nobel prize-winner Wangari Maathai in 1977, is dedicated to large-scale

---

Patents on Life: Working Group Update," GeneWatch 15 (2002): 3, http://www.gene-watch.org, whose position is that no forms of life should be patented. Also see Vandana Shiva, *Biopiracy: The Plunder of Nature and Knowledge* (Brooklyn and Boston: South End Press, 1997).

[19] Vandana Shiva, *Earth Democracy: Justice, Sustainability, and Peace* (Brooklyn and Boston: South End Press, 2005), 120-1.

[20] Cheryl Doss, *The Role of Women in Agriculture*, ESA Working Paper no. 11-02, (Rome: United Nations Food and Agriculture Organization, 2011), http://www.fao.org/docrep/013/am307e/am307e00.pdf.

[21] Shiva, *Earth Democracy*, 133. According to the Women's Earth Alliance, http://womensearthalliance.org/, women are responsible for between 60% and 80% of food production in developing countries, and over 70% of employed women work in agriculture.[21] As Shiva describes in *Staying Alive: Women, Ecology and Development* (London: Zed Books, 1982), women also are the rural land laborers, providers of water, custodians of the fields and forests, soil managers, seed selectors, fuel providers, animal keepers, and knowledge keepers of how to survive and provide for their families and communities.

reforestation (planting 50 million trees and counting), prevention of soil erosion, and empowerment of women by teaching ecological conservation, forestry, food production, and related skills.[22] Numerous NGOs have now followed similar models, such as the Women's Earth Alliance, which runs training programs in the Karataka region of India for women to lead and teach seed saving, sustainable farming practices, and resilience to climate disruption[23]; the Women's Organization for Rural Development in Tamil Nadu, India,[24] which promotes seed saving, sustainable farming, and water conservation and purification, among other projects; the Brahma Vidya Mandir community described above; and others. Some are indigenous organizations, while others are international NGOs partnered with local organizations.

Techniques of Nonviolent Farming in India and Africa

In Masanobu Fukuoka's poetic and almost mystical, yet eminently practical account of his development of "natural farming," in *The One-Straw Revolution*, he describes how he came to understand what was wrong with the way agriculture was then being practiced in Japan, which had adopted some of the newer Western methods introduced by the U.S. and others after the second World War, and which relied on chemicals and machinery. Born in Japan in 1913 and engaged in research on fungal diseases in rice as a young man, he had an epiphany in which he realized he understood little about how life worked, despite his education, concepts, and training. In that moment, "...something one might call 'true nature' stood revealed."[25] It was as if Fukuoka suddenly saw through ignorance and duality to realize that "all the world was part of one central truth," according to Partap Aggarwal, who met Fukuoka and adopted his methods (see above).[26] This unexpected experience liberated Fukuoka's thinking, by his own account, and he went on to spend the next decades "testing whether or not I have been mistaken"[27] by develop-

---

[22] Green Belt Movement, https://www.greenbeltmovement.org/. The GBM is now a large NGO in both Kenya and internationally.

[23] Women's Earth Alliance, "Traditional Agriculture Solutions for Women Farmers in India," http://womensearthalliance.org/projects/2013-shakti-green-foundation-training/#.

[24] Women's Organisation for Rural Development, "Our Services," http://mywordindia.org/services.php?p=environment_conserva.

[25] Masanobu Fukuoka, *The One-Straw Revolution: An Introduction to Natural Farming*, ed. Larry Korn, trans. Chris Pearce, Tsune Kurosawa, and Larry Korn (Mapusa, Goa, India: Other India Press, 1992), 8.

[26] Fukuoka, *One-Straw Revolution*, preface by Partap C. Aggarwal, xii.

[27] Fukuoka, *One-Straw Revolution*, 9.

ing unique approaches to farming rice, vegetables, and orchard fruit trees, using methods that were neither wholly traditional nor using modern chemical and machine-based practices.

It is worth reflecting on the principles on which Fukuoka based his methods, because they align closely with the foundational spiritual principles of a deep, nonviolent ecology and economy approach described in Chapter 8. Fukuoka describes four principles and "gentle measures" that guided his practice[28]: 1) no cultivation, i.e., no plowing, tilling, or turning of the soil; 2) no use of chemical fertilizer or prepared compost—instead, using a prior ground cover of white clover, a covering of threshed straw on the fields, and a little poultry manure; 3) no weeding by tillage or herbicides—instead, managing (but not eliminating) weeds and seed-eating birds by means of straw mulch, interplanting with clover, and occasional temporary flooding; 4) no dependence on chemicals—instead, growing grain crops without any pesticides, chemical fertilizers, or fossil fuels. He believed in cooperating with, not conquering, nature and insisted that resident volunteers live simply and mainly off the land, as he did himself, to better understand the ways of nature. And, as Larry Korn comments in the introduction to *The One-Straw Revolution*, Fukuoka believed that natural farming "proceeded from the spiritual health of the individual…[and] *the healing of the land and the purification of the spirit to be one process* [my emphasis]."[29]

Although there were setbacks, crops flourished and grew steadily sturdier over the decades that Fukuoka and his helpers farmed. Even severely degraded soils were enriched and kept intact by humus, mulch, and roots, rather than depleted and polluted; water usage was reduced; and water quality was preserved. Because the crops and trees were not artificially fed by chemical inputs, strong weeds such as crabgrass, which took over many fields with conventional methods, did not reappear. He also demonstrated that, contrary to widespread belief and practice, rice could be grown successfully without flooding fields during the growing season, as it had traditionally been grown. Last, he demonstrated that the labor involved in using his methods was far less than that required in other farming methods and preserved the dignity and autonomy of those working on the land. His work, and that of his students, including the successful implementation of his methods by Aggarwal at

---

[28] Fukuoka, *One-Straw Revolution*, 33-4.

[29] Fukuoka, *One-Straw Revolution*, introduction by Larry Korn, xxxi.

Rasulia,[30] provided clear empirical evidence of the success of his methods, in part because he conducted research on his own evolving practices, such as applying various treatments in experimental plots and comparing the results with untreated control plots. Aggarwal points out that some aspects of Fukuoka's methods, such as no plowing and tilling, and the planting of traditional foods such as tubers, wild grains, and vegetables, had been widely practiced in India for centuries but were being lost. He also notes that most of the old, hardy local varieties of wheat had mostly been lost, too, and that highly modified varieties fared poorly without chemical inputs.[31]

A related example, in this case restoring traditional farming methods in a desertified region of northern Africa, is described in the form of a parable, by the prominent agroecologist Pierre Rabhi.[32] He, like Fukuoka, Shiva, and others, emphasizes how desertification and desecration of the land reflects a spiritual barrenness and a failure to revere the earth, and speaks of how over-reliance on the false promise of modern technologies has helped destroy indigenous peoples' relationship to their culture, their ways of feeding and clothing themselves, and their spiritual connection to the land, resulting in a climate of violence against each other and the earth. In his story, Rabhi's protagonist describes in detail how observing and understanding patterns in nature—how each of the plants and animals, from microorganisms to mammals and trees, are interconnected—and doing the patient work of restoring soils, tending plants that are right for the soil and climate, composting, conserving, and constantly listening and watching are all necessary to grow food. Rabhi, in an interview, also argued that, to bring about a change in hearts as well as minds, we must be being willing to speak in the public arena of a sense of the sacredness, beauty, and wonder in nature without separating that from the rational scientific and technical aspect of agroecology, as if only one is fundamental to the work. [33]

[30] Partap Aggarwal, "Natural Farming Succeeds in Indian Village," undated, at http://satavic.org/natural-farming-succeeds-in-indian-village/. Original source: *The Illustrated Weekly of India.*

[31] Aggarwal, "Natural Farming."

[32] Pierre Rabhi, *As in the Heart, So in the Earth: Reversing the Desertification of the Soul and the Soil,* trans. Joseph Rowe (Rochester, VT: Park Street Press, 2006). First published in 1996.

[33] Rabhi, *As in the Heart,* 139.

Can Agroecology Work in Industrialized Countries?

In some important respects, the practice of agroecology in richer and highly industrialized countries presents different challenges from those in poorer, less industrialized countries. Since the 1950s, however, there has been a growing convergence of common concerns due to the global dominance of large-scale or transnational industrial agricultural businesses, land ownership, farming methods, and patenting of life-forms and the extent of ecological destruction resulting from industrialized farming methods. In richer countries, agriculture has been industrialized and mechanized for decades longer than in the poorer world, and increasingly monopolized by a small number of transnational agribusiness conglomerates such as Cargill, Arthur Daniels Midland, and ConAgra. Much of the produce we consume is processed and much is consumed far from its origins. The challenges of restoring more holistic, local, and nonviolent farming methods in richer countries may be as great, if somewhat different from, as those in poorer countries. And even in the U.S., although food and water are generally abundant, varied, and reliably available, food insecurity has become a reality for more and more people, due to a complex of causes ranging from the climate crisis and the use of unsustainable agricultural practices to poverty and the monopolization of food production and markets.

Many of the same agroecology principles that have been preserved or restored in poorer countries apply to the development of agroecology in richer countries. The common goal is threefold: to counteract the negative impacts of mass industrialization and commodification of agriculture on local ecologies, labor, and wildlife; to regenerate soils, landscapes, and wildlife that have been damaged; and to restore control of sustainable and healthy food provision to local communities. Despite obvious imbalances in economic power, a flourishing local food movement has emerged among small farmers in the U.S. and elsewhere, devoted to small-scale, organic food production and local farmers' markets. In some cases, farmers and conservers have held on to traditional farming practices, sometimes in the face of stiff competition from agribusinesses; in others, younger people have taken up organic farming or backyard gardening for the first time.

However, the lessons from agroecology are not just about the victory of small farmers over agribusiness, as this begs the question of whether small-scale agroecology and similar farming methods can provide enough food to sustain our burgeoning global population. Large-scale or transnational industrialized agriculture has indeed greatly increased the food productivity of many regions around the world over the past half century, at least in the short term. But, as described in Chapter 1, the reliance of transnational industrialized agriculture on unsustainable methods and globalization, together with the pursuit of short-term economic priorities over long-term sustainability and care for other life-forms, has involved increasingly unsustainable costs. In sum, we have now come up against the limits of the earth's biological capacity to sustain such practices. To put in context the reasons to change to deeper agroecology approaches in richer countries, it is worth reminding ourselves of the range of costs, which involve not only declining food productivity of the land but also significant costs to local communities and to domesticated animals and wildlife, thereby violating many of the principles of a deep ecology and economy described in Chapter 8. These costs include:

- Increased use of factory farming methods and the suffering of animals
- Control of methods of farming, including the (threatened or actual) control of seed availability
- Overuse of chemical fertilizers and pesticides, antibiotics, and hormones
- Resulting air, food, soil and water pollution
- Ecological destruction through overtilling rather than crop rotation or allowing fallow periods; deforestation; soil erosion; the stripping of vegetation by grazing animals, etc.
- Food processing with the addition of preservatives, coloring, and related compounds, some of which are toxic to humans or ecosystems
- Packaging with plastics and nonbiodegradables, along with associated energy and material costs and waste-disposal problems
- Long-distance transportation, warehousing, refrigeration, and distribution and associated energy and material costs
- Exploitation of low-paid, temporary domestic and foreign labor
- Increasing concentration of agribusinesses into transnational conglomerates that control large-scale agricultural production and prices, and thus food and water accessibility in multiple countries, rendering small farmers everywhere unable to compete and survive
- The risk of political and related "resource wars" for food and water in some countries
- Excess food waste (approximately one-third of food is wasted globally, about 10 times as much wasted per capita in the U.S. and Europe than in

Southeast Asia and Africa),[34] whether due to inadequate storage or wasteful methods of mechanized harvesting; insistence on particular standards of size, shape and appearance; transportation and storage losses; or the discarding of food in our kitchens and restaurants

- Increasing alienation and separation of people from the land, other life-forms, and local ecologies; from traditional farming practices; and from convivial livelihoods

To address the questions, Can we "feed the world" with its exponentially increasing populations without destroying the very ecosystems on which we depend? Can we provide adequate, affordable nourishment for our populations by using smaller-scale, locally controlled, traditional, or organic methods rather than industrialized agribusiness? it is becoming clear that we must consider not only our methods of *producing* food but also our ways of *consuming* and *wasting* food, which, as we saw in Chapter 1, dictate not only land use and ecological impacts such as greenhouse gas emissions but also are a major driver of the types of agriculture we practice.

In terms of food production, as both the economic and ecological costs of large-scale industrialized agriculture become unsustainable, as indicated above, we clearly must feed ourselves in much more sustainable and life-enhancing ways. This does not mean throwing the baby out with the bathwater—there is no simple black-and-white answer as to whether large-scale food production can be achieved in sustainable, safe, and technologically appropriate ways or whether farming can be sustained on a smaller scale and still feed burgeoning urban populations. We may well need a wise combination of appropriate technologies, methods, and scales of operation and some new-old syntheses of methods, such as those described below. One thing is clear, however: The debate has gradually shifted away from agribusiness-dominated toward more ecologically focused approaches. The primary challenge has become: How we can change our food production and consumption patterns to conserve soils, waters, and the wellbeing and survival of animals, wildlife, and ecosystems over the long term while providing sufficient food for our survival in a long-term, sustainable way?

---

[34] United Nations Food and Agriculture Organization, "SAVE FOOD: Global Initiative on Food Loss and Waste Reduction," http://www.fao.org/save-food/resources/keyfindings/en/.

Integrating Traditional and New Approaches

In the U.S. and elsewhere, there has been a renewal of interest in indigenous farming and land conservation practices in recent decades, as well as in traditional farming methods brought by European and other nonindigenous settlers. For example, the extent of Native Americans' impact on the land is generally considered to be minor compared with that generated by the arrival of outside settlers and their descendants, but over many thousands of years, they changed landscapes in various and significant ways, including clearing of vegetation, leading to changes in ecosystems and the appearance of savannah and grasslands, and local and seasonal controlled low-intensity or broadcast burning of forests and woodland for food growing and other purposes.[35] The practice of controlled burning was suppressed in recent times, but changes in forestry management practices combined with the scale of climate-related wildfires have led to a resurgence of this practice.[36] Interest in Native American farming techniques has also been revived, such as the widely practiced "companion" method of growing squash, corn, and beans (known as "three sisters") close together in mounds, which allows each of the plants to symbiotically benefit the growth of the others.[37]

Traditional farming practices have typically depended on the long, slow observation and experience of what works for the local soil, topography, water supplies, and seasonal weather patterns, and what methods best serve the land and the farmer alike. Some modern farming operations have also begun to include methods that eschew nonsustainable and damaging practices and machinery and industrial-scale operations that render much labor redundant. The aim is to restore ecologically sound traditional practices and integrate them with innovations such as permaculture and biodynamic farming (see below). At present, less than 1% of the US labor force now works in agriculture, but this may start to increase with a renaissance of small-scale

---

[35] "Native American Use of Fire in Ecosystems," Wikipedia, https://en.m.wikipedia.org/wiki/Native_American_use_of_fire; W.G. Williams, "Aboriginal Use of Fire: Are There Any 'Natural' Plant Communities?," in *Wilderness and Political Ecology: Aboriginal Influences and the Original State of Nature*, eds. C.E. Kay and R.T. Simmons (Salt Lake City: University of Utah Press, 2002), 179-214.

[36] Dale Brockaway, Richard Gateway and Randi Paris, "Restoring Fire as an Ecological Process in Shortgrass Prairie Ecosystems: Initial Effects of Prescribed Burning During the Dormant and Growing Seasons," *Journal of Environmental Management* 65 (2002), 135-52, https://doi.org/10.1006/jema.2002.0540.

[37] "Three Sisters (agriculture)," Wikipedia, https://en.wikipedia.org/wiki/Three_Sisters_(agriculture).

farming. At the same time, the image of the "traditional farmer" in the U.S. is changing: According to *Forbes*, 30% of farmers in the U.S. are women, a threefold increase since 1970.[38] Where possible, these new farmers integrate conservation and regeneration of depleted soils, the growth of seasonally and geographically appropriate crops using organic methods, humane animal husbandry, and appropriate technologies.

For example, the overuse of tractors and heavy machinery leads to excessive packing down of soil—increasing runoff into streams and rivers and decreasing penetration of rain into the soil—as well as placing large financial burdens on small farmers. Low-till or no-till methods and the reduced use of heavy machinery increase the need for human labor and may better preserve soils, improve yields, and reduce overall costs to the farmer. In addition, new landscaping and land-use approaches for water conservation, such as keylining, first developed by P.A. Yeomans in the 1950s,[39] can take advantage of natural watercourse patterns, trees, topography, and human structures on the land in ways that conserve and allow for reliable water supplies for crops. Restoration and regeneration of previously overcropped land and depleted or pesticide-laden soils is an integral part of long-term sustainable farming and wildlife conservation. (For example, Quaker friends in my local area are experimenting in restoring the depleted soil of a farm formerly used primarily for tobacco, by planting nitrogen-fixing plants, by composting, and by leaving parcels of land fallow or rotating crops.) Soil and water conservation and restoration are critical both to good farming practices and to dealing with pollution. For example, scientists are experimenting with biochar, a stable charcoal made from the pyrolysis of biomass,[40] as a way to sequester carbon in soils, amend soil, and improve water retention, and thus contribute to the mitigation of climate disruption. However, as with all such methods, the total carbon budget must be taken into account, and the effectiveness of the

---

[38] Eve Turow Paul, "More Women Are Starting Companies From The Ground Up, Literally," *Forbes*, August 11, 2016, https://www.forbes.com/sites/eveturowpaul/2016/08/11/more-women-starting-companies-from-the-ground-up-literally/#3ceff1e56ee2.

[39] P.A. Yeomans, *The Keyline Plan* (Sydney: P.A. Yeomans, 1954), https://www.soilandhealth.org/wp-content/uploads/01aglibrary/010125yeomans/010125toc.html. Interestingly, Yeomans integrates an approach that has echoes of both Gandhian concepts of permanent economy and a Taoist approach to allowing water— and nature—to flow naturally and without resistance to gift us with life.

[40] See, for example, Dominic Woolf et al., "Sustainable Biochar to Mitigate Global Climate Change," *Nature Communications* 1 (2010), 1-9, http://www.doi.org/10.1038/ncomms1053.

method is still under investigation. Untoward effects on other vital soil mi-croorganisms, including bacteria, yeasts, fungi, earthworms, and insects, also must be investigated.[41] Whether biochar soil treatments can be scaled up to make a significant contribution to carbon drawdown remains to be seen.

Wendell Berry is one of our most well-known, eloquent, and constant voices, as a poet, essayist, and farmer, for a renewed relationship with the earth and the miracle of life. For decades, he has made connections between reverence for all life, a nonviolent ecology, human needs, and the reciprocal relationship between them, as expressed in the way we grow and consume our food. He has also advocated for the use of traditional agricultural practic-es, small farms, and local economies, based on his experience of farming in a small community in Kentucky, while working with scientists and ecologists, such as Wes Jackson and others at the Land Institute,[42] to (re)discover sus-tainable practices for conserving and using the land. Berry describes himself as "a conservationist and a farmer, a wilderness advocate and an agrarian..."[43] and draws an important conclusion from his experiences in each of these aspects. He writes:

> I decided not long ago that I would not endorse any more wilderness preserva-
> tion projects that do not also seek to improve the health of the surrounding
> economic landscapes and human communities...my decision...has
> helped me to see more clearly the compatibility and even coherence of
> my two allegiances. The dualism of the domestic and the wild is, after
> all, mostly false and it is misleading.... Domesticity and wildness are in
> fact intimately connected. What is utterly alien to both is corporate in-
> dustrialism—a displaced economic life that is without affection for the
> places it is lived and without respect for the materials it uses.[44]

What Berry is pointing to is the practical reality of our interconnection. Humans are an integral part of the ecology of the earth; the "wild" and the domestic (or domesticated) are not ultimately separable (and animals are homemakers and change their landscapes, too); conservationists are farmers

---

[41] Sarah E. Hale et al. "Short-term Effect of the Soil Amendments Activated Carbon, Biochar, and Ferric Oxyhydroxide on Bacteria and Invertebrates," *Environmental Science and Technology* (2013), 47: 8674-83, http://www.doi.org/10.1021/es400917g.

[42] The goal of the nonprofit Land Institute, based in Salinas, Kansas is to "create an agri-culture system that mimics natural systems in order to produce ample food and reduce or eliminate the negative impacts of industrial agriculture," https://landinstitute.org/.

[43] Wendell Berry, "Conservationist and Agrarian," in *Citizenship Papers: Essays by Wendell Berry* (Washington: Shoemaker and Hoard, 2003), 165.

[44] Berry, "Conservationist and Agrarian," 166.

because we all eat; and we are all connected and coresponsible. As explored in Chapter 5, the danger arises from distancing and the illusion of separation from each other and nature—and the lack of care, of response and responsibility, and of reciprocity that accompanies this illusion. Distancing leads to violence to the earth and the people who share it with all life. Our task is not to set up a false dichotomy between the needs of people and the rest of life, whether they be indigenous people or urban dwellers, but to seek to break down those barriers and forces that separate us from knowing, understanding, and living in a "continuous harmony"[45] between agriculture, human culture, and the wider natural world.

Permaculture and Biodynamic Farming

Permaculture and biodynamic methods of farming specifically employ methods to ensure soil vitality and, increasingly, restored carbon sequestration of the soil, while growing food that is healthy and sustainable. The principles and practice of permaculture were developed in the late 1970s by David Holmgren[46] and Bill Mollison. These principles aim to enable appropriate, and nonviolent, ways of interacting with the wider natural world and to address long-term essential needs without excess waste or damage to other living systems.[47]

Biodynamic farming is based on the principle that farming should be a self-contained and self-sufficient system, i.e., all that is needed for the farm's vitality, including the health of the soil, the prevention of disease and pests, and the conditions for growing should be provided by the farm itself. The farm, in other words, should be a self-reliant organism. Developed first in the

---

[45] Thomas Hornbein, quoted by Wendell Berry in the frontispiece of Wendell Berry, *A Continuous Harmony: Essays Cultural and Agricultural* (San Diego and New York: Harcourt, Brace and Jovanovich, 1975).

[46] David Holmgren, *Permaculture: Principles and Pathways Beyond Sustainability*, revised ed. (Hepburn, Victoria, Australia: Holmgren Design Services, 2017). First published in 2002.

[47] The 12 principles embodied in permaculture include detailed observation and interaction with the wider natural world; harvesting solar energy, water, hay, plant compost, building materials, and food sources when they are plentiful and storing for when they are scarcer; obtaining useful yields (in food, or other forms) from whatever work is done; understanding and applying self-regulation and feedbacks (to preclude nonsustainable consequences now or in the future); using renewable gifts of nature; reducing overconsumption; avoiding waste; recognizing and using patterns in nature; integrating rather than segregating, and understanding interrelationships; using small and slow solutions; using and valuing diversity of natural forms; valuing the marginal (thinking outside the box, for example); and creatively using and responding to change (with a vision of how things should and could be).

1920s, biodynamic methods include no or little tilling, growing cover crops to fertilize or control weeds, using animal compost, controlling grazing to encourage perennial grass conservation, diversifying crops to encourage natural biological pest control, rotating leguminous plants to return nitrogen to the soil, and setting aside at least 10% of the land for wildlife.[48]

The goals are to ensure sustainable yields into the future without external inputs, to sustain wildlife, and to regenerate and increase the capacity of soil and vegetation as the second major carbon sink after the oceans. Elizabeth Candelario (managing director of Demeter USA, the body that certifies biodynamic farms) reports that the organization has also begun to add soil testing for carbon sequestration to its program to assist farmers in building biologically active and carbon-sequestering soils. As she states, "The time has come to reimagine farming."[19]

Changing the Way We Eat

We cannot reimagine farming for food without reimagining the way we eat. How do we do this, in countries with highly industrialized agriculture, where, as discussed above, our food supply is controlled by a few transnational corporations, often comes from thousands of miles away, is highly processed and highly packaged, and may be lacking in nutrition while containing ingredients we can't pronounce and don't know what they are doing to us or other life-forms?

As described in Chapter 1, the globalization of markets and changing food preferences and fashions mean that vast amounts of food (and increasingly, bottled water) are shipped around the world; in addition, vegetable and meat products are widely used in nonfood goods from cosmetics to gasoline additives to leather jackets. For example, according to one estimate, although only 15% of food overall is imported into the U.S., an estimated 50% of fruit, 20% of vegetables, and 80% of seafood comes from outside the country.[49] We are often unaware of the ecological and human impacts in far-off countries of changes in food production or food choices, which happen with

---

[48] Elizabeth Candelario, "Biodynamic Agriculture, Regenerative Farming and Climate Change," At the Epicenter, August 11, 2017, http://www.attheepicenter.com/biodynamic-agriculture-regenerative-farming-climate-change/.

[49] Margaret A. Hamburg, "Food Safety Modernization Act: Putting the Focus on Prevention," https://www.foodsafety.gov/news/fsma.html.

increasing rapidity as market forces and fashions change, and that can lead to devastating consequences that are largely hidden from the end consumer.

To name just one example, the production of palm oil—which is causing mass deforestation and the draining and burning of peatlands in some parts of the world, particularly in Malaysia and Indonesia—accounts for between 2% and 9% of the world's carbon emissions, according to a recent report.[50] Palm oil is used in a wide array of products from foods to biofuel additives, from cleaning products to cosmetics. Part of the increase in demand has resulted from the move away from trans fats in our diets, for which palm oil has been a useful substitute. Recently, however, campaigns to protect forests and peatlands have partially succeeded in slowing the rate of increase in plantations, although overall use is still expanding.

Despite increased globalization of food markets over the past 30 years, there has also been a shift over the past two decades or more toward locally-sourced foods, together with an increase in consumer demand for organically-grown, non-genetically-modified produce, meat, eggs, and dairy. The shift reflects a combination of human health and animal welfare concerns as well as ecological concerns, from the carbon footprint of livestock and "food miles" to pesticide and animal waste pollution (see below and Chapter 1).[51]

Organic or Non-organic Food Production?

The extensive debate around the pros and cons of conventional vs. organic agriculture illustrates the number of factors that need to be weighed in a comprehensive analysis. An example of this was described in a recent web article by Nathanael Johnson.[52] His original question was, Does organic farm-

---

[50] Union of Concerned Scientists, "Palm Oil," https://www.ucsusa.org/global-warming/stop-deforestation/drivers-of-deforestation-2016-palm-oil.

[51] Figures regarding the percentage of organic farms in a country depend in part on the definitions used. In the U.S., for example, the percentage of organic farms certified by the U.S. Department of Agriculture (USDA) was less than 1% of all farms at their 5-year census in 2012, but is growing rapidly, as is the percentage of food from local producers. (See, for example, data on organic and local food production from the National Sustainable Agriculture Coalition's blog, "2012 Census Drilldown: Organic and Local Food," May 16, 2014, http://sustainableagriculture.net/blog/2012-census-organic-local/. According to the USDA, organic food now accounts for about 4% of food sales in all categories in the U.S., some of which is imported from other countries. (USDA Economic Research Service, "Organic Agriculture," https://www.ers.usda.gov/topics/natural-resources-environment/organic-agriculture/.

[52] Nathanael Johnson, "Do Industrial Agricultural Methods Actually Yield More Food Per Acre Than Organic Ones?," Grist, October 14, 2015, https://grist.org/food/do-industrial-agricultural-methods-actually-yield-more-food-per-acre-than-organic-ones/.

ing give higher or lower yields per acre than conventional methods? His investigation yielded a more complex rather than a simple conclusion. Yield depended on a number of interrelated factors. A major factor is nitrogen input, which is typically provided by synthetic fertilizers in industrial farming, but organic farming must obtain nitrogen by manure and plowed-in leguminous or other plant matter, which requires crop rotation or more land to grow such plants and the need to harvest them first. He reports that some researchers find comparable yields; others, 20%–30% less yield from organic farming. The size of the farm was important in poorer countries—probably related to more labor-intensive farming, with smaller farms yielding more than bigger farms—but was not so clearly important in industrialized countries.

If we add in the enormous problem of food waste from farm to table, relatively small differences in farm yields may be less critical than addressing waste, pollution, and carbon emissions. Both synthetic and organic fertilizers can wash out of the soil and cause pollution downstream (albeit at different rates, and much of the nitrogen from synthetic fertilizers ends up in water or air rather than in food). However, organic material used as fertilizer binds the soil and prevents soil erosion better than synthetic fertilizers, whereas the production of synthetic nitrogen fertilizer incurs a large carbon footprint, representing the largest energy input in industrialized agriculture. If synthetic fertilizer can be made using clean energy, as has been demonstrated with ammonia production, some of that footprint can be shrunk, with a possible role for combinations of synthetic and organics in the future.

Small Is Bountiful: Food from Backyards, Rooftops, and Vacant Lots

I first heard Majora Carter speak at a "Black, Brown and Green Alliance" conference in North Carolina in 2009. Bringing together the concerns of racial justice, ecojustice, and ecologically sustainable food provision, she has developed urban revitalization and conservation strategies that include growing food horizontally and vertically, on rooftops, in vacant lots, in window boxes, and in other tiny plots in dense urban environments such as the South Bronx. This work is part of a comprehensive strategy for land, water, and energy use; waste management and environmental restoration; and the generation of "green" jobs.[53] According to the UN's Food and Agriculture Organi-

---

[53] Majora Carter founded the nonprofit Sustainable South Bronx in 2001, later incorporated into the HOPE program in Brooklyn. See
https://web.archive.org/web/20080801075618/http://ssbx.org/mission.html.

zation, some 15% of the world's food is now grown in urban areas, and this proportion is rising.[54] In richer countries with otherwise-abundant food supplies, far from being an "elite" form of gardening practiced only by people with a lot of money and time, such programs increasingly give a measure of food security and independence and more sustainable and healthy diets in communities whose food choices from supermarkets are often limited by income and lack of choice. Garden-sized plots can yield up to 15 times more produce than comparable rural farms, according to some estimates,[45] and storage, transport, and distribution costs are minimized. Numerous such initiatives now exist in urban areas, often taking an integrated approach to ecojustice and jobs as well as food provision.[55] Many proponents of backyard and the well-known "square-foot"[56] gardening methods have revived and reimagined ways to encourage growing food more in the style of many in our grandparents' generation (except they mostly planted in rows, not squares or mounds), demonstrating, as my own family knew well, that you can feed four (or more)—and some neighbors—on a few square feet of well-nourished soil, without the need for weeding, hoeing, or artificial pesticides and fertilizers, with a lower carbon footprint, and plentiful choices of fruits and vegetables to eat. Local governments have also stepped up to, for example, allocate vacant lots for community gardens or permit chickens, goats or bees to be kept in urban backyards.

We have barely begun to change our food consumption habits in favor of more ecologically sustainable practices in many industrialized countries, despite the fact that many of our parents or grandparents, in the 1950s and earlier, produced and ate food in very different ways, with less food imported from distant regions or abroad, less waste, and less packaging, for example. It was relatively easy for our grandparents to eat according to the ways listed below, depending on what country or region they lived in. Still, the rapid rise of organic food, the local and "slow" food movements, community-supported agriculture, and farmers' markets are changing the way we can choose to eat in more areas of the U.S. and other countries. Together with the popularity and success of eating guides such as the succinct "Eat food,

[54] United Nations Food and Agriculture Organization, "Urban Agriculture," http://www.fao.org/urban-agriculture/en/.

[55] Food Tank recently listed 26 inspiring urban agriculture projects around the world: https://foodtank.com/news/2015/07/urban-farms-and-gardens-are-feeding-cities-around-the-world/.

[56] Mel Bartholomew, *All New Square Foot Gardening: Grow More in Less Space*, revised ed. (Franklin, TN: Cool Springs Press, 2006).

not too much, mostly plants" message of Michael Pollan, for example,[57] more people are finding it possible to do some or all of the following (if medical, financial, or availability conditions permit):

- Eat "not too much" food and waste less of it.
- Eat less or no meat and dairy.[58] Avoid meat from factory farms or concentrated animal feeding operations (CAFOs). Eat from local organic farmers raising animals with due care for their wellbeing in pastures and fields without the need for hormones, unnecessary antibiotics, and non-organic feed.
- Eat less or no fish from unsustainable wild-caught sources[59] or from fish farms.
- Eat or grow locally and organically grown, unprocessed, fresh vegetables and fruit in season (see, e.g., the "slow" food movement[60]), without excess packaging or demand for perfection in shape, size, color, etc.
- Eat minimally packaged and processed (and locally sourced) food where possible (e.g., grains, nuts, lentils, peas, beans, rice, dried fruits, etc.)
- Where water supplies are safe and regulated by local municipalities, buy less or no bottled water or soft drinks, especially if imported and/or made by private companies using municipal water or a country's vital sources of drinking water, and bottled in plastic (see Chapter 1).

However, many people in urbanized industrialized countries have little opportunity to follow any or all of the steps outlined above, for a variety of reasons, several of which relate to accessibility, choice, money, and time. Many people live in areas dominated by only one or two supermarket chains,

---

[57] Michael Pollan, *In Defense of Food: An Eater's Manifesto* (New York: Penguin Books, 2009).

[58] Many reasons exist to consider avoiding or reducing meat and dairy consumption, including animal welfare concerns, human health concerns, and the conditions of workers in e.g., the meat packaging industry. Globally, meat (particularly beef) and dairy consumption are significant contributors to greenhouse gas emissions, deforestation, the destruction of wildlife habitats, and contaminated and depleted soils and water. Avoiding meat and dairy in richer countries may be the single most effective way to reduce our ecological impact (Marco Springmann et al., "Options for Keeping the Food System within Environmental Limits," *Nature* 562 (2018), 519-25, https://doi.org/10.1038/s41586-018-0594-0. (See also Chapter 1.)

[59] The IUCN maintains a "red list" of threatened species, including marine and freshwater fish (https://www.iucnredlist.org/). Over 1,400 species are endangered, including at least 10 of commonly harvested species (https://animals.howstuffworks.com/endangered-species/top-10-most-endangered-fish.htm).

[60] The goals of the slow food movement include improving the taste of food, increasing biodiversity and local food production, growing and eating foods in season and preserving traditional cooking, and increasing collaboration between local food producers. See for example, Slow Food USA, https://www.slowfoodusa.org/.

which may or may not supply a wide range of food. The problem of food insecurity has become more acute in the U.S. and elsewhere. There are "food deserts" where local foods or fresh vegetables and fruits are unavailable or require long journeys to buy, or are prohibitively expensive for poorer families. Work and other obligations may leave minimal time for shopping, cooking, and eating—much less growing—our food, so we have become accustomed to eating fast food, quick-to-prepare processed foods, and factory-farmed or imported foods, which may be most of what's available in our supermarkets or convenience stores.

Growing Food Together: Community Support for Farmers

Small-scale farming still must compete with agribusiness and is subject to the unpredictability of seasonal weather and climate-related downturns. As well as diversifying what is grown and raised, one way that small farms can be made less financially precarious is via the principle of community-supported agriculture (CSA), in which members buy "shares" in the season or year's produce at a given CSA farm in exchange for weekly supplies of produce, for example. This model has flourished in many parts of the U.S. and elsewhere in recent decades, as a way to secure a stable and reliable income for small farmers.[61] Other ways include garnering commitments from cooperative and community-owned grocery stores to carry local produce, setting up web-based buyer's clubs to order and deliver produce, and selling at local farmers' markets at low overhead. In turn, farmers and cooperatives are committing to their local communities by, for example, giving to food banks, or raising donations so that local farmers can both grow and provide healthy food and eliminate hunger in some of their poorest neighborhoods and public schools.[62]

In sum, to seek to live from a deep ecology perspective is to recognize both our dependence on the wider natural world and the right of all life-forms to exist, but it does not mean pitting of the needs of "nature" against

---

[61] For example, in my local area in the Eastern Piedmont of North Carolina, dozens of small farms are within a 30-mile radius or so of the town I live in, including a number of CSAs and scores of small "backyard" fruit and vegetable growers or keepers of bees and laying hens. These farmers and growers are supported by three cooperatively owned grocery stores, a farm and food network, local farmers' markets, and a community land trust that helps foster sustainable land use.

[62] See for example, the Farmer Foodshare project in North Carolina, which supports local farmers, distributes food for schools and hunger-relief organizations, and is supported by donations and help from individuals, local restaurants, artists and musicians, and farmers' markets. http://www.farmerfoodshare.org/.

those of humans, as if we are either less than or more than a part of nature and the commonwealth of life. Nor is it a hopeless ideal, a utopian vision that is belied daily by our all-too-familiar violence to the earth in which so many of us are wittingly or unwittingly complicit. It is worth remembering that in less than 30 years, more and more citizens in some of the richest countries have become familiar with the need for conservation, the impact of our life-styles on animals and plants on the other side of the earth, fair-trade and local food movements, the inestimable value of our threatened wildlife, and simply spending more time connecting with nature. The practice of deep ecology does not mean becoming a drop-out or mystic so much as simplifying, slowing down, and falling in love with that which gives us life, something that we may have forgotten but are inherently born to do. It means learning how to live in greater alignment and reciprocity with nature; it means living more locally, and paying attention to place, seasons, the intricate webs of connections in nature. Finally, it means learning, or relearning, how resilient and adaptable life in the wider natural world is. We cannot, ultimately, destroy all life, but we are morally responsible to ourselves and all life for the suffering and destruction that is ours to avoid.

Chapter 10

The Practice of Deep Economy

...since consumption is merely a means to human well-being, the aim should be to obtain the maximum well-being with the minimum of consumption.

—E.F. Schumacher[1]

Building a local economy will mean...ceasing to worship markets as infallible and consciously setting limits on their scope.... We will have to make the biggest changes to our daily habits in generations—and the biggest change, as well, to our worldview, our sense of what constitutes progress.

—Bill McKibben[2]

As we saw in Chapters 1 and 2, it has become increasingly apparent over the past 40 years that we are rapidly reaching the limits to global economic growth. A major shift in our economic thinking is clearly called for at the local, regional, national, and supranational levels if we are to move from our current growth-dominated economies to economies in which all people have the basic right to the essential means to survive and thrive on an unpolluted planet, and that acknowledge the intrinsic right of other life-forms to live, as explored in the previous chapter. Concerned thinkers, from economists and environmentalists and ethicists to religious thinkers, have argued that we need a new, morally grounded economy.[3] Michael Lerner calls for a "new bottom line," based "not only on economic success but also on our deepest spiritual values...love, generosity, kindness, responsibility, respect, gratitude, humility, honesty, awe and wonder at the grandeur of the universe."[4] If our current

---

[1] E.F. Schumacher, *Small is Beautiful: Economics As If People Mattered* (New York: Harper Colophon, 1975), 54. First published in 1973.

[2] Bill McKibben, *Deep Economy: The Wealth of Communities and the Durable Future* (New York: Henry Holt and Co., 2007), 2.

[3] For example, see Tom Head, *Envisioning a Moral Economy*, Pendle Hill Pamphlet No. 410 (Wallingford, PA: Pendle Hill Publications, 2010).

[4] Michael Lerner, *The Left Hand of God: Taking Back Our Country from the Religious Right* (New York: HarperCollins/HarperSanFrancisco, 2006), 228-9.

economic systems—dependent on growth, capital accumulation, and concentrated economic power—are unsustainable, then what alternative, "deep economy" approaches, to use Bill McKibben's phrase, are called for? What might a socially and environmentally just and long-term, ecologically sustainable economy, based on the principles (explored in Chapters 5 and 6) of nonviolence, integrity, simplicity, and equality in community, look like? And could materially simpler ways of living in richer countries yield more happiness and health, rather than less? How might we put the principles of a deep economy described in Chapter 8 into practice?

There is a wide and creative range of practical ways in which these goals might be met. Many economic experiments have been and are being tried around the world within the context of current macroeconomic systems. Several of these movements have been guided explicitly or strongly influenced by Gandhian, Buddhist, Christian, Muslim, Jewish, or other religious and indigenous traditions, as well as by practical activism by conservationists, ecojustice activists, and others. The core goals and characteristics of these experiments are remarkably consistent, from Gandhian-inspired village economies[5] to Quaker-led economic experiments[6] and the ethical "new economics" based on the work of thinkers such as E.F. Schumacher, Herman Daly, Michael Lerner, Ivan Illich, Vandana Shiva, and Wendell Berry. They have many fundamental aspects and goals in common, including:

- Moving toward a no-growth or minimum-growth economy and minimizing ecological impacts on the wider natural world, so that society as a whole can remain well within ecologically sustainable limits into the foreseeable future;

- Moving toward no-poverty, no-wealth economies in which every individual's essential needs are met, and economic disparities are addressed to achieve this; and

- Empowering individuals and local communities to participate meaningfully, responsibly, and democratically in their own governance, to foster dignity and cooperative self-reliance and to mitigate the concentration of political and economic power in the hands of the few.

---

[5] M.K. Gandhi, *Sarvodaya (The Welfare of All)*, ed. Bharatan Kumarappa (Ahmedabad, India: Navajivan Publishing House, 1954), 8-28; A.T. Ariyaratne, *Buddhism and Sarvodaya: Sri Lankan Experience*, ed. Nandasena Ratnapala (Delhi, India: Sri Satguru Publications, 1996).

[6] See, for example, the Quaker Institute for the Future's (www.quakerinstitute.org) Moral Economy Project.

To underline the most critical point, *the principles that underlie ethical sustainable human economies are precisely those needed to ensure ecological sustainability and vice versa.* In other words, we cannot have sustainable, secure, and dignified livelihoods and human economies without sustainable ecologies, nor sustainable ecologies without sustainable and just economies.

A Deep Economy Is a Nonviolent Economy

Perhaps no one has articulated the concept of nonviolent economics and experimented with putting its principles into practice on a widespread scale more than Gandhi and those subsequently influenced by his work (see Chapters 5 and 8). Gandhi himself was drawing explicitly on the ancient philosophies of both Hindu and Buddhist traditions in his economic and political thinking (as well as on the ideas of Tolstoy, Ruskin, and others), grounding it in the principle of *advaita,* the unity of all life and being, and in nonviolence, equality and simplicity in living.

Gandhi insisted, following Ruskin's series of essays "Unto This Last," that "true economics is the economics of justice," that true wealth lies in human happiness, and that amassing riches at the expense of others or paying unjust wages in the name of competition leads to oppression, cheating, and active resistance of those who labor. If the real goal of economics is to foster human happiness and spiritual and cultural growth,[7] it requires economic equality, so that everyone has the means to provide for their essential (or "natural") needs. It also calls for voluntary simplicity, since nature has more than enough for everyone's needs but not for everyone's wants. Only then, Gandhi insisted, could we speak of a nonviolent society.[8]

While wholesale ecological destruction was not an explicit concern in the way it is today, and a certain amount of violence to other life-forms was, of course, necessary for survival, it could be minimized—Gandhi eschewed meat eating, for example, and wrote repeatedly of cultivating an attitude of sacredness and respect to all living beings. As J.C. Kumarappa, Gandhi's economic partner, wrote, "Gandhi was not interested in economic side of things for its own sake. He was interested [only in] truth, and all things that lead to untruth…and violence he wanted to remove from society."[9]

---

[7] Gandhi, *Sarvodaya,* 33, 36.

[8] Gandhi, *Sarvodaya,* 14, 34.

[9] J.C. Kumarappa, *The Non-Violent Economy and World Peace* (Sarva-Seva-Sangh, Wardha, India: A.W. Sahasrabuddhey, 1958), 40.

In Gandhi's Constructive Program, the principles of a "permanent" economy, expounded by Kumarappa,[10] were put into practice in what he called "independent village republics," decentralized economies based on the relatively small community units of the many thousands of villages in which the majority of India's population lived in during and beyond his lifetime.[11] The principles embodied in the Constructive Program—*sarvodaya* (the wellbeing or welfare of all), *swadeshi* (the duty to serve one's neighbors, or collective self-reliance), and *swaraj* (self-government), underpinned by the striving for a nonviolent society through *satyagraha* (truth or soul force)[12]—closely correspond with the Quaker principles of simplicity, equality, and nonviolence in the service of human and ecological sustainability (see Chapter 6). Gandhi and Kumarappa also emphasized that reliance on nonrenewable materials and of ever-expanding distant markets and demand for products increased the risks of poverty, malnutrition, the exploitation of labor and ecologies, and conflict and war over scarce resources.[13]

By emphasizing local production for local needs, Gandhi sought to achieve independence from imported foods and goods; reliance on local labor and skills; and the alleviation of poverty and ill-health. He also paid close attention to what was suitable and sustainable based on indigenous species and local soil, water, and climatic conditions. Above all, the local growing of food wherever possible was considered essential.[14] The ability to do so rested on village land ownership and self-reliance as far as practicable in food production, before the growing of "cash crops" would be considered. Local land ownership became the cornerstone of the well-known *Bhoodan* movement founded by Vinoba Bhave (one of Gandhi's followers) in the 1950s, in which landowners were persuaded to gift a portion of their land to poor, landless villagers. Later, less successfully, larger tracts of land constituting whole villages, in the *Gramdam* movement, were sought in a form of equal distribution

---

[10] J.C. Kumarappa, *The Economics of Permanence: A Quest for a Social Order Based on Non-violence* (Varanasi, India: Sarva Seva Sangh Prakashan, 1948. First published in 1945.

[11] According to 2011 census data for India, close to 70% of India's population lives in rural communities of less than 5,000 people. (Source: Registrar General and Census Commissioner, Indian Ministry of Home Affairs, at http://censusindia.gov.in/2011-prov-results/paper2/data_files/india/Rural_Urban_2011.pdf.)

[12] Gandhi, *Sarvodaya*, 8-10, 22-5, 35, 81-4.

[13] Kumarappa, *Non-Violent Economy*, 42, 78-9.

[14] Kumarappa cites an example of a village where rice had been the traditional crop, but the land was sold and converted to coconut plantations, used to manufacture oils for soaps and other products in mills elsewhere, leaving the villagers without rice or coconuts (Kumarappa, *Non-Violent Economy*, 37-8.)

of land under common ownership.[15] The village "republics" could also become self-reliant in the production of locally grown, spun, and woven cotton cloth, or *khadi*,[16] examples both of appropriate technology and of resistance to the colonial import of spun cotton products and the corresponding displacement of indigenous livelihoods.

In present-day India, Gandhi's influence and the principles of his Constructive Program have arguably largely waned in significance, although several organizations dedicated to land reform and agricultural and ecological sustainability specifically trace their nonviolent guiding principles to Gandhian principles. For example, Ekta Parishad, based in Bhopal, conducts land-reform campaigns and nonviolence training, and promotes self-reliant village economies and protection of the earth along the lines of Gandhi's Sarvodaya movement.[17] The well-known Chipko movement in the Himalayan region of Uttar Pradesh (in which local women protected trees, under threat of logging by commercial development, by holding onto or "hugging" them to prevent the loggers from cutting them) owed its inspiration in part to Mira Behn and other followers of Gandhi.[18] As noted in Chapter 9, Gandhi's influence can still be traced from the Quakers in Rasulia via Partap Aggarwal and others to the agroecology experiments using Masanobu Fukuoka's methods from Japan. In addition, Gandhi's experiments have seen a new flourishing in Sri Lanka in the form of the Sarvodaya Shramadana movement (described below), in a model that has also inspired experiments in Nepal and elsewhere.[19]

---

[15] See Lanza del Vasto, *From Gandhi to Vinoba: The New Pilgrimage* (London: Rider and Company, 1956), and a description and bibliography by Mark Shepard, http://www.markshep.com/peace/GT_Vinoba.html.] Although the movement faltered in the late 60s, several million acres were obtained in this way, and the experiment undoubtedly helped inspire land-reform movements in other countries. (See also Chapter 9).

[16] Although relatively few villages produce locally grown, spun, and woven cloth today, during several weeks of travel in India to see present-day Gandhian economic experiments in practice, I met more than one elderly follower of Gandhi who still proudly wore *khadi*. The *charkha*, a portable hand spinning wheel, is still used as the central and unmistakable symbol associated with Gandhi's life and work.

[17] See http://www.ektaparishad.com/en-us/about/mission.aspx. When I visited Ekta Parishad in Bhopal, in Madhya Pradesh, in 2007, the organization was planning a long march to Delhi, in the Gandhian tradition, to fight for land-reform efforts.

[18] The Chipko movement has been used as a potent example of women's empowerment as well the protection of subsistence agriculture and nature. See, for example, Vandana Shiva, *Staying Alive: Women, Ecology and Development* (London: Zed Books, 1982), 67-77 and elsewhere.

[19] Sarvodaya USA, http://www.sarvodayausa.org/.

The Sarvodaya Shramadana Movement in Sri Lanka

Gandhi's Sarvodaya movement has also been the model for the present-day Sarvodaya Shramadana movement in Sri Lanka. Sarvodaya Shramadana, meaning "the awakening of all by the voluntary sharing of labour and other resources,"[20] was founded by A.T. Ariyaratne in the late 1950s. The movement combines Gandhian and Buddhist principles[21] to achieve an "integrated, holistic, and sustainable approach to satisfying the 10 basic needs of each human being" and to meet the three core goals of a Sarvodayan society—no poverty, no affluence and freedom from conflict. The movement has led the development of village-wide programs in almost half of the more than 30,000 villages in Sri Lanka. It is strongly supported by an international network, including a center in the U.S., and ultimately envisions a global awakening of all in the cultural, spiritual, moral, economic, political, and social spheres of human life and embedded within the living ecosphere.[22] The goals of the movement include:

- A clean and beautiful environment
- A clean and adequate supply of drinking water
- Adequate supplies of clothing
- Adequate and balanced nutrition
- Simple housing
- Basic healthcare
- Basic communication facilities
- A minimal supply of energy
- Holistic education
- Satisfaction of spiritual and cultural needs and peacebuilding[23]

Crucially, Ariyaratne's articulation of the 10 essential needs of human beings starts and ends with spiritual and moral awakening as its core, and how "each of the Buddhist principles laid out in the eightfold path [can] be put into a form that can be easily practiced."[24] The ultimate vision of the move-

[20] A.T. Ariyaratne, *Buddhism and Sarvodaya: Sri Lankan Experience*, ed. Nandasena Ratnapala (Delhi, India: Sri Satguru Publications, 1996), 3.

[21] A.T. Ariyaratne, *Schumacher Lectures on Buddhist Economics* (Ratmalana, Sri Lanka: Sarvodaya Vishna Lekha Publication, 1999), 1, 4.

[22] Ariyaratne, *Schumacher Lectures*, 24.

[23] Ariyaratne, *Schumacher Lectures*, 30-31. See also http://www.sarvodaya.org/philosophy-and-approach and http://www.sarvodaya.org/about/development-model/.

[24] Ariyaratne, *Schumacher Lectures*, 18.

ment is to develop in concentric circles from individual to family to village to urban communities to national and global awakening.[25] At ground level, the programs have developed multiple microenterprises supported by microbanking and by environmental, cultural, and educational projects, all of which must be decided on by the participation of all village members. Microfinancing and community banking has also flourished in many other poorer countries, one of the most well known being the Grameen banking system originated in the 1970s by Muhammad Yunus in Bangladesh.[26]

Ecological awareness is woven into the fabric of the movement, not as a "new" concern, but from its inception as what it means to have the "wellbeing and awakening of all" as the core principle. Ariyaratne writes that this means practicing agriculture in nonviolent ways that take account of seasons, climate, soil, indigenous plants and animals, and natural cycles in sustainable ways—working according to the seasons and limits of the local ecology, working collectively, equitably sharing what is harvested,[27] and preserving biodiversity, as well as providing clean drinking water and self-sufficiency in food at the village level. The program also sponsored the building of a model ecovillage at Lagoswatte, which, when I visited it as a volunteer in 2007, was housing some 50 or more families displaced by the 2004 tsunami. They were living in simple four-room dwellings, built primarily with local materials, and used sustainable technologies such as rainwater conservation, simple ultraviolet water purification, and less-polluting cooking fuels. More recently, the organization has been heavily involved in relief efforts during the increasing number of floods and other climate change-related severe weather events. (As a short-term voluntary participant, I could gain only an overview of the work, but they clearly had a deep understanding of the interdependence of spiritual and cultural needs, self-sufficiency, empowerment, and equality with ecological and human harmony and nonviolent ways of living. This does not of course mean that such movements have readily overcome widespread poverty or the pressures of modern development and conflicts.)

India, Sri Lanka, Africa, and other countries with so-called emerging economies still have large rural populations in village-sized communities. However, they are rapidly urbanizing and becoming part of a globalized, multinational world, as well as increasing in population. While the underlying

[25] Ariyaratne, *Buddhism and Sarvodaya*, 229.
[26] Grameen Bank, Bank for the Poor, http://www.grameen.com/.
[27] Ariyaratne, *Schumacher Lectures*, 19.

principles of Gandhian and Buddhist economics, as exemplified by the present-day Sarvodaya movement, are being adapted and modeled in urban as well as rural settings—for example in microenterprises such as the provision of clean water and sanitation in some of the poorest slums in Mumbai, Chennai, and elsewhere—it remains to be seen whether more equitable development can withstand the pressures of a globalized economy that wrests control of land and resources from local populations and uses cheap labor for production of goods for elsewhere, leaving many without basic necessities while ecological destruction proceeds apace.

Nonviolent Economics in the Global North— Utopianism or Emerging Reality?

An obvious question arises: Do such examples such as the Sarvodaya movement in countries like India or Sri Lanka have any relevance for predominantly urban and hyperdeveloped countries in the global North? If, as argued throughout this book, the need to heed such fundamental principles to create more peaceful, equitable, and ecologically sustainable—and hopefully happier—societies is as necessary and urgent in the global North as in the South, is it possible to imagine and experiment with ways that adapt and integrate the principles underpinning Gandhian and Buddhist economies with existing traditions and local economies in highly developed countries? Let's start by looking at the vision and work of E.F. Schumacher and those who collaborated and followed his vision, which was strongly influenced by Christian, Buddhist, and Gandhian perspectives as well as his practical experience as an economist in postwar England.

E.F. Schumacher was one of the earliest postwar thinkers to both critique the economic models and practices in Western industrial society and articulate the principles of a nonviolent economy. Schumacher's work focused on the core principles of human-scale, appropriate technology, along with egalitarian forms of economic wellbeing, ownership, and control and the preservation of the natural world to ensure a viable future for all life. Equally as important, Schumacher and others developed practical economic and appropriate technology programs that could be applied to both richer and poorer countries.

In the essay "Buddhist Economics" (originally called "Nonviolent Economics") in his seminal book *Small is Beautiful*,[28] Schumacher writes:

> …while the materialist is mainly interested in goods, the Buddhist is mainly interested in liberation…[but this is] in no way antagonistic to physical well-being. …*the keynote of Buddhist economics, therefore, is simplicity and non-violence* [my emphasis]…. [S]ince consumption is a means to human well-being, the aim should be to obtain the maximum of well-being with the minimum of consumption.[29]

In this view, spending excessive labor, effort, and resources to produce more goods (often using cheap materials, changing fashions, or advertising to increase "productivity") reduces the time available for one's cultural, artistic, and spiritual life and increases both stress and the likelihood of conflict over resources as well as multiple ecological pressures. As explored in Chapters 8 and 9, Schumacher felt that the almost exclusive emphasis on efficiency, uniformity, mass production and quantification, which sacrifices the dignity of labor, creativity, craftsmanship, and quality, is also a form of violence.[30] He argued that the Buddhist would view work as the "chance to utilise and develop [our faculties]; to overcome…ego-centredness by joining with other people in a common task" as well as producing needed goods and services.[31] Full, meaningful, dignified, and creative employment would be the primary focus of the economy, not the production of goods.

Small—and Local—Is Beautiful

E.F. Schumacher also argued that dependence on producing and selling goods at great distance is a sign of failure, not progress. He writes:

> …from the point of view of Buddhist economics…production from local resources for local needs is the most rational way of economic life, while dependence on imports from afar and the consequent need to produce for export to

---

[28] Schumacher, *Small is Beautiful*, 50-8. After his sudden death in 1977, Schumacher's writings and ideas were published in E.F. Schumacher, *Good Work* (New York: Harper and Row, 1979) and expanded by others in, e.g., Schumacher's colleague George McRobie's *Small is Possible* (London, Abacus, 1982) and in the work of the E.F. Schumacher Society, founded in 1980, now the Schumacher Center for a New Economics. To many who met or knew him (including myself), he combined rare spiritual insight with equally impressive intellectual and practical insights into ways in which economics and technology can serve the needs of people and the earth. A former economic advisor to the UK National Coal Board, he could speak persuasively both to industrialists and economists about appropriate technologies and "nonviolent" or "Buddhist" economics as well as to grassroots activists, ecologists, and environmentalists of many stripes.

[29] Schumacher, *Small is Beautiful*, 54.

[30] E.F. Schumacher, "Nonviolence," Transcription of a lecture delivered in Berkeley, CA, 1976, at http://www.centerforneweconomics.org/content/nonviolence.

[31] Schumacher, *Small is Beautiful*, 51.

unknown and distant peoples is highly uneconomic and justifiable only in exceptional cases and on a small scale.[32]

Such patterns of consumption increase the use of both energy and other materials and mean that we are increasingly distanced from the effects of our consumption on other ecosystems and communities. He also goes on: "from a Buddhist point of view…[n]on-renewable goods must be used only if they are indispensable, and then only with the greatest care and the most meticulous concern for conservation. To use them heedlessly or extravagantly is an act of violence…against nature which must inevitably lead to violence between men."[33] One of Schumacher's unique contributions was to rethink the question of size and scale, whether in the form of the economic paradigm of "more, bigger, faster, and newer is better" (as discussed in Chapter 2), the waste in exporting and importing or transporting goods across great distances, or the need for local control and participation at the community level, as exemplified by the Shramadana Sarovodaya model described above.[34]

Notably, neither Gandhi and Schumacher, nor the majority of those who have followed, have argued for a rejection of all modern development and growth, technologies, international trade, and so on. That would be a case of throwing the baby out with the bathwater. Schumacher always emphasized the Buddhist principle of a "middle way" and "right livelihood" in its broadest social and ecological meaning, which he saw as a way between unfettered material growth and accumulation on one hand and traditional stagnation or immobility on the other. But by *prioritizing* the foundational spiritual and ecological principles and values he articulated, he argued that it is absolutely possible to meet both material and spiritual needs—self-reliance, dignified work, social cooperation, mutual respect, equitable provision of essential needs, and the flourishing of cultural, artistic, and spiritual development—without sacrificing the natural world or our future lives. Let's examine further how some of these ideas have been articulated and put into practice by Quakers and others.

---

[32] Schumacher, *Small is Beautiful*, 55-6.

[33] Schumacher, *Small is Beautiful*, 57. See also Kirkpatrick Sale, *Human Scale Revisited: A New Look at the Classic Case for a Decentralist Future* (White River Junction, VT: Chelsea Green Publishing, 2007). An update of the author's classic *Human Scale* (New York: Coward, McCann & Geoghegan, 1980).

[34] Schumacher, *Small is Beautiful*, 59-70.

Right Livelihood and Right Sharing

Right livelihood can be defined as a means of living that is ecologically sustainable over the long term; provides for a modest but sufficient provision of essential physical, cultural, and spiritual needs; and ensures the dignity and enjoyment of one's labor. If we imagine a virtuous rather than a vicious circle whereby a person's basic wellbeing (health and education) needs are met by a commitment of the whole community (whether at the country level or village level), and material consumption is reduced due to individual frugality, or reductions in built-in obsolescence and advertising, for example, then this circle may yield greater freedom to refuse soul-destroying work, long hours, or stressful or hazardous working conditions in which one has little control over one's work—in other words, a greater freedom to realize right livelihood. At the same time, living more simply typically means less ecological impact.

The social contract, in the form of universal healthcare and education and social security provisions, for example, enabled by the (tax) contributions of all members of the society, contributes to the dignity and security of labor. (Where such provisions exist, for example in Scandinavian countries, there is little convincing evidence that citizens stop working, as some politicians have argued, but rather tend to engage in more meaningful and enjoyable vocations.[35]) Similarly, *common ownership* or employee-owned models of companies, rather than failing to provide adequate wages or benefits and improved productivity, may in fact do better than employer-owned companies, in which the financial rewards primarily go to shareholders and managers, and where wages, benefits, and good working conditions are considered a drain on profits and should be minimized.[36] In addition, multiple examples of community-owned food and production cooperatives and intentional communities, whether secular or religious in focus, have conservation and reducing ecological footprints as an integral part of the concept of right livelihood and an equitable economy.

---

[35] See, for example, George Lakey, *Viking Economics: How the Scandinavians Got it Right and We Can Too* (Brooklyn: Melville House Books, 2016).

[36] See, for example, the Scott Bader commonwealth model, http://www.scottbader.com/about-us/.

Convivial Societies

Ivan Illich defines a "convivial" society as "a modern society of responsibly limited tools"[37] (including as tools, hardware, machines, factories, and systems of production) and describes conviviality as "individual freedom realized in personal interdependence and...an intrinsic ethical value."[38] A convivial society is predicated on the three values of *survival, justice (both participatory and distributive), and self-defined work.*[39] It is "designed to allow all its members the most autonomous action by means of tools least controlled by others."[40] He sees the growth of tools beyond a certain point as decreasing autonomy, creativity, and joy and increasing regimentation, exploitation, and powerlessness.[41] In other words, *conviviality is contingent upon a deep understanding of limits.* If we sacrifice dignified labor, education, and the production of goods and services to constantly increasing demands of efficiency, growth, speed, and productivity, in the interests of managers and owners rather than those whose labor produces those goods and services, then we move toward deceptively and shoddily produced mass-made goods; the loss of traditional skills, knowledge, and time-honored tools and trades; and turning people into dependent appendages of those machines and systems in their daily work.[42]

What such systems of accelerated growth and production result in, beyond certain limits, is, ironically, a greater sense of separation and alienation in the name of the increasing demands for the satisfaction of material wants, instead of solidarity, interdependence, and dignity. Illich writes, "As conviviality is reduced below a certain level, no amount of industrial production can effectively satisfy the needs it creates among society's members."[43] Although Illich himself did not emphasize the ecological implications, such demand also increases the likelihood of ecological damage via overconsumption and waste, which may be exacerbated by this very loss in satisfaction and value in one's daily work as we try to find compensatory pleasure in material goods. Finally, Illich points out that, as discussed in Chapter 2, the "solution" to the social dissatisfactions and alienation thus generated is to not to do more of

[37] Ivan Illich, *Tools for Conviviality* (New York: Harper and Row, 1973), xxiv.
[38] Illich, *Conviviality*, 11.
[39] Illich, *Conviviality*, 13.
[40] Illich, *Conviviality*, 20.
[41] Illich, *Conviviality*, 20.
[42] Charlie Chaplin's 1936 classic movie, *Modern Times*, set in a rapidly industrializing America, is a telling—and hilarious—illustration of this dehumanizing process.
[43] Illich, *Conviviality*, 11.

the same—apply more technology, more management, and so on—as this escalates rather than solves the crisis. [44]

We clearly will need large changes at *all* levels of society, from the supra-national to the individual, and there is no *a priori* reason that these levels cannot act synergistically. Nevertheless, as I will explore below, the case is compelling for action on the more local, state, regional, and community lev-els. The most far-reaching modern social movements (e.g. around slavery, women's enfranchisement, workers' rights, and gay rights) indicate that changes at higher levels rarely happen except as the result of dogged, often decades- or centuries-long grassroots struggles, and the gains are always im-perfect and fragile. These are the levels at which regionally appropriate eco-nomic models and democratic controls can work most effectively, according to the subsidiarity principle. As exemplifed by Gandhian and Schumacherian economics, for example, the goal is to uphold the rights of individuals in community to their dignity and freedom *and* the rights of the wider natural world. This is best done by local and regional institutions supported by gov-ernments through e.g., infrastructure and transport policies.

Subsidiarity does not mean that in areas that must be dealt with at the national and international levels, such as global energy policies or the impacts of trade globalization, larger institutions do not have a major role and respon-sibility. Indeed, there may be areas where only such institutions can effect necessary actions and change on the scale required (see below). Further, a real danger exists that the idea of local governance and control becomes conflated with a political libertarian or neoliberal push for "small" government. The latter is too often a thinly veiled mask for failing to support infrastructure, conservation, healthcare and other large-scale services and projects, stripping away regulations that protect human health and wellbeing and the wider natural world, and for allowing greed to flourish without regard to the needs of the poor or the survival of the whole earth community.

Below, I will first briefly review the arguments for and feasibility of steady-state or no-growth economic systems at the macroeconomic level, and then look at some examples of existing attempts to address ecological impacts and consumption at the macro, community, and individual levels. I will em-phasize experiments in deep economy that integrate with a deep ecology perspective and the principles of integrity, nonviolence, justice, simplicity, and community explored in Part II.

---

[44] Illich, *Conviviality*, 9.

Deep Economy at the Macro Level: Steady-state Economics

Herman Daly, an academic formerly at the World Bank, was one of the first economists, together with John Cobb, to develop the theory of a steady-state economy and to link it to ecological sustainability.[45] Daly also addresses the criticism that a steady-state economy will necessitate an increase in unemployment, an issue dealt with in detail by economist Peter Victor, who argues that no rule exists that requires constant economic growth to ensure full or almost full employment or that environmental policies such as reducing greenhouse gases will necessarily increase unemployment.[46]

The idea of a steady-state economy has gained considerable ground over the past 30 years, as part of the emerging "new economics" thinking—bringing us back to the Meadows' *Limits to Growth* models described at the beginning of Chapter 1. The irony of the "new economics" thinking in one sense is that it simply reflects the reality of the world—and societies—we actually live in, rather than the world of mainstream economics that assumes, for example, that growth is imperative and ecological limits and damage are "externalities" that can be ignored. Economic theory also assumes that people are "rational actors": behaving as self-interested and isolated individuals intent on maximizing their needs and desires; with perfect knowledge, choice, and capacity; and as if we are all mere economic "units"—of workers, producers, and consumers of goods, services, and flows of money, rather than members of communities and cultures living together on a finite planet. (In a sense, businesses and corporations are behaving as "rational actors" if they do everything to maximize profits in the short term, justifying this on the grounds of shareholders' investments; but in fact, many companies do act in more complex ways, or actively pursue a "triple bottom line" of trying to integrate the needs of "people, profit, and planet" and still make a fair profit.)

---

[45] See, for example: Herman Daly and Kenneth Townsend, eds., *Valuing the Earth: Economics, Ecology, Ethics* (Cambridge, MA: MIT Press, 1993), and Herman Daly and John B. Cobb Jr., *For the Common Good: Redirecting the Economy Toward Community, the Environment, and a Sustainable Future*, 2nd ed. (Boston: Beacon Press, 1994). Daly cofounded the journal *Ecological Economics*, developed the Index of Sustainable Welfare, and writes extensively about ecological economics and ethics.

[46] Peter A. Victor, *Managing without Growth: Slower by Design, Not Disaster* (Cheltenham, UK: Edward Elgar Publishing, Ltd., 2008), 169-85. Simulations of various growth scenarios for Canada, including different rates of greenhouse gas (GHG) reductions, suggest that slowing the rate of growth to a low level for a period of time, followed by no growth, is compatible with a concurrent substantial reduction in GHG while protecting employment.

"Doughnut Economics"

Building on such work and that of Daly and others, the new economic thinking recognizes not only that wellbeing and growth are not synonymous but also that the absolute necessity of living within ecological limits and the welfare of all must be central to any new economic strategies. For example, Kate Raworth, an economist at Oxford University, describes an alternative model, captured in her elegant "doughnut" diagram, of how to think about the relationships between the economy, community, and ecology (Figure 10-1).

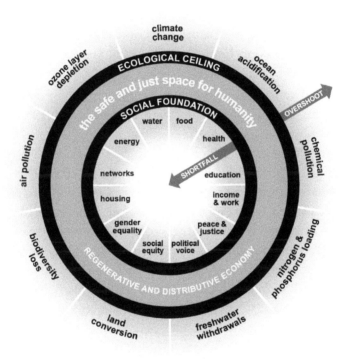

Figure 10-1. The "doughnut" model of the economy. Living in the "hole" in the center of the doughnut (the "shortfall" area) means deprivation of human needs for food, water, sanitation, education, housing, healthcare, and democracy. Living outside the outer ring of the doughnut (the "overshoot" area) means exceeding the ecological limits of the earth with respect to climate breakdown, biodiversity loss, pollution, and disruption to the natural cycles that maintain life. The aim is to live between the social foundation and the ecological ceiling, i.e., within the doughnut ring or zone. Reprinted from Raworth, *Doughnut Economics*, with permission.[47]

---

[47] Kate Raworth, *Doughnut Economics: Seven Ways to Think Like a 21st Century Economist* (London: Penguin Random House, 2017), 44.

Instead of conventional economic ideas of linear growth with inputs and outputs in a system that take no account of finite planetary limits, inequalities, non-market values, etc., Raworth proposes seven new ways to think about economics. The new principles include: change the goal [thriving in balance rather than increasing Gross Domestic Product (GDP)]; embed the economy in society (government, voluntary and domestic work, the commons, etc.) and nature, not just the market; nurture human nature (going beyond the idea of the rational consumer); understand that we are part of a dynamic, interdependent system (using systems thinking as described in Chapters 1 and 5); design systems that distribute income, wealth, and potential, not concentrate them; encourage a regenerative, cyclical economy that mimics nature, not degenerative designs that deplete the environment; and have as the key criterion whether the economy helps us thrive within the doughnut, rather than whether it grows.[48]

The idea of a steady-state economy has been taken up by government advisory bodies such as the Sustainability Commission in the U.K.,[49] but there are few signs that governments and their economic advisors are actively advocating such policies. Further, it is not clear whether, first, ecological balance can be achieved without a rapid *negative growth* phase in many countries, and second, whether either can be achieved within the current capitalist system. Several economists and others have argued that even a steady-state economy as currently conceived will be insufficient to avoid further ecological collapse or to begin to *restore* ecosystems and social equity; only after a long period of negative growth, or "degrowth," and global contraction to bring our footprint well within the limits of the earth's systems, could we maintain steady-state economies. For example, in a declaration from a Paris conference in 2008 on degrowth and social equity, participants stated that the "right-sizing" of global economies to bring the global ecological footprint within sustainable limits will require countries whose footprint exceeds this limit to make reductions, while in the poorest countries "right-sizing implies increasing consumption by those in poverty as quickly as possible, in a sustainable way, to a level adequate for a decent life, following locally determined pov-

---

[48] Raworth, *Doughnut Economics*, 25-30.

[49] Tim Jackson, UK Sustainability Commission, *Prosperity Without Growth? The Transition to a Sustainable Economy*, March 2009, https://research-repository.st-andrews.ac.uk/bitstream/handle/10023/2163/sdc-2009-pwg.pdf.

erty-reduction paths rather than externally imposed development policies."[50] The declaration also emphasized that wealth and income distribution within and across countries was an essential component of this process. The political economist Gar Alperovitz and others have also argued that a steady-state economy is not only unfeasible in the absence of more equitable distribution of income and wealth but also requires far greater control over the actions of corporations and the restoration of community cohesion, including the "reconstruction and nourishing of community as a political and cultural experience."[51] Alperovitz names cooperative worker- or community-owned enterprises as one of the ways in which such nourishment and cohesion can be achieved.

Deep Economy at the Community Level: Transition Communities

How can the macro-level concepts articulated above be translated into action at the regional and community levels? One approach is exemplified by the "Transition Towns" movement founded by Rob Hopkins and others in the mid-2000s.[52] Inspired by the thinking of E.F. Schumacher and many others, the transition concept is underpinned by six guiding principles, listed below. These principles underline the absolute necessity for a good deal of groundwork and community education and preparation before any plan for each area of action can be drawn up and then implemented.

- Visioning—creating a clear vision of the desired goals and outcome
- Inclusion—including business, local government, citizens, and everyone in dialogue, innovation, and action

[50] Declaration by participants, Conference on Economic DeGrowth for Sustainability and Social Equity, Paris, April 18–19, 2008, http://events.it-sudparis.eu/degrowthconference/en/Declaration%20on%20Degrowth%20EN.pdf. For further research on degrowth, see, for example, https://degrowth.org/.

[51] Gar Alperovitz, "Some Requirements of a Steady-State Economy," (undated), https://www.humansandnature.org/economy-gar-alperovitz.

[52] See Rob Hopkins, *The Transition Handbook: From Oil Dependency to Local Resilience* (Totnes, Devon, UK: Green Books, 2008); Rob Hopkins, *The Transition Companion: Making Your Community More Resilient in Uncertain Times* (Totnes, Devon, UK: Green Books, 2011); Jacqi Hodgson and Rob Hopkins, *Transition in Action: Totnes and District 2030, An Energy Descent Plan* (Totnes, Devon, UK: Transition Town Totnes, 2010); Rob Hopkins, *The Power of Just Doing Stuff: How Local Action Can Change the World* (Cambridge, UK: UIT/Green Books, 2013); Shaun Chamberlin, *The Transition Timeline: For a Local, Resilient Future* (Totnes, Devon, UK.: Green Books, 2009).

- Raising awareness—educating each other about fossil fuels, climate change, soil depletion, conservation of local ecologies, etc.
- Resilience—the ability of the community to not only reach a zero carbon state but also build resilience in food security and all areas of basic needs
- Psychological insights—developing ways to affirm people's concerns, empower cooperative action, etc.
- Credible and appropriate solutions—developing schemes that are realistic and appropriate on a community scale[53]

Perhaps the most remarkable aspect of this movement is that it has been put into practice in several local communities of varying types in the U.K. since its inception in the early 2000s (mostly in small towns, but also in urban districts) and has spread to become an international movement, with experiments in the U.S., Australia, New Zealand, and elsewhere. Such experiments provide local participants and others with multiple "lessons learned" by means of a range of "resilience indicators," as well as carbon footprinting, to gauge how well different plans are working, what projects need to be adapted or dropped, and how well the community is working with rather than against nature. Monitoring also allows people to share their expertise and experiences with other communities on an ongoing basis. The movement has focused on building resilience on a local level to climate disruption and economic downturns, particularly on reducing energy consumption by means of its "energy descent action plans,"[54] but it covers virtually all core aspects of community resilience for sustainable essential needs well into the future—from local currencies (about which more below) to clean and reliable water supplies, healthcare, farming practices and food security (with reliance on permaculture and related low-impact agricultural methods), education, housing, and transport—and also emphasizes the need for a flourishing culture and the arts, protection of both human livelihoods and biodiversity, and local governance. At bottom, the movement emphasizes the need for what the authors call an "inner transition," i.e., an inward, spiritually grounded change in thinking, to foster greater cooperation, sharing, and understanding of our relationship to the wider natural world.[55]

For example, the energy descent and resilience plan for Totnes in Devon (a town in southwest England, currently with a population of about 8000

[53] Hopkins, *The Transition Handbook*, 141-2.
[54] Hodgson and Hopkins, *Transition in Action*, 120-67.
[55] Hodgson and Hopkins, *Transition in Action*, 251-5.

people) is one of the most detailed blueprints for practical action yet produced. The plan, described in full in *Transition in Action*, includes detailed
energy-use analyses, carbon and energy budgets, and a series of plans to increase energy efficiency and reduce consumption in households, services,
industry, and transport using energy from solar, wind, hydro, biomass and
other crops, animal and plant waste, and sewage, together with options for
mass transit and more. It also covers land use; farming; conservation; food
security; employing agroecology; community-supported agriculture; the conservation of wildlife habitats; afforestation schemes; restoring soil integrity;
planting fibers such as jute, flax, and hemp for commercial use; and other
projects tailored to the local ecology and human needs combined with the use
of renewable energy sources wherever possible.

Local Currencies and Time Dollars

Numerous experiments in local exchange trading systems (LETS) have
been introduced in the U.S. and elsewhere. Perhaps the most well-known and
successful in the U.S. are Berkshares, a local currency project launched in
2006 in the Berkshires region of Massachusetts, assisted by the E.F. Schumacher Society, now expanded as the Schumacher Center for a New Economics. The basic principle behind the project is to create a local currency to
ensure that money generated in a community stays in the community, thereby
strengthening the local economy, provided that local businesses, banks, and
residents agree to buy and sell in the local currency (as well as or instead of
the national currency).[56] Some local currency schemes, like PLENTY (Piedmont Local EcoNomy Tender) in a town neighboring my own, are confined
to one town or district, and although some have eventually folded, some have
succeeded on a small scale.[57] Another concept is that of "time dollars," a
form of alternative exchange or time banking for services, in which participants exchange person-hours of work rather than monetary payment for
services. Originally an idea developed in the 1830s by socialist labor reformers
in Britain, it was taken up in the U.S. in the 1990s by Edgar Cahn.[58] Typically,

[56] The Schumacher Center for New Economics promotes sustainable economies via
programs including community land trusts, community-owned industries, micro-credit
initiatives, and local currencies, including Berkshares.
https://centerforneweconomics.org/apply/local-currencies-program/.
[57] Wikipedia, "List of Community Currencies in the United States," June 2018,
https://en.wikipedia.org/wiki/List_of_community_currencies_in_the_United_States.
[58] Edgar Cahn, *Time Dollars: The New Currency That Enables Americans to Turn Their Hidden
Resource-Time-Into Personal Security & Community Renewal* (Emmaus, PA: Rodale Press, 1992).

participants agree to exchange skills of varying types at a common rate (e.g., an hour of editorial work is "worth" the same as an hour of lawn mowing, etc.) to foster reciprocity and sharing in the community. Some of these schemes, such as "Ithaca (New York) HOURS," have been successful on a fairly wide community level, while others have not.[59]

Can Individual Actions Make a Difference?

The "answer," as one might expect, isn't a simple yes or no. In one sense, few if any actions are in reality "individual" or carried out independently of other people, circumstances, or social and political structures. For example, while individuals such as John Muir or Arne Naess or Martin Luther King may have individually pioneered visions, they were influenced in turn by other thinkers, religious traditions, spiritual or political leaders, and transforming those visions into effective action took the work of countless people and institutions.

As discussed in Chapters 5 and 8, there can be complementarity, interdependence, feedback, and creative synergism between individual and collective actions, as there can be between actions at the local, state, national, and international levels, if we reframe our habitually atomized and individualized ways of thinking and acting. As many Quakers and others attest, we can each, as George Fox advocated, be "patterns and examples" as we go about our lives, answering to the sacredness of each living being and to our own consciences, whether or not our actions seem to have a wider impact in the short term. It is critical to act individually according to our individual consciences and leadings, and it is also critical to remember that the most effective action is that taken in concert with others at the community, state, national and international levels, whether in the form of participation in local farming initiatives, designing and deploying clean energy technologies, political and educational campaigns, or voting. As described below, many issues, such as the globalization of consumer capitalism, climate breakdown, and the loss of biodiversity worldwide, can only be addressed on the scale now required at the corporate, governmental, or international levels. This calls for spiritually and morally

---

[59] A small group of friends and I experimented with a similar "time dollar" system in my local community some years ago. It ran for about a year or more and was only partly successful, but taught us several valuable lessons, such as how to take into account different skill sets (which would have differing economic value in the marketplace); the time to travel to perform a service for more distant members; and the time and effort required to organize contacts, monitor times and match needs.

grounded political action in concert with many other concerned citizens to put pressure on such bodies while building alternative structures and living more simply wherever possible.

A number of corporations and environmental campaigns have focused on "green" lifestyle choices as a way for individuals to act. One question is whether this emphasis distracts from the deeper changes that are needed at both the collective and individual levels if we are to create a deep and sustainable economy or whether such emphases are both ineffective or easily distorted by corporate or policy interests (such as "greenwashing" attempts by governments to appear to be taking action on the environment but in a superficial or deceptive way). "Green living" risks becoming yet another commodity or money-making consumer fashion, another way to profit from "alternative" lifestyles and products, and also sidesteps the question of whether such choices are options that poorer people may not have, as in the example of the lack of availability of organic and fresh food described above. As discussed in Chapter 2, consumer "sovereignty" as economists like to call it, is predicated on both *knowledge* (of e.g., alternatives, relative impacts of one product over another, etc.) and *choice*, and both of these are typically less available to poorer communities and individuals than richer ones. A further, practical question is the extent to which individuals, acting either alone or in small groups, can adopt ways of living in simpler and ecologically less damaging ways within highly developed societies, whether or not we are working for more structural changes at the community or wider level.

Nevertheless, for those of us who have the money and means to do so, it may be possible to choose how we travel and what we eat and buy, for example, both individually and cooperatively. Ideally, every time we buy something—an article of clothing, a smartphone, or a pound of grapes—we could ask questions such as whether we really need it; where the article came from, how was it made, who produced it and under what working conditions and wages; who profits; what relationship the producers have to the wider economy and the nation in which they operate; whether animals were involved in the production and under what conditions; and the ecological impacts of production. I can choose not to buy the article, or not to buy it online; I could buy a secondhand article; or I could buy an article from a fair-labor, sustainable, nonviolent producer and country. I can buy articles that are designed to last, take care of them, and eventually pass them along rather than throwing them away. On a broader level, I could, for example, choose to move my savings or any investments or not to work in certain industries, or leave them. As acts of what I call "conscientious protection" on the part of individuals and collective movements, they are acts of faith and commitment, whether or not we see immediate changes at the level of corporate or governmental behavior. Nevertheless, there is a limit to the choices available to me to make in the absence of larger structural, societal changes. (For example, I may be able to make individual choices about food, energy use and sources or personal transport, and thus help lower my carbon and ecological footprint. It is not nearly as easy to make individual choices about infrastructure, such as the millions of buildings, highways and other structures that are made of concrete, although the greenhouse gases emitted during its production are surpassed among materials only by coal, gas and oil emissions.[60])

Rich in Ends: Voluntary Simplicity

It is eminently possible for many of us in richer countries to live at much lower levels of consumption, but this will require structural rather than only individual changes in lifestyles. In some of the richest countries in the world, particularly the U.S., our average levels of material consumption are 10 times or more of the average in most countries in Asia and Africa, and *even almost double that of most European countries*, including some of the Scandinavian countries that offer excellent healthcare, education, and social care as well as high standards of living, as George Lakey has described.[61] However, it is easy to confuse plain or simple living as a choice with poverty as a condition of material deprivation and limited life choices. We have great inequality and poverty even in the richest countries: In the U.S., for example, at least 13 million Americans live below the official poverty line ($12,140 a year for an individual or $25,100 for a family of four as of 2018). Or, if we take a broader and more realistic definition of poverty, based on a "low income" of double the federal poverty line and including the Supplemental Poverty Measures,[62] roughly a third to 40% of all Americans live in near-absolute poverty and struggle each month to make ends meet. When environmentalists, conservationists, and

[60] Jonathan Watts, "Concrete: The Most Destructive Material on Earth," *The Guardian*, February 25, 2019, https://www.theguardian.com/cities/2019/feb/25/concrete-the-most-destructive-material-on-earth.

[61] Lakey, *Viking Economics*.

[62] Institute of Policy Studies, *The Souls of Poor Folk: Auditing America 50 Years After the Poor People's Campaign Challenged Racism, Poverty, the War Economy/Militarism and Our National Morality*, eds. Saurav Sarkar, Shailly Gupta Barnes, and Aaron Noffke (Washington: Institute of Policy Studies, April 2018), 9, https://ips-dc.org/wp-content/uploads/2018/04/PPC-Audit-Full-410835a.pdf.

deep ecologists call on us to reduce our carbon footprints, or our ecological footprints, it not only seems like asking people to make sacrifices rather than experience gains but also appears to ignore the very real inequalities and poverty that exist in the midst of the richest countries. In other words, advocating that people live more simply seems at best utopian and at worst elitist.

However, within certain constraints, many of us in richer societies can live materially more simple lives as individuals and communities, and multiple ways to do this have emerged, as both the voluntary simplicity movement and the transitions towns movement and other new economics experiments have exemplified. Collectively, individuals, families, and small communities could live at considerably less than the average per-capita consumption level in the richer world. In fact, we could in fact have a higher quality of life, with more control over our daily lives; more equality; more attention paid to the equitable provision of essential goods and services such as healthcare and education; more time for the cultivation of our cultural and spiritual life; and a more sustainable, healthy, and nourishing environment, as exemplified by the goals of the Sarvodaya movements described above.

We could actually be liberated into a new form of richness—a more egalitarian life where we are not imprisoned in a cycle of wage slavery and uncertainty to stay afloat in a society of insecure income, inadequate healthcare and educational opportunities, with no time to think about nature, never mind take steps to avoid what is happening to the earth.[63] In Chapter 6, I described the principle of simplicity from a Quaker perspective. In this view, simplicity has both a material and spiritual aspect, and it is the latter that guides those of us who seek to practice it in our lives.[64] What this means in practice is that rather than sacrificing something (parts of our consumer lifestyles, for example), we gain the possibility of a greater a sense of inner freedom and peacefulness, as well as the restoration of the wider natural world on which we depend materially and in so many ways culturally and spiritually. We could learn to live, to paraphrase deep ecologist Bill Devall,

---

[63] Joe Dominguez and Vicki Robin's bestseller *Your Money or Your Life: Transforming Your Relationship with Money and Achieving Financial Independence* (New York: Penguin Books, 1993) reframed the relationship between money, life energy, work, and values, not only to achieve financial independence, or to free oneself from a stress-filled treadmill of work, money, and debt, but also to live in a more materially simple and more meaningful way. A life of sufficiency allows greater freedom (p. 282-3) and a potentially lower impact on the earth. A criticism of their work is that, for many in poverty, such life choices may be highly restricted by what it takes to survive in our present social structures.

[64] See, for example, Richard B. Gregg, *The Value of Voluntary Simplicity*, Pendle Hill Essays No. 3 (Wallingford, PA: Pendle Hill Publications, 1936).

simpler in means and richer in ends,[65] and this involves action ranging from changing our personal consumption to collective political and social action.

Joining Individual and Collective Actions: The Power of Synergy

While individual lifestyle changes can and do make a difference, they would be scarcely enough by themselves to turn around the ecological crisis—even if many of us could reduce our footprints—if the larger structural forces that are putting enormous pressure on the planet were still in place. Many of the economic and social changes required call for cooperation and organizing as communities at the local, regional, or city level, and up to the national and even supranational levels. For example, choosing as individual consumers to ride a bicycle, walk, install solar panels, or not fly might affect fossil-fuel extraction and burning, but only if done by many and if accompanied by clean energy policies, mass transit, and an end to fossil-fuel extraction, by divestment from fossil-fuel companies,[66] government support for solar energy projects and so on, and this requires active campaigns from the community to the national level and beyond.[67] At the same time, we can press for the adoption of policies that address ecojustice in several ways: to redress the inequalities of poorer communities being hit hardest by pollution, waste, and climate breakdown, and to ensure that people have the means and opportunity to eat good food or switch to clean energy, for example, while protecting the wider natural world. In other words, we can only bring about the no poverty, no wealth, nonviolent and ecologically sustainable world envisioned by Gandhi, Ariyaratne, Schumacher and others by addressing the issues of poverty, inequality and the need for social and ecological action at all levels of society and beyond our national borders.

---

[65] Bill Devall, *Simple in Means, Rich in Ends: Practicing Deep Ecology* (Layton UT: Gibbs Smith Publishers, 1988).

[66] The fossil-fuel divestment movement has gained considerable ground in the past decade, for example, https://en.wikipedia.org/wiki/Fossil_fuel_divestment.

[67] In my own state, NCWARN, the North Carolina Waste Awareness and Reduction Network (https://www.ncwarn.org/) is an example of a highly effective, local clean-energy movement that, for 30 years, has combined active education and a program of clean energy installation with campaigning against fossil-fuel use and pollution by Duke Energy (one of the largest power utilities in the U.S.) and others. It also promotes a "Clean Path 2025" strategy that supports solar-power installation, improved battery storage, energy conservation and green jobs across the state. (NCWARN, "Clean Path 2025: Achieving an Economical Clean Energy Future for North Carolina." https://www.ncwarn.org/our-work/clean-path-2025/.)

The Need for Good Global Governance

Economic change on the scale and depth now called for clearly requires the participation of governments and businesses as well as people at large. Further, at the macroeconomic level, large-scale shifts in economic practices require the underpinning of changes in *global* governance and cooperation; i.e., legislative and policy action must be taken on international as well as national and local levels in support of a whole earth economy.

Peter Brown and Geoffrey Garver spell out four forms of global institutional governance they consider necessary to support this, by providing the means to monitor the state of the planet; to protect the earth's commons in a fairer way; to make enforceable rules and regulations; and to review the performance and compliance of the institutions and the application of their rules.[68] The four institutions would consist first of a *Global Reserve*, which would guide the global economy—based on an ecological "life support" budget that monitors both ecological impacts and consumption and the distribution of costs and benefits across countries—and define the limits that the ecosphere imposes on human economic activity. *Global Trusteeships* would protect the earth's commons—the many areas of the planet that are shared in common, from land to sea to rivers to atmosphere. The *Global Federation*, an international policy and regulatory body to link the Global Reserve and Trusteeships, would protect global security for humans and other life-forms, and set global quotas for extraction of minerals, fishing, and so forth. Finally, a *Global Court* would oversee and enforce the rules laid down by the various global agencies.[69] Whether macroeconomic systems (even if overseen by such global bodies) can alter the current trajectories of "growth at all costs" and vast imbalances in power, wealth, and costs, and still protect the wider natural world and avoid ecological catastrophe, remains to be seen, especially when, in Brown and Garver's scenarios, they continue to operate on the basis of taxation, pricing, and cap-and-trade policies as well as regulation. Nevertheless, some successes by existing supranational bodies provide framework models for future global governance, including the European Union, the UN Environment Programme, and the UN Green Climate Fund, backed up by multidisciplinary scientific and monitoring studies from international bodies or NGOs such as the UN Intergovernmental Panel on Climate Change,

---

[68] Peter G. Brown and Geoffrey Garver, *Right Relationship: Building a Whole Earth Economy* (San Francisco: Berrett-Koehler Publishers, Inc., 2009), 111.

[69] Brown and Garver, *Right Relationship*, 113-37.

World Wildlife Fund, Worldwatch Institute, and others.[70] Another example is
the 1982 UN Convention on the Law of the Sea, which, while weaker than its
proponents wished, nevertheless enshrined the concept of protection of the
marine commons in law. This law has been ratified by over 160 countries and
the European Union as of 2016.[71]

The scale and speed of ecological and climate breakdown have reinforced
arguments for large-scale programs at the international and national levels,
with calls for urgent action on the scale of a "global Marshall plan," first put
forward by Al Gore,[72] or the rapid mobilization and conversion of industry
on a scale comparable to military conversions at the beginning of the second
World War. Others have called for programs of the type that the Roosevelt
administration instigated during the Great Depression of the 1930s, with the
mobilization of the Civilian Conservation Corps, for example. The idea of a
"Green New Deal," initially put forward by the UK's New Economics Foundation in 2008,[73] has been taken up in different forms by international organizations such as the UN Environment Programme and other NGOs, and
received a recent boost from newly-elected members of the US Congress, the
US Green Party,[74] and others in the form of a related proposal. In the US
version, the proposed program seeks to address the combined predicaments
of climate breakdown, job insecurity, and poverty based on a four-part program consisting of an economic "bill of rights"—a transition program to a
sustainable economy, financial reform, and democratic reforms. However, as
noted in Chapters 2 and above, the idea that such programs can, as some of
its proponents suggest, "boost economic growth" while avoiding from ecological destruction and climate breakdown without more radical reforms, is
questionable. Absent major economic reforms and significant reductions in
economic growth and consumption in the richest countries, such efforts will

---

[70] Brown and Garver, *Right Relationship*, 160.

[71] United Nations Division for Ocean Affairs and the Law of the Sea, "The United Nations Convention on the Law of the Sea of December 10, 1982,"
http://www.un.org/Depts/los/convention_agreements/texts/unclos/unclos_e.pdf.

[72] Al Gore, *Earth in the Balance: Ecology and the Human Spirit* (New York: Rodale Press, 2006),
295 et seq. First published in 1992.

[73] New Economics Foundation, "A Green New Deal: Joined-up Policies to Solve the
Triple Crunch of the Credit Crisis, Climate Change and High Oil Prices,"
https://neweconomics.org/2008/07/green-new-deal.

[74] The Green Party of the United States, "Summary of the Green New Deal,"
http://www.gp.org/green_new_deal. See also the new youth-led Sunrise Movement
campaigning for the Green New Deal in the US Congress,
https://www.sunrisemovement.org/gnd.

likely fall well short of what is required, particularly the drastic reductions in GHG emissions now needed (see Chapter 1).

Appropriate Technology

When E.F. Schumacher developed the concept of "appropriate" or "intermediate" technology, he saw it as an integral part of a nonviolent economy. The approach of his Intermediate Technology Group, later renamed Practical Action,[75] is aligned with the principles explored in the examples from Schumacher, Gandhi, and Ariyaratne, described above, and is currently focused primarily on helping local communities in poorer countries. Schumacher believed that poorer, rural communities would continue to be poor unless small-scale technologies were available for use, but that "it cannot be assumed that that the level of technologies used by affluent countries is the only possible level, let alone that it is necessarily the best for poor societies."[76] The goals and practical application of appropriate technology, based on these principles and examples, might be summarized as follows:

- Serve the essential needs of a local community first, *according to priorities determined by the local community*
- Use indigenous skills and local labor and ensure dignified work
- Use locally-adapted or traditional technologies, agriculture, health practices, etc. wherever possible
- Use the simplest technologies consistent with satisfying needs
- Use technologies that remain under the economic and political control of the local population in terms of skills, equipment, materials, machines, agricultural supplies, etc., to preserve and increase community self-reliance
- Minimize or actively restore damage to, local ecologies and life-forms

---

[75] Practical Action, https://practicalaction.org/. For example, the simple expedient of raising the level of village wells, using dirt and brick and a bit of cement, has saved thousands of residents in Bangladesh from having to drink contaminated water during increasingly frequent flooding due to climate change; placing bicycle-driven pumps in fields using a simple bucket method allows for more irrigation; rainwater conservation methods help protect against drought, simple water-distillation technologies provide clean drinking water. Methods for such technologies are freely available via the organization's technical advice services or on their website. The organization lobbies for policy changes at the state, national, and international levels to, for example, ensure equitable access to sustainable energy and technology.

[76] E.F. Schumacher, *Good Work*, 95.

- Ensure that agricultural, industrial and infrastructure technologies are economically and ecologically sustainable over the *long* term
- Align and integrate technologies with the economic, social, cultural and spiritual needs of the community

Schumacher adopted a Gandhian approach in not eschewing technology out of hand. Instead, technology should meet definite criteria. Specifically it should not displace local dignified work, be affordable and controllable at the local level, not build in obsolescence, and provide first and foremost for needs, not superfluous consumption. An example is the biosand filter, which provides point-of use drinking water by means of filtration of pathogens and suspension of solids through simple filters installed in containers of various sizes, upon which microorganisms grow that consume pathogens, and then through graded layers of sand (Figure 10-2).

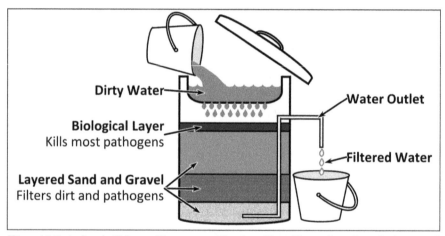

Figure 10-2. A simple "biosand" water-purification filter. Figure based on designs used worldwide by a number of NGOs and related organizations, such as Friendly Water for the World.[77]

Appropriate technologies based on these criteria clearly apply equally in richer countries, with the emphasis here of reducing excess consumption rather than developing capacity. Small, simple, and equitable applies equally to the disparities in wealth in poor and rich countries as to the need to tread more lightly on the earth. As Godfrey Boyle and Peter Harper wrote in the preface to their book on "radical technology" in the 1970s, "this is…about technologies that could help create a less oppressive and more fulfilling socie-

---

[77] Friendly Water for the World, https://watercharity.com/partner/friendly-water-world.

ty."[78] In the 1970s and beyond, a wide range of projects and campaigns emerged in the U.K., U.S. and Europe as awareness of the limits to growth and the problems of pollution became evident, from the first solar energy installations to protesting overpackaging and the phasing out of returnable bottles. Ideas for how appropriate or intermediate technology could be applied to every sector of industrial economies flourished, from food, energy, housing, communications, and infrastructure to ways families can use solar energy, compost, or wind as alternative energy sources.[79]

One of the key challenges we face in the era of climate crisis and increasing ecological destruction is whether technological approaches can be developed and deployed that, first, satisfy the principles of appropriate technology described above and in Chapter 8; second, whether they can work on a large enough scale to bring about the radical decreases in GHG and related pollutants that are now needed (see Chapter 2), i.e., whether they can be brought into production on a scale and in time to avoid the worst impacts of ecological destruction. Methods to generate renewable and clean energy, in the form of solar, wind, water and ocean wave technologies, are rapidly spreading worldwide and becoming cheaper than fossil fuels, for example, although material shortages or accessibility to some components may become an issue. Such a shift will require a massive change in our business-as-usual economic calculus and significant interventions at many levels from community to governmental and international levels (see Chapter 2). There is no shortage of "solutions," as Paul Hawken and colleagues have recently demonstrated with respect to an array of technologies to curb global warming[80]; but, if their implementation depends primarily on short-term economic considerations as much as technical feasibility, and these continue to trump the long-term needs of human life and the wider natural world, we may not act in time to avoid runaway climate breakdown and ecological collapse.

Contraction and Convergence—A Model for Equity

"Contraction and convergence" is a concept that is best known as an approach to the progressive and equitable reduction in global greenhouse gas

[78] Godfrey Boyle and Peter Harper, eds. *Radical Technology* (London: Wildwood House Ltd, and New York: Pantheon Books, 1976), 5.

[79] The Staff of Mother Earth News®, *The Mother Earth News® Handbook of Homemade Power* (New York: Bantam Books, 1974).

[80] Hawken, Paul, ed. *Drawdown: The Most Comprehensive Plan Ever Proposed to Reverse Global Warming* (New York: Penguin Books, 2017).

emissions, but which can, in theory, be applied to the distribution of the burdens and costs of ecological damage and of resources in equitable and just ways within and across countries. In the early 1990s, Aubrey Meyer and his colleagues developed the Contraction and Convergence (C&C) global framework for equitably reducing global warming and avoiding climate catastrophe, an approach since supported by the United Nations Framework Convention on Climate Change (UNFCCC), businesses, and environmental organizations.[81] The underlying principle of the C&C framework is simple: to reach and stay below a target concentration of atmospheric greenhouse gases agreed upon by the international community, by reducing overall global GHG emissions in an equitable manner. This is done by first determining the global per-capita GHG emissions level that will ensure this target is met and maintained. Richer countries typically exceed the target per-capita GHG level, but poorer countries typically do not. Under the equitability framework, poorer countries could still develop their economies and emit more GHGs up to this level for some years, while richer countries would be required to reduce per-capita GHG the most. If implemented successfully, the process of contraction and convergence means that the global target level of GHG is reached equitably by a given agreed date, as shown in Figure 10-3.

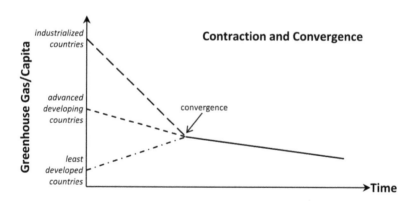

Figure 10-3. A schematic of contraction and convergence of per capita GHG emissions by type of country to reach a given global emission target by a specified time.

Even in theory, calculating a per-capita allocation of GHG emissions is complex, requiring first a detailed understanding of how much and at what rate global GHG reduction is needed to stay below the agreed threshold level.

---

[81] Aubrey Meyer, *Contraction and Convergence: The Global Solution to Climate Change*, Schumacher Briefings No. 5 (Totnes, Devon, UK: Green Books, Ltd., 2000).

Second, how can this amount be allocated equitably, on a global basis? How do we account for the cumulative historical emissions from the richest countries, for example? What mechanism can we bring to bear to effect this policy? Rereading the history of the original 1990s proposal and its fate some 28 years later gives pause for reflection, as we watch GHG concentrations pass the approximately 400 ppm compatible with keeping global warming below 2°C. Nevertheless, the UN and other agencies and governments, up to and including at the 2015 Conference of the Parties (COP) 21 climate meetings in Paris, have each supported such an approach to the climate crisis as both just and pragmatic. However, there appears to be little chance that participating countries will reduce GHG to the target levels agreed upon within the specified time periods (see Chapter 1), although countries' "intended nationally determined contributions" (INDCs) to the Paris agreement are supposed to basically reflect this approach.[82] Nevertheless, the basic principles of contraction and convergence arguably represent the most equitable and just ways in which carbon emissions and other forms of pollution can be reduced on a global basis, together with the sharing of the costs of pollution control.

In sum, experiments with putting deep economies in practice seek to embody many of the principles and characteristics described above. These include a commitment to nonviolence, right livelihood, and right sharing; minimizing ecological destruction and conflict; participatory democratic structures, including of labor; a sense of community solidarity and responsibility; a sense of belonging and care for land and place; human scale (smaller, less, slower, more local, and self-reliant communities); a sense of sufficiency and simplicity; basic material and bodily security; dignified work; attention to distributive justice, morality, and conviviality; and the prioritization of spiritual, moral, and cultural values over those of short-term growth economies.

Many of the most effective approaches are being carried out at the community level, and a number are inspired by Gandhi's Constructive Program and Ariyaratne's Shramadana Sarvodaya program, by Schumacher's ideas on Buddhist economics, Quaker testimonies, and other faith traditions. Action guided by such deep ecology and deep economy principles is needed on all levels from the individual to the global, if we are to change our way of thinking and living sufficiently to avoid ecological catastrophe.

---

[82] David King, "Towards Decarbonising the Global Economy: The Direction of Travel After COP-21," presentation to the International Energy Agency, Paris, January 29, 2016, at http://www.gci.org.uk/Documents/King_IEA_29-Feb-2016.pdf. See also World Resources Institute data on the Paris INDCs at http://cait.wri.org/indc/.

Chapter 11

The Practice of Deep Peace

Our truth is an ancient one: that love endures and overcomes; that hatred destroys; that what is obtained by love is retained, but what is obtained by hatred proves a burden. This truth, fundamental to the position which rejects reliance on the method of war, is ultimately a religious perception, a belief that stands outside of history.

—American Friends Service Committee[1]

What leads to peace is not violence but peaceableness, which is not passivity, but an alert, informed, practiced, and active state of being.... The key to peaceableness is continuous practice.

—Wendell Berry[2]

How can we bring about a more peaceable earth for ourselves and for all life? The path to nonviolence and a peaceable earth is an integral one—integrating the inner contemplative spirit and outer action; humans, nature and whatever we call the Source or Divine or All; individual action and collective action—and to realize, as explored throughout earlier chapters, that we cannot build a peaceable, just and sustainable life with Earth without seeking a more just, equitable and peaceful way of living with each other, and within ourselves. In other words, *thinking and acting nonviolently toward the earth is an act of peacemaking, and peacemaking is an act of ecological restoration.* Each reinforces the other in interdependent ways. First, we can first practice nonviolence to all other life-forms and the ecosystems, soils, oceans, rivers, and air they and we depend on and begin to repair the existing violence to the earth, and in myriad ways. As described in Chapters 5, 6 and 9, this can be done through overcoming our sense of separation and distancing from the wider natural world

---

[1] Stephen G. Cary et al., *Speak Truth to Power: A Quaker Search for an Alternative to Violence*, American Friends Service Committee (1955), iv, http://www.quaker.org/legacy/sttp.html.

[2] Wendell Berry, "Thoughts in the Presence of Fear," in *In the Presence of Fear: Three Essays for a Changed World*, (Great Barrington, MA: Orion Society, 2001), 7-8.

and the sacredness of all life; by conserving, preserving, and restoring soils, waters, and air; protecting wildlife and habitats; preventing deforestation, erosion, and pollution; preserving native species and landscapes; cleaning up polluted rivers, oceans, and landscapes; planting trees; caring for threatened animals and plants and habitats; spending time in nature; learning about the holistic nature of the universe and the systems view of life; doing science in more holistic and less hubristic ways; and reducing our overall human consumption and healing ecological destruction in equitable and just ways, both within and across countries. Second, as I will explore below, we can seek to live more peaceably among ourselves and prevent more war and conflict and we can seek to heal the inward splits and projections in ourselves so that we are less likely to act out of fear, hatred, greed and power-seeking in the world.

In previous chapters, we have seen how violence to each other and to the earth both reinforces and is reinforced by the other in a positive feedback loop—overconsumption and resource grabbing, the climate crisis, and scarcity of the needs for life give rise to conflicts; ecological damage wreaked by armed conflicts increases the risk of "resource wars"; and the displacement of millions of climate or ecological refugees creates further tensions and conflicts. As described in Chapter 6, in 18th-century America, the Quaker John Woolman made the connections between, on the one hand, wanton cruelty to animals, the slave trade, the treatment of the poor, and the possession of great wealth, and on the other, the "seeds of war"; and in 20th-century England, E.F. Schumacher wrote that we cannot have peace without a "permanent" (i.e., steady-state, sustainable, and equitable) economy. Robert Swann, cofounder of the Schumacher Center for a New Economics and a conscientious objector, concluded that the main root causes of war were the commodification of land, the exclusive control of currencies by national and international governments and banks, and the loss of community due to the forces of larger economic interests and globalization (see Chapter 10).

I also explored ways that we can practice nonviolence to the earth through such things as nonviolent science, nonviolent technology, nonviolent economy, nonviolent social justice, and nonviolent ecology, with numerous examples of how nonviolent practices have been applied in each of these areas. As we saw, many of these experiments were and are grounded spiritually in the teachings of the ancient sages, prophets and mystics of the great religions, as practiced by modern visionaries, from Woolman to Gandhi and from to Schumacher to Ariyaratne, and countless others. This spiritual ground, as explored in Chapters 5 and 6, is the foundation of ultimate sustainability—and the primacy of life, beauty, truth, and love—for both the commonwealth of human life and for the conservation and integrity of all of life in the wider natural world.

Nonviolence in the world is a positive action, a constructive, creative, and restorative force. It is not just a matter of striving not to cause physical harm or not engaging in killing, conflict, or wars; it is a matter of acting nonviolently toward all beings, and the soils, waters, and air that support all life in its intricate interdependence. It is intimately dependent on working toward inward psychospiritual integration, on spiritual and material simplicity, on a recognition of the intrinsic equality of all beings and the reciprocity and integrity of all that lives on the earth, and on the sharing of the common wealth of life with each other and the wider natural world in "permanent economies," i.e., in nonviolent and egalitarian ways that minimize harm to other life-forms and allow for long-term sustainability of human and other life unto the nth generation.

It is undoubtedly easier for many of us to envisage ways to protect nature and reduce our ecological footprints than to reduce wars and conflict, as utopian and quixotic as both of those goals may seem at present. But, again, we need to remember that nonviolence to the wider natural world can foster nonviolence to each other and nonviolence to each other can foster nonviolence to the wider natural world, and that the same underlying principles that we need to apply to preventing violence to the earth apply to preventing violence to each other. They are connected to each other by the same spiritual principles of integrity, unity and reciprocity, nonviolence, simplicity, equality and community, and, ultimately, the practice of love.

To repeat the underlying principles of integrity and nonviolence we explored in Chapters 5 and 6, which apply to both the human realm and the wider natural world: first, all beings and all life are ultimately one unity; second, all life is sacred and worthy of love; third, as violence leads to more violence, so nonviolence leads to more peace; fourth, hatred cannot overcome hatred; and fifth, love has the transformative and creative power to overcome fear and violence. Thus, the ground of nonviolence is a felt bond of kinship and love. And love, as we have seen, flourishes when we are not distanced from one another and nature by fear, insecurity, greed, hatred, justification, or a sense of separation.

The Inner Landscape of Nonviolence

In the human realm, nonviolence does not deny that violence is real, or that it can be overcome merely by the absence of war or passive accommodation with those who perpetrate violence. Nonviolence is an *active* force that resists violence and conflict in all its forms. As many Quakers and others can testify, along with modern leaders such as Gandhi and King, nonviolence, to be effective and sustainable, must be grounded in a deep spiritual understanding if one is to have the courage to outwardly resist war and conflict and to stand nonviolently for truth and justice. It involves a commitment to loving relationships in our personal lives—with family, friends, and everyone with whom we come into contact. It also requires us not to contribute to the many types of structural violence—from racism, sexism, and other forms of discrimination to economic injustice and the unjust exploitation of others' labor.

As discussed in Chapter 4, many of the forces that drive violence to the earth are the same as those that drive violence among people, while others are unique to the realm of human conflict. First, as the Buddha reminds us, we are driven both by desires—from egotistical satisfaction and power to a desire for happiness and pleasure—and by fear and insecurity—of disease, starvation, or death from natural phenomena, war, or violence to each other. We seek to predict and control nature and others even as we know we cannot do so; we seek permanence in a world of constant change, and joy and love without suffering. Our desires can drive us to seek to dominate and tame natural forces and can make us (perhaps unconsciously) rage against the unpredictability and essential uncontrollability of nature. The untrammeled desire for more wealth, power, and possessions drives us to go far beyond using natural materials and life-forms for our essential needs, resulting in structural forms of violence to each other—by putting profit or power over people and nature in industrial production, globalized commerce, pollution or overexploitation of soil and labor, and wars over land and resources.

Around the world, many of us, even in or arguably particularly in the richest countries, increasingly suffer from symptoms of profound disquiet or discontentment; from addictions or depression; from a sense of meaningless, cynicism, or a failure of trust in systems; and from a deep-seated, if diffuse, anxiety—about nuclear war, the economy, the creaking institutions of our governments, and what we are doing to the earth, our only home. While many of us even in rich countries suffer from extreme material insecurity, unemployment and poverty, many of us can't seem to find lasting happiness or a sense of security in increasing consumption, or our work, even as we continue to do them more and faster and longer. Nor do we do well with living in the present, being grateful for what we experience. We are habitually future-oriented, imagining that we will achieve some goal in the future, or fearing that we will lose what we have, and failing to live in the only moment we have, the present, and we cling to what we do have. We also don't do well with impermanence or uncertainty. We may realize that we want to break the cycle of addiction to our ways of getting, having, and doing, with their diminishing returns, and their ever-increasing costs to our quality of life and to the wider natural world, but we don't seem to know how to get off the treadmill. The dangers of the kinds of hyperactive, rushing, never-satisfied, frantic ways many of us live can also apply to those who are attempting to bring change in the world. "Frenzied activism,"[3] no matter how noble the effort, can, as both Thomas Merton and Thomas Kelly have pointed out, become a form of violence, when, in an attempt to carry many concerns at once, we lose our ability to discern and listen, and lose our contact with the Inner Guide, the Source, that we need if the work is to be wisely directed and effective.[4]

As described in Chapters 4 and 5, Carl Jung believed that one of the critical tasks facing humanity, if we are to avoid destroying ourselves through conflict, and now, ecological devastation, was to learn to mutually withdraw the projections of the unwanted, repressed or denied "shadow" aspects of ourselves on to others, or onto a natural world that we fear or find uncontrollable, and want to dominate. We are as a house divided against itself—the rational mind or head seems pitted against the heart, the emotional self; the creaturely self and fear-based ego conflict with the wisdom of the deeper self, the soul, or conscience; the masculine aspect seems to oppose the feminine aspect; and so on. From the conflicted self, feelings of anger, rage, fear, frustration, anxiety, and shame can arise, and they can be projected as violence,

---

[3] Thomas Merton, *Confessions of a Guilty Bystander* (New York: Doubleday, 1968), 86. Merton writes: "To allow oneself to be carried away by a multitude of conflicting concerns, to surrender to too many demands, to commit oneself to too many projects, to want to help everyone is to succumb to violence. More than that, it is cooperation in violence. The frenzy of the activist neutralizes his work for peace. It destroys his own inner capacity for peace. It destroys the fruitfulness of his own work, because it kills the root of inner wisdom which makes work fruitful."

[4] Thomas Kelly, *A Testament of Devotion* (San Francisco: HarperCollins, 1992), 89-90, 95. First published in 1941. Kelly writes: "Our professional status, our social obligations, our membership in this or that very important organization, put claims upon us.... But if we *center down*...and live in that holy Silence which is dearer than life, and take our life program into the silent places of the heart...[t]here is a reevaluation of much that we do or try to do, which is done for us, and we know what to do and what to let alone."

the desire to dominate, control, and punish. Violence to each other is also driven by fear and hatred of the other; by the desire for revenge among those who have suffered violence and injustice; and as a result of justification. Only when we deeply examine the justification and consequences of conflict and ecological destruction might we be led to question whether it can be prevented by nonviolent means. At bottom, these forces of violence break the felt bond of unity with all beings; blind us to the realization that we are all interconnected and interdependent, held in a reciprocal universe; and instead create in us envy, fear, anger, insecurity, and hate rather than love and reciprocity, responsibility, and common cause. As we have forgotten how to listen to the earth, so we have forgotten to listen to each other and to the promptings of love and truth in our own hearts.

Nonviolence to each other and the earth is perhaps one of the most misunderstood and difficult psychospiritual conditions to understand and practice among the many moral and ethical problems we wrestle with in human societies, yet it is the practice that most deeply calls upon us to act individually and inwardly but also, essentially, *collectively*. For people with enough money and time, a wide array of spiritual practices is on offer today. Many focus on individual liberation, or on individual ways to gain insight, inner peace, or enlightenment, whether through meditation techniques, following gurus, or spending time in retreats, workshops, or monasteries. Such practices can miss not only the underlying meaning of the interconnectedness of all things and all beings, but also the need for both outward and collective action in the world. We remain in an illusory state of separation, seeking personal liberation alone; paradoxically, we may experience an isolated sense of aloneness, even as we intellectually realize that we live in a reciprocal universe of dependent co-arising. The individual search for inner peace and awakening might lead to a realization of our interdependency and an awareness of the multiple ways we need to act peacefully in the world, or to a kind of narcissism of individualized experience. We need both inward reflection and self-knowing to integrate aspects of ourselves that seem separate or opposed, and we need to realize and reflect on ourselves as integral members of the whole earth community. As we explored in Chapter 5, while integration and spiritual awakening are tasks of the inner, psychospiritual realm, they must, if we are to heal the violence and woundedness in the world and live nonviolently, awaken our commitment and obligation to act collectively to care for all beings, rather than restricting ourselves to caring for me and mine, realizing that in our care for all beings ultimately lies our own healing.[5] They lead us to heed the call to put love into action in the outward world, in whatever ways we are able.

One of the critical tasks in the inner realm, in my experience, is to understand the essential paradox that we gain, bit by bit, a greater measure of inner peace when we let go of our grasping desires to dominate, to accumulate, to achieve, to prove ourselves, to control everything, to not be humiliated or shamed, to cling to relationships and achievements to satisfy our ego, and to avoid pain, suffering, and loss. In a vital sense, we have only the present moment: It is the nature of life to be in constant dynamic flow, and we cannot therefore cling to things as if they could never die, change, or pass away. If we begin to understand that suffering has much to do with resisting change and loss; that pain and pleasure and the cycles of life and death are two inseparable sides of one coin; that the idea of a separate "I" is in a real sense an illusion, in that we are inwardly a unity of thinking, feeling, sensing and intuiting, without which "we" cannot exist as conscious beings; then we can begin to integrate these apparently separate aspects of our being, even those that seem to be in opposition or lost, including the feminine aspect, which I will describe more fully below. We can develop a deeper awareness of what it means to live more fully in the ongoing, ever-changing, living stream of life. And if we become aware of how we are intimately connected to all life, to All That Is, we can begin to love it and to feel more at home in the world. As explored in Chapters 5 and 6, love is not necessarily a feeling state, like passion or attachment; it is the deepening sense of the I–Thou bond that eventually sees them as an inseparable One, like the yin-yang symbol—each aspect is necessary to complete the other in reciprocity and complementarity. It is Thomas Berry's call to see the earth as "the larger sacred community to which we belong."[6]

If we can grasp this, we actually do achieve a greater sense of freedom. Paradoxically, we become *more* ourselves than before; we become less alienated than before, more relaxed and less anxious or vulnerable, and more at peace, as we let life flow rather than pushing it. Grasping and clinging are essentially future-orientated. If we can also learn to live more fully in the present, to notice all that we are connected to now, out to the farthest corners

---

[5] Judith Plant, "The Circle is Gathering," in *Healing the Wounds: The Promise of Ecofeminism*, ed. Judith Plant (Santa Cruz, CA: New Society Publishers, 1989), 242-53.

[6] Thomas Berry, *The Dream of the Earth* (San Francisco: Sierra Club Books, 1990), 81.

of the cosmos, to begin to feel joy in what the gift of life is offering us in this moment, we can begin to lessen both (unsatisfiable) cravings for future satisfaction and aversions to the many things we want to avoid or get rid of. To the extent to which we can let go of our inner struggles, with the insight that our various pairs of apparently opposite aspects are actually aspects of one unity, we don't need to overcome one with the other. Rather, we need to undergo the alchemy of joining them and transforming them into our whole Self-in-relation. The alchemy of love for all beings also can then begin to emerge without effort. It is not forced but flowing, like a spring bubbling up from the soil beneath our feet.

The point to emphasize is that the gradual increase in the richness of our inner lives; the increase in a sense of inward peace; and the lessening of the need for outward possessions, status, power, and achievements to fill our seemingly bottomless need for security, control and pleasure have obvious implications for lessening our collective impact on the earth and for watering the seeds of nonviolence toward each other. To say this is emphatically *not* a plea for ignoring poverty, deprivation, inequality, injustice, and violence in the world but rather the opposite. To repeat, the process of liberating oneself inwardly turns out not to be an individualistic exercise in spirituality but an awakening of one's sense of unity and love. We are more likely to feel liberated and empowered to become active on behalf of all life—human and other-than-human—when we deeply experience this truth.

Reintegration of the Feminine Aspect

In many ways, the feminine aspect is more attuned to this inward yielding, integrating, letting be, and relationality than the masculine aspect, particularly as these aspects have been developed or repressed in traditional Western cultures. The masculine aspect, if integrated with the feminine, can provide outward energy, rationality, and drive, not to conquer and divide but to connect, care, and unify. In the outer realm, the feminine aspect is arguably more attuned to reconciliation, listening, seeing connections, and resolving violent conflict and separation than the masculine aspect. This applies to both interpersonal violence and violence to the earth. How then might the feminine aspect be restored to be an equal, complementary, and reciprocal aspect of a whole psyche and a whole world?

As described in Chapter 4, the ecofeminist perspective centers on the argument that male-dominated human-to-human violence parallels violence to the earth—and that the rape of a woman and the rape of the earth have some of the same origins. In addition, ecofeminists argue that traits associated with the feminine aspect, whether biologically or culturally acquired or both, allow this aspect, typically predominant in women but also present in men, to identify more easily with the wider natural world, to recognize and value interconnectedness, and to use nonviolent but empowered means to learn from, protect and restore nature.

The work of protecting and restoring the earth requires humility and radical love, patience, care, and inward endurance, traits that are more strongly part of the feminine aspect of both men and women, but traditionally culturally and socially encouraged as women's roles. What we are beginning to see, perhaps, in the 21st century is not simply a blending of the masculine and feminine in people but a transformation of both—women, traditionally subservient to men, are asserting not dominance but their strength and autonomy and right to equality in ways that do not mean imitating men but that bring something new to their roles. The evolution of feminism, in my view, is not about taking combat roles in the military, or becoming ruthless in business, or taking chainsaws and bulldozers to threatened forests, but about having stronger voices and roles with supportive men to create a nonviolent, just, and sustainable world in more nonhierarchical, cooperative, nonviolent, and equal ways. A deepening awareness of interconnectedness, reciprocity, and the kinship of all beings, each the realm of the heart and soul, whether of women or men, is not to "take over" the masculine aspect but to balance, complement, and transform both. This awareness can lead to a deeper reverence for each other and nature, and a greater potential for reconciliation, reciprocity, and nonviolent coexistence, among both men and women.

Practicing Nonviolence in the Real World

In one sense it is true that we must overcome violence within ourselves first in order to practice nonviolence in the world, and that we cannot achieve inward peace if our mind and consciences are troubled and divided. Nevertheless, it is also true that if we wait until we have somehow purged ourselves of our anger and potential for violence, the chances are we will never act but will instead feel incapable of practicing nonviolence at all in a hostile world. It is notoriously difficult to "overcome" our resentments, greed, envy, hatreds, judgments, jealousies, and anger about personal and political injustice. If we have a highly developed sense of justice, we may find it even more difficult not to respond without anger or outrage—in fact, anger is often a vital sign of when injustice and unfairness has occurred.

It is helpful to remember that engaging in outward nonviolent work for peace, justice, and ecological sustainability helps foster inward nonviolence in ourselves and others, and, in turn, outer conditions of security, peaceableness, and justice will nourish the seeds of nonviolent reciprocity within us. In the end, there is no separation. We also need to remember that we are engaged in a *process* and a *practice* (as in practicing any skill or technique or habit to get better at it). It may take us all of our lifetime (some would say, many lifetimes) to get better at practicing nonviolence. As the Quaker saying has it, the more we practice living up to the Light we are given, the more we are given; and as we practice, and as the world moves toward more nonviolent ways, so habits of thought change too. We do not need to, nor can we, wait until we are no longer angry or until we are full of loving feelings toward our fellow humans or the natural world before we can act. While the seeds of inner peace, and the seeds of love, *do* need to be planted in our hearts and minds, this is not to deny or belittle the difficulty of practicing nonviolence, whether inwardly or outwardly. If we are in the middle of a war; a famine; a drought; wildfires; or a massive oil spill that poisons the water supply for thousands of people, animals, and plants; it is beyond most of us not to succumb to fear and anger or even to react violently against an aggressor or threat. This is why Gandhi, King, and others insisted that nonviolence is a lifelong discipline that we must learn and teach each other; it is also why we must do everything to *prevent* the multiple causes of violence and ecological destruction from escalating; and it is why, if we are wise, we extend compassion to ourselves and others when we are afraid, hurt, angry, and prone to reacting violently in the face of danger and injustice.

In Chapter 6, I identified several interrelated grounds on which individuals or groups have based nonviolent action, including pragmatic or strategic; ethical or moral or philosophical; scriptural, creedal, or doctrinal; and spiritual or mystical. A given person or group may act nonviolently from one or more of these grounds. In many ways, they inform each other. First, in the realm of human conflict, we may realize that we are simply outgunned, outnumbered, or outmaneuvered in many cases. We may therefore resist by using nonviolent means, such as civil disobedience or negotiation, for pragmatic reasons. We might find ourselves in a similar situation with a herd of angry elephants, a pack of wild dogs, or a bear protecting her cubs, and decide to walk away rather than attempting to kill or trap the animals. Second, we may ground our practice of nonviolence specifically on scriptural authority and the moral and ethical principles that derive from them, where these teach us to be nonviolent to all humans and the wider creation. Third, we may choose nonviolence based on a philosophical understanding, or gained through insight or experience, that violence creates more violence, and violent means cannot lead to nonviolent ends, a lesson that appears frequently in the writings of Hindu and Buddhist sages, among other wisdom traditions. Fourth, we may be called to nonviolence based on the inward, mystical experience or realization of a felt bond of unity with all beings, and a direct experience of the transforming power of love. This can be described as the "experiential conviction" of spiritual nonviolence. As many Quakers and others have attested, we may feel so compelled to obey our consciences or Inner Light that we are prepared to accept any consequences, from rejection and persecution to death. For pacifists and nonviolent activists called to act nonviolently as a matter of conscience or obedience to a religious calling, the strategic probability of "success" (especially in the short term) is not the primary motivating factor. What *is* required is an inward conviction, a calling from the depths of one's being, and an unconditional commitment to the nonviolent ideal.

Considerable evidence indicates that nonviolent means of dealing with conflicts and oppression can be more successful and less costly than violent means in terms of lives, suffering, and destruction. For example, a 2008 award-winning and wide-ranging study of political civil resistance conflicts against generally superior forces compared violent campaigns and nonviolent campaigns, including methods such as boycotts, strikes, and noncooperation. This study showed that nonviolent methods were twice as successful as violent methods, albeit that even the former succeeded only about 53% of the time.[7] However, despite studies, books, and movies[8] pointing to such evidence, it is rarely sufficient by itself to shake the common belief in the dominant paradigm—that only force met with counterforce can "win" (reinforced daily by most media coverage)—particularly if the criteria for "winning" focus only on the immediate short term and a narrow definition of winning. In the

---

[7] Maria Stephan and Erica Chenoweth, "Why Civil Resistance Works: The Strategic Logic of Nonviolence," *International Security* 33 no. 1 (2008): 7-44, https://www.mitpressjournals.org/doi/pdf/10.1162/isec.2008.33.1.7.

[8] See, for example, Gene Sharp, *The Politics of Nonviolent Action* (3 volumes) (Boston, MA: Porter Sargent Publishers, 1973; Richard B. Gregg, *A Discipline for Non-Violence*, Pendle Hill Pamphlet No. 11 (Wallingford, PA: 1941) and *The Power of Nonviolence* (Philadelphia: J.B. Lippincott Co., 1935). Revised editions 1959, 1960, https://civilresistance.info/sites/default/files/thepowerofnonviolence0206.pdf; P. Ackerman and J. DuVall, *A Force More Powerful: A Century of Nonviolent Conflict* (New York: Palgrave Macmillan, 2000); also the documentary and accompanying PBS series, directed by Steve York, 1999, 2000.

same way that we seem to be convinced that we cannot limit economic growth to "save the planet," we appear to be so convinced that the only "answer" to aggression is counter-aggression that we are prepared to risk incalculable costs in life, treasure, infrastructure, and ecological devastation for the sake of this belief. Thus wars and conflicts continue unabated, fueled in turn by the enormously profitable military-industrial complex that supports them.

The Power of Nonviolence in Practice

There is a moral and spiritual *power* in nonviolent action, a power that, in the long run, is generative and creative. In his nonviolent resistance movement, Gandhi experienced the power of *satyagraha* (truth force or soul force) in the heat of political engagement, not in a sheltered library or ashram. His campaigns, and those of many others, demonstrate that nonviolence is not a utopian philosophy with little or no chance of practical success, but a powerful principle that can be effective, and in fact, transformative, in the real world when it is practiced in the spirit of love and truth, and not just as a technique or as an expedient due to fear or a lack of violent means. In the 20th century, Martin Luther King Jr., Danilio Dolci, Vinoba Bhave, Badshah Khan, Lanza del Vasto, and many others also have taught and lived a philosophy of nonviolence in the human sphere, inspired by movements such as the satyagraha movement in India and the nonviolent civil rights movement.

Many Quakers have also taken a similar path throughout their history. As described in Chapter 6, from George Fox's refusal to serve in the military force of his day by famously insisting that "I [live] in the virtue of that life and power that takes away the occasion of all wars"[9] to what became the basis of the peace testimony in their declaration to King Charles II in 1660[10] onwards, Friends have been willing to suffer imprisonment, loss of property and income, and even death because they must obey their conscience, inner Truth, and integrity. The "politics of eternity," as Quakers wrote in the 1950s, "works not by might but by spirit."[11]

---

[9] George Fox, *Journal of George Fox* (1643), ed. John Nickalls (Philadelphia: Religious Society of Friends, 1985), 65.

[10] George Fox et al., "A Declaration from the Harmless and Innocent People of God, called Quakers, Against All Plotters and Fighters in the World...Concerning Wars and Fighting," (London: Wilson, 1660), F1786, http://www.qhpress.org/quakerpages/qwhp/dec1660.htm.

[11] Stephen Cary et al., "An Affirmation," in *Speak Truth to Power*, 67, http://quaker.org/legacy/sttp.html.

It is often difficult to understand and predict the complex conditions that lead to interpersonal violence or armed group conflict and thus to act preventively. Failure to prevent conflicts, which often escalate beyond the control of the initial disputants, helps explain why trusting in the power of nonviolence can seem like a crazy, utopian, and even suicidal option. Prevention is clearly far more effective than attempts to stop or resolve conflicts once underway.[12] If, as argued in Chapters 4 and 5, we can identify the seeds of violence and work to prevent these roots from sprouting, we stand a chance of not finding ourselves faced with invading armies, or in our living room with our family facing a gunman, trying to decide what to do. It is one of the reasons why various versions of the Quaker peace testimony emphasize opposition to making *preparations* for, as well as participating in, war.

Learning to Practice Nonviolence

We typically must learn nonviolence by actual *practice*, i.e., though training and education in self-discipline in our daily relationships and civic and political lives. Gandhi's satyagraha movement,[13] Badshah Khan's nonviolent army,[14] the civil rights movement in the 1960s under Martin Luther King Jr., and the Student Nonviolent Coordinating Committee (SNCC) involved extensive training of participants to ensure that nonviolent discipline could be maintained. Only then were participants ready to carry out acts of nonviolent protest or even civil disobedience, whether facing armed troops, police with dogs, or local militias. As 20th-century examples illustrate, the moral and spiritual courage required for nonviolent resistance has answered physical strength and armed opposition in potentially transformative ways—ways that violent resistance does not. Such techniques do not always "win the day" in

---

[12] To use an analogy from my own field of public health, it is typically easier and more effective to prevent disease than it is to try to treat disease once it has taken hold, particularly in the case of population-level epidemics. For example, long before vaccines and antibiotics, public health workers had begun to trace the spread of infectious disease to poor sanitation and hygiene, cross-infection due to overcrowding, and inadequate nutrition. The most effective strategies in public health were not only or even done by the practitioners of "heroic medicine"—the surgeons, specialists, and pharmacologists—but the preventive work done by community health workers and doctors (such as Josephine Baker) who went out into cities and towns to teach hygiene, or to immunize patients, and who agitated for improved housing, sanitation, and health education.

[13] A description of the methods developed in Gandhi's satyagraha movement are scattered throughout his writings, and are described in detail in his autobiography, Mohandas K. Gandhi, *An Autobiography, The Story of My Experiments with Truth*, trans. Mahadev Desai (Boston: Beacon Press, 1957). First published in 1927 and 1929.

[14] See Eknath Easwaran, *A Man to Match His Mountains: Badshah Khan, Nonviolent Soldier of Islam* (Petaluma, CA: Nilgiri Press, 1984).

the short term. But whether gains are made or not, the commitment, if genuine, must stay firm.

Training and practice in nonviolence techniques apply equally to the realm of interpersonal relations and to social action, whether in the context of group conflict and war-making or in resisting forces engaged in ecological destruction, such as the Keystone oil pipeline protests by indigenous tribes and others.[15] In the 1950s, Lawrence Apsey and a small group of Quakers developed the first Alternatives to Violence Project (AVP) program.[16] The process emerged from the experience of training participants in civil rights and war resistance movements to remain nonviolent during protests and actions.

The underlying principles included, first, the belief that everyone has the power for peace and good and this has the potential to transform conflict; and second, that there are nonviolent alternatives to violent responses in any conflict situation. These principles in turn are grounded in the Quaker belief in the transforming power of love, of seeing that of good or God in everyone. This power, called forth by the techniques used in AVP that emphasize process rather than content, has been shown empirically to change lives among thousands of AVP participants in prisons and elsewhere and to spur positive social change. (As a participant in an AVP program, I was deeply impressed by the way simple means and role-playing are used to teach the skills of conflict prevention, management, and nonviolent response. The approach builds trust, communication, listening skills, honesty, mutual respect, and cooperation so that anger and conflict can be managed or resolved nonviolently. Conflicts can actually be productive and creative, if they are dealt with openly and honestly but respectfully and with a genuine desire to reach a place of reconciliation.)

Nonviolent communication, an approach developed by Marshall Rosenberg in the 1960s and beyond,[17] has also been used widely to teach ways to

---

[15] Wikipedia, "Keystone Pipeline,", *Wikipedia*, https://en.wikipedia.org/wiki/Keystone_Pipeline.

[16] Sally Herzfeld and Alternatives to Violence Members, *This We Can Do: Quaker Faith in Action Through the Alternatives to Violence Project*, The James Backhouse Lecture. (Australia Yearly Meeting of the Religious Society of Friends (Quakers), Inc., 2015) 8, https://www.quakersaustralia.info/sites/aym-members/files/pages/files/FINAL_BL2015.pdf.

[17] See Nonviolent Communication, http://www.nonviolentcommunication.com/aboutnvc/aboutnvc.htm; also the Center for Nonviolent Communication, https://www.cnvc.org/.

reduce interpersonal and social conflict in families, relationships, schools, organizational negotiations, and other potential conflict situations. Similar in a number of ways to the goals of the AVP programs, but different in approach, nonviolent communication seeks to help people learn effective strategies for getting universal human needs met without resorting to culturally learned forms of violence to oneself, another, or society at large. It is based on the belief that all humans have the capacity for compassion, love, understanding, and cooperation, and that it is when basic needs—for love, acceptance, nurturance, and justice—are not met by nonviolent means that violent means are turned to.[18] Rosenberg refers to the spiritual ground of the work as becoming conscious of divine love or energy. Many hundreds of groups, meetings, and workshops now teach the process and methods of communicating in nonviolent ways.

Peaceful Production: A Possibility

In Chapter 1, I described how wars and conflicts destroy both human lives and millions of other lives in nature, and how they represent one of the largest costs to our planet in direct damage, resource consumption, and treasure spent on armaments and conflicts. Global military expenditures represented close to an estimated 1.7 *trillion* dollars in 2017 alone,[19] similar to trends for previous years. If even a small portion of such expenditures and efforts were diverted to preventing and repairing what are by far the single biggest threats to our security, climate breakdown and ecological destruction (see Chapter 1), we could potentially convert fossil fuel-dependent economies to clean energy, reduce the ecological damage from wars and conflicts and other sources, and start to restore soils, forests, oceans and waterways and the millions of life-forms we have lost. In addition, reducing military production would increase the possibility of reducing conflicts and war and fostering nonviolence to each other, which, as described in Chapter 4 and above, are intimately intertwined with practicing nonviolence to the earth. In many areas the connections between militarism, poverty, inequality and the ecological crisis have not been clearly made, and thus actions to foster peace, justice and environmental action have not been integrated. Nevertheless, a number of

---

[18] Marshall Rosenberg, *Nonviolent Communication: A Language of Compassion* (Encinitas, CA: Puddledancer Press, 2001).

[19] Nan Tian et al., *Trends in World Military Expenditures, 2017* (Stockholm: Stockholm International Peace Research Institute, May 2018), https://www.sipri.org/sites/default/files/2018-04/sipri_fs_1805_milex_2017.pdf.

organizations and activists have paid increasing attention to emphasizing the need to integrate these concerns, as have, for example, a number of Quaker organizations, the ecojustice movements, and new "fusion" movements such as the Poor People's Campaign (see Chapters 6, 7 and 9).

As described in Chapter 10, there have also been calls for a "new bottom line" and the need to challenge militarism, economic and ecological injustice as part of a single approach, as articulated by Michael Lerner and others, and for a massive mobilization of capital along the lines of a "global Marshall Plan," or "green Marshall Plan" to foster the development of green infrastructure and industries. In view of the urgency of the need to rapidly decrease greenhouse gas emissions within the next decade as called for by the UN's Intergovernmental Panel on Climate Change (see Chapter 1), some initiatives are now calling for the conversion of fossil fuel-dependent and other extractive industries along the lines of the rapid mobilization undertaken by the U.S. and other countries to switch to a war economy in the 1940s, achieved in a matter of months.

Most of these initiatives focus on the civilian production sector and on generating the necessary capital from the private banking industry. However, the idea of focusing industrial production on "socially useful" and "green" goods and services began to be taken up in the 1970s and into the 1980s in some sectors of the military-industrial complex as well. Such experiments (which largely failed at the time), as well as the new campaigns in the U.S. and elsewhere that are calling for a green Marshall plan and a Green New Deal (see Chapter 10), are generating a new debate about what constitutes our real security in an age of climate and ecological breakdown, and provide a potential model for peaceful and sustainable production.[20] Such models also represent an opportunity for job creation and more equitable and dignified work, as well as socially and ecologically enhancing, nonviolent production.

In sum, as we see that many of the drivers of our violence to each and other and the earth have common roots (see Chapter 4), so we can see that

---

[20] For example, Lucas Aerospace engineering workers in the U.K. initiated an "alternative corporate plan" in the early 1970s to convert aerospace production to "socially useful" production, including mass transit and hybrid vehicles, medical equipment, heat pumps, solar panels, clean energy technologies, and other social and environmentally useful products. Participating economists designed the plan to be commercially viable, and it was supported by a wide range of organizations, including E.F. Schumacher's Intermediate Technology Development Group and academic resources in the U.K. such as the Center for Alternative Industrial and Technological Systems and the Energy Research Group, among others. See Hilary Wainright and Dave Elliott, *The Lucas Plan: A New Trade Unionism in the Making?* (London: Allison and Busby, 1982), especially 100-8, 135-8, 154-7, 168-9.

healing our violence to each other is inseparable from healing our violence to the earth and vice versa. This requires integrated work in the inner, psychospiritual realm and the outer realm of economic, scientific, technological and political activity, in the realm of human social affairs and the realm of ecological sustainability.

In other words, a deep ecology, economy, and peace are all of a piece; all call for an inward realization of our unity with all beings, and the realization that violence to each other and violence to the earth result in violence to ourselves and to the future of the earth. Whether we are calling for an end to ecological destruction, or for more equitable, peaceable and sustainable economies that support the poorest among us while preserving the sanctity of all life-forms, we begin to realize that all these concerns are indivisible, as are the principles that guide our actions in the world. We begin to realize that acting on behalf of the wider natural world is the way to our own peace, our own security, and our future lives, and that, ultimately, we are being called to love each other and the earth as one indivisible commonwealth of life.

Afterword: Tipping Point or Turning Point?

Which future will be our path? Are we reaching a tipping point of full-scale global ecological (or nuclear) disaster, condemning all life to suffer the consequences of mass starvation, global conflict, and the destruction of much of the life we know on earth? Will our human legacy be a failure to act in time due to an inability to grasp the enormity of our predicament and the finitude of the earth, or our collective inertia and habits of focusing only on our short-term interests? Will we maintain our blind faith in the kinds of technological, economic or political fixes and business-as-usual approaches we have been applying or to date, even though they have thus far failed to bring about the necessary shifts in our ways of living on a large enough, fast enough scale to avoid catastrophe? Or, as climate and ecological breakdown looms ever closer, and with it, the "threat multipliers" of war and conflict, will we be able to put on the brakes just in time to avoid the worst?

If we fail to avoid ecological catastrophe, it will not, I believe, be because we—particularly those of us who live in the richer countries of the world or who have the most wealth and power—did not know which way to turn, but rather because we believed that there was no alternative to our current economic and political systems and our ways of thinking, or were unwilling to transform our structures of power and our ways of living. It may appear to many of us that we are being exhorted only to give up our lifestyles, but we stand to gain not only our very survival, but the things of the heart, mind, and spirit. By realizing our ultimate unity, interconnection and interdependence as the spiritual roots of our being, we gain much in the outer sphere as we begin to live in more sustainable, nonviolent and equitable ways, whether it be in material sufficiency, in art, culture, and good, meaningful and creative work, or in the love that informs our kinship with each other and the whole earth community in all its wonder, beauty and numinosity.

As explored in these pages, such life-enhancing ways of being in the world, grounded in our oldest spiritual traditions, indigenous wisdoms, and the teachings of the great sages and mystics of many traditions, are not only possible but are being put into practice in many ways by millions around the world, integrating and transforming each of the interconnected spheres of ecology, science, technology, economics, politics, and peacemaking. They are an integral part of the evolution of a new, radical, yet ancient spirituality for the 21st century, and of a deep ecology, economy and peace on behalf of the commonwealth of life.

The challenges we face are formidable, and it may seem as if bringing about such a transformation, and an earth restored, is simply utopian, naive, or impossible. Nevertheless, as reinforcing feedbacks can result in tipping points and accelerating change in the climate or ecosystems, paradigm shifts in society can also happen very rapidly once a critical point is reached. The very urgency of the ecological crisis can tip us either in the direction of conflict and ecological collapse, or turn us toward a new way of living and a new, ecozoic era. As Joanna Macy writes, for example:

> The most remarkable feature of this historical moment on Earth is not that we are on the way to destroying the world....It is that we are beginning to wake up, as from a millennium-long sleep, to a whole new relationship to our world, to ourselves and to each other....We imagine [future generations] will look back at us...and say, "Oh, those ancestors. They were taking part in the Great Turning."[1]

Quakers, among others, have always been called to act based on conscience and being faithful to the leadings of the Inner Light, irrespective of the seeming impossibility of the tasks ahead, whether it be the abolition of slavery, the prevention of war, the injustices of racial and economic inequality, or ecological breakdown, knowing that nonviolent action, rooted in love, is ultimately more powerful than separation, division, opposition, and violence. We do not know what the next decades will bring, and there is no certainty that we will avoid enormous suffering to ourselves and other lifeforms, although we cannot ultimately destroy the resilience and capacity of life itself to survive and thrive. We don't need a false optimism so much as the courage, wisdom, compassion and humility to stay rooted and to keep faith with our commitment to do what we are called to do, grounded in the power of life and love. As Rabbi Tarfon, quoted in the front of this book, reminded us, it is not our responsibility to complete the work, but neither are we to abandon it. As Friends say, we can do no other.

---

[1] Joanna Macy, quoted in "Joanna Macy and the Great Turning," http://www.joannamacyfilm.org/about/.

Acknowledgments

Writing this book has been the work of many years. Following preliminary work, I was able to spend a year at Pendle Hill in 2005-6 as the Henry J. Cadbury Scholar in Quaker studies, where I had the unique opportunity to deepen my understanding of Quaker principles and practice and the evolution of Friends' testimonies in relation to peace, justice and ecological concerns, and participate in a thriving, spiritually-grounded, and diverse community—a living example of love in action. I am also deeply grateful to Friends in my home Meeting in Durham, North Carolina, and in the wider Quaker community in the U.S. and beyond, many of whom have helped support my spiritual life and my commitment to contemplative action in community.

I owe much to many people I have met during years of traveling widely for work or study, and from whom I've learned much about resilience, living in greater harmony with the wider natural world, and traditional wisdoms, as well as the devastating effects of poverty, globalization and ecological breakdown; also to many colleagues in public health whose dedication to the goal of a healthy and sustainable world has inspired my own efforts. I also owe an incalculable debt to the many beloved people in my personal life who've sustained me over the years. When writing felt like sailing a paper raft into the eye of a growing storm, they were there to encourage me, and all of us, to go on. In all these ways, the explorations in this book are not the work of one person, or even a particular group, but part of the ways many of us are seeking to integrate human life with the whole earth community.

Preparing the present manuscript would not have been possible without Pat French, my editor, and Andrea Shapiro, who laid out the book, produced the figures, graphics, and cover design, and much more. If there are any remaining errors, they are mine.

Thanks also to W.W. Norton and Co. for permission to use a line from the poem "Still" by A.R. Ammons in the *Complete Poems*, Vol. I (Norton, 2017); to Kate Raworth, for permission to reproduce the "doughnut" diagram in *Doughnut Economics: Seven Ways to Think Like a 21st Century Economist* (Penguin Random House, 2017); and to Vensim (http://www.vensim.com) for permission to use their Model Reader x32 and their version of the Meadows' World3 model. Images for the illustrations and cover design are from online open sources (Wikimedia Commons, kissclipart.com, and openclipart.org).

Bibliography

Abbott, Margery Post, Mary Ellen Chijioke, Ben Pink Dandelion, and John Oliver, Jr. *Historical Dictionary of the Friends (Quakers).* Lanham MD and Oxford, U.K.: The Scarecrow Press, Inc., 2003.

Ackerman, P. and J. DuVall. *A Force More Powerful: A Century of Nonviolent Conflict.* New York: Palgrave Macmillan, 2000.

Adams, Carol, ed. *Ecofeminism and the Sacred.* New York: Continuum Publishing Co., 1993.

Adler, Gerald, with Aniela Jaffe, eds. *Letters of C. G. Jung,* Vol. 2, 1951-1961. Translated by R.F.C. Hull. London: Routledge and Kegan Paul, 1976.

Aggarwal, Partap C. Preface. In Masanobu Fukuoka, *The One-Straw Revolution: An Introduction to Natural Farming,* edited by Larry Korn, and translated by Chris Pearce, Tsune Kurosawa, and Larry Korn. Mapusa, Goa, India: Other India Press, 1992, ix-xx.

———. "Natural Farming Succeeds in Indian Village." Undated. http://satavic.org/natural-farming-succeeds-in-indian-village/. Original source: The Illustrated Weekly of India.

Alcott, Blake. "Jevons' Paradox." *Ecological Economics* 54 (2005): 9-21. https://doi.org/10.1016/j.ecolecon.2005.03.020.

Alperovitz, Gar. "Some Requirements of a Steady-State Economy." (Undated). https://www.humansandnature.org/economy-gar-alperovltz.

Ambler, Rex. "Befriending the Earth: A Theological Challenge." *The Friends' Quarterly* 26 (1990): 7-17.

Ammons, A.R. The *Complete Poems of A.R. Ammons,* Vol. I, edited by Robert West. New York: W.W. Norton and Company, 2017.

Angell, Stephen W., and Ben Pink Dandelion, eds. *The Oxford Handbook of Quaker Studies.* New York and Oxford, UK: Oxford University Press, 2013.

Anon. *The Dhammapada: The Path of Perfection.* Translated by Juan Mascaro. Harmondsworth, UK: Penguin Books, 1973.

Ariyaratne, A.T. *Buddhism and Sarvodaya: Sri Lankan Experience,* edited by Nandasena Ratnapala. Delhi, India: Sri Satguru Publications, 1996.

———. *Schumacher Lectures on Buddhist Economics.* Ratmalana, Sri Lanka: Sarvodaya Vishna Lekha Publication, 1999.

———. "Awakening for All." Interview with A.T. Ariyaratne by Matthew Weiner, *Tricycle,* Winter 2008, https://tricycle.org/magazine/awakening-all/.

Armitage, Wilson. *Anthony Benezet: From the Original Memoir [Roberts Vaux], Revised with Additions.* London: A.W. Bennett and Phildelphia: Lippincott and Company, 1859.

Attfield, Robin. "Christian Attitudes to Nature." *Journal of the History of Ideas* 33 (1983): 369-86. https://orca.cf.ac.uk/48961/1/Journal%20History%20Ideas_Christian%20Attitudes%20Nature.pdf.

Barbour, Ian. "Justice, Participation and Sustainability at MIT." *Ecumenical Review* 31 (1979): 380-87. https://doi.org/10.1111/j.1758-6623.1979.tb02528.x.

Barlow, Maude, and Tony Clarke. "The Lords of Water." In *Troubled Water: Saints, Sinners, Truth and Lies,* edited by Anita Roddick and Brooke Shelby Biggs, 16-21. Chichester, UK: Anita Roddick Publications, Ltd., 2004.

———. "Evian Backward Is Naive." In *Troubled Water: Saints, Sinners, Truth and Lies*, edited by Anita Roddick and Brooke Shelby Bigg, 62-73. Chichester, UK: Anita Roddick Publications, Ltd., 2004.

———. *Blue Gold: The Battle Against the Corporate Theft of the World's Water*. London: Earthscan, 2002.

Barnhill, David Landis, and Roger S. Gottlieb, eds. *Deep Ecology and World Religions: New Essays on Sacred Ground*. New York, NY: State University of New York Press, 2001.

Bartholomew, Mel. *All New Square Foot Gardening: Grow More in Less Space*. Revised Edition. Franklin, TN: Cool Springs Press, 2006.

Bateson, Gregory. *Mind and Nature: A Necessary Unity*. New York: Bantam Books, Inc., 1980. First published in 1979.

———. *Steps to an Ecology of Mind*. Chicago: University of Chicago Press, 1972.

Beardslee, William. Institute of Medicine Steering Committee on the Medical Implications of Nuclear War. "Children's and Adolescents' Perceptions of the Threat of Nuclear War: Implications of Recent Studies." In *The Medical Implications of Nuclear War*, edited by Fred Solomon and Robert Q. Marston, 413-34. Washington: National Academies Press, 1986.

Benezet, Anthony. Letter to David Barclay (1782), quoted in Wilson Armitage, *Anthony Benezet: From the Original Memoir [Roberts Vaux], Revised with Additions*. London: A.W. Bennett and Philadelphia: Lippincott and Company, 1859.

———. Letter to John Smith (1758), quoted in Donald Brooks Kelley, " 'A Tender Regard to the Whole Creation': Anthony Benezet and the Emergence of an Eighteenth Century Quaker Ecology." *Pennsylvania Magazine of History and Biography* 106 (1982): 69-88.

———. Letter to Israel, John, and James Pemberton (1778), quoted in Donald Brooks Kelley, " 'A Tender Regard to the Whole Creation': Anthony Benezet and the Emergence of an Eighteenth Century Quaker Ecology." *Pennsylvania Magazine of History and Biography* 106 (1982): 69-88.

Benson, Lewis. *Prophetic Quakerism*. Philadephia, PA: Friends Book Store, 1943.

Berkedal, Carla. "Spirituality and Sustainability." In *Sustainable Development: The Challenge of Transition*, edited by Jurgen Schmandt and C.H. Ward, 101-12. Cambridge, U.K.: Cambridge University Press, 2010. First published in 2000.

Berry, Thomas. *The Dream of the Earth*. San Francisco: Sierra Club Books, 1990. First published in 1988.

———. *The Great Work: Our Way Into the Future*. New York: Bell Tower, 1999.

———. Interview with Derrick Jensen. In Derrick Jensen, *Listening to the Land: Conversations About Nature, Culture, and Eros*, 36. White River Junction, VT: Chelsea Green Publishing Company, 2004.

Berry, Wendell. *A Continuous Harmony: Essays Cultural and Agricultural*. San Diego and New York: Harcourt, Brace and Jovanovich, 1975.

———. "Thoughts in the Presence of Fear." In *In the Presence of Fear: Three Essays for a Changed World*, 1-9. Great Barrington, MA: Orion Society, 2001.

———. "In Distrust of Movements." In *In the Presence of Fear: Three Essays for a Changed World*, 35-44. Great Barrington, MA: The Orion Society, 2001.

———. "Conservationist and Agrarian." In *Citizenship Papers: Essays by Wendell Berry*, 165-74. Washington: Shoemaker and Hoard, 2003.

Blanco, Gabriel, Reyer Garlag, Sangwon Suh, John Barrett, Heleen de Coninck., Cristobal Felix Diaz Morejon, Ritu Mathur et al."Drivers, Trends and Mitigation," In *Climate Change 2014: Mitigation of Climate Change. Contribution of Working Group III to the Fifth Assessment Report of the Intergovernmental Panel on Climate Change*, edited by O. Edenhofer, R. Pichs Madruga, Y. Sokona, E. Farahani, S. Kadner, K. Seyboth, A. Adler et al. Cambridge, U.K.: Cambridge University Press, 2014. https://www.ipcc.ch/report/ar5/wg3/.

Bleier, Ruth, ed. *Feminist Approaches to Science*. New York, NY: Pergamon Press, 1986.

Boff, Leonardo. *Cry of the Earth, Cry of the Poor*. Translated by Phillip Berryman. Maryknoll, NY: Orbis Books, 1997.

Bohm, David. *Wholeness and the Implicate Order*. London: Routledge, 1980.

Bolan, Janis. "Essentialism, Constructionism, and Feminist Psychology." *Psychology of Women Quarterly* 17 (1993): 5-21. https://doi.org/10.1111/j.1471-6402.1993.tb00673.x.

Bookchin, Murray. "Social Ecology versus Deep Ecology: A Challenge for the Ecology Movement." *Green Perspectives, Newsletter of the Green Program Project*, Nos. 4-5, Summer 1987.

Bourgeault, Cynthia. *The Holy Trinity and the Power of Three*. Boston: Shambhala Publications, Inc., 2013.

Boyle, Godfrey and Peter Harper, eds. *Radical Technology*. London: Wildwood House Ltd. and New York: Pantheon Books, 1976.

Bradshaw, Corey J.A., and Barry W. Brook. "Human Population Reduction Is Not a Quick Fix for Environmental Problems." *Proceedings of the National Academy of Sciences of the United States of America* 111 (2014): 16610-15. https://doi.org/10.1073/pnas.1410465111.

Branger, Frederic, Oskar Lecuyer, and Phillippe Quiron. "The European Emissions Trading Scheme: Should We Throw the Flagship Out with the Bathwater?" *WIREs Climate Change* 6 (2015): 9-16. https://doi.org/10.1002/wcc.326.

Britain Yearly Meeting. *Quaker Faith and Practice (Fifth Edition)*. London: Britain Yearly Meeting of the Religious Society of Friends, 2013.

Brock, Peter. *The Quaker Peace Testimony, 1660-1914*. York, UK: Sessions Book Trust and NY: Syracuse University Press, 1991.

Brockaway, Dale, Richard Gateway, and Randi Paris. "Restoring Fire as an Ecological Process in Shortgrass Prairie Ecosystems: Initial Effects of Prescribed Burning During the Dormant and Growing Seasons." *Journal of Environmental Management* 65 (2002): 135-52. https://doi.org/10.1006/jema.2002.0540.

Brooke, John, and Geoffrey Cantor. *Reconstructing Nature: The Engagement of Science and Religion*. Edinburgh, Scotland: T. and T. Clark, 1998.

Brown, Lester. *World on the Edge: How to Prevent Environmental and Economic Collapse*. Earth Policy Institute, 2011. New York: W.W. Norton & Company, 2011. http://www.Earth-policy.org/books/wote.

Brown, Patrick T., and Ken Caldeira. "Greater Future Warming Inferred from Earth's Recent Energy Budget." *Nature* 552 (2017), 45-50. http://dx.doi.org/10.1038/nature24672.

Brown, Peter G., and Geoffrey Garver. *Right Relationship: Building a Whole Earth Economy*. San Francisco: Berrett-Koehler Publishers, Inc., 2009.

Brunnschweiler, Christa, and Erwin Bulte. "Natural Resources and Violent Conflict: Resource Abundance, Dependence, and the Onset of Civil Wars." *Oxford Economic Papers* 61 (2009): 651-74. https://doi.org/10.1093/oep/gpp024.

Buber, Martin. *I and Thou*. Translated by Walter Kauffman. New York: Charles Scribner's Sons, 1970.

Buckley, Paul. "The Origin of the SPICES." Talk given at South Central Yearly Meeting, 2012. http://concordfriendsmeeting.org/sites/all/files/documents/241.0496TheOrigin OfTheSPICESbyPaulBuckley_bookfold.doc.

Cadman, David, and John Carey, eds. *A Sacred Trust: Ecology and Spiritual Vision*. Temenos Academy Papers No. 17. London: The Temenos Academy, 2002.

Cahn, Edgar. *Time Dollars: The New Currency That Enables Americans to Turn Their Hidden Resource-Time-Into Personal Security & Community Renewal*. Emmaus, PA: Rodale Press, 1992.

Candelario, Elizabeth. "Biodynamic Agriculture, Regenerative Farming and Climate Change." At The Epicenter, August 11, 2017. http://www.attheepicenter.com/biodynamic-agriculture-regenerative-farming-climate-change/.

Cantor, Geoffrey. "Quakers and Science." In *The Oxford Handbook of Quaker Studies*, edited by Stephen W. Angell and Ben Pink Dandelion, 520-34. New York and Oxford, UK: Oxford University Press, 2013.

Capra, Fritjof. *The Tao of Physics: An Exploration of the Parallels Between Modern Physics and Eastern Mysticism*. Fifth Edition. Boston, MA: Shambhala Press, 2010. First published in 1975.

———, and Pier Luigi Luisi. *The Systems View of Life*. Cambridge, U.K.: Cambridge University Press, 2014.

Carbon Disclosure Project. *The Carbon Majors Database: CDP Carbon Majors Report 2017*. London: UK: CDP, 2017. https://b8f65cb373b1b7b15feb-c70d8ead6ced550b4d987d7c03fcdd1d.ssl.cf3.rackcdn.com/cms/reports/docume nts/000/002/327/original/Carbon-Majors-Report-2017.pdf.

Carrington, Damian. "The Anthropocene Epoch: Scientists Declare Dawn of Human-Influenced Age." *The Guardian*, August 29, 2016. https://www.theguardian.com/environment/2016/aug/29/declare-anthropocene-epoch-experts-urge-geological-congress-human-impact-Earth.

Cary, Stephen G., James E. Bristol, Amiya Chakravarty, A. Burns Chalmers, William B. Edgerton, Harrop A. Freeman, et al. *Speak Truth to Power: A Quaker Search for an Alternative to Violence*. Philadelphia: American Friends Service Committee, 1955.

Ceballos, Geraldo, Paul Ehrlich and Rodolfo Dirzo. "Biological Annihilation via the Ongoing Sixth Mass Extinction Signaled by Vertebrate Population Losses and Decline." *Proceedings of the National Academy of Sciences of the United States of America* 114 (2017). https://doi.org/10.1073/pnas.1704949114.

Center for Ecozoic Studies. http://www.ecozoicstudies.net/.

Center for Nonviolent Communication. https://www.cnvc.org/.

Centre for Alternative Technology. http://www.cat.org.uk/.

Ceroni, Marta. "Beyond GDP: US States Have Adopted Genuine Progress Indicators." *The Guardian*, September 23, 2014. https://www.theguardian.com/sustainable-business/2014/sep/23/genuine-progress-indicator-gdp-gpi-vermont-maryland.

Chamberlin, Shaun. *The Transition Timeline: For a Local, Resilient Future.* Totnes, Devon, UK: Green Books, 2009.

Chapple, Christopher Key. *Nonviolence to Animals, Earth and Self in Asian Traditions.* Albany, NY: State University of New York Press, 1993.

———, ed. *Jainism and Ecology.* Cambridge MA: Harvard University Press, 2002.

Charnas, R. Council for Responsible Genetics. "No Patents on Life: Working Group Update." *GeneWatch* 15 (2002): 3. http://www.gene-watch.org.

Clark, John. "A Dialogue with Arne Naess on Social Ecology and Deep Ecology." *Trumpeter* 26, no. 2 (2010): 20-39. http://trumpeter.athabascau.ca/index.php/trumpet/article/view/1176/1527.

Clowney, David, and Patricia Mosto, eds. *Earthcare: An Anthology of Environmental Ethics.* Lanham, MD: Rowman and Littlefield Publishers, Inc., 2009.

Cobb, John B. Jr. "Envisioning a Just and Peaceful World." *Religious Education* 79 (1984): 483-94. https://doi.org/10.1080/0034408400790402.

———. "Ecology, Ethics and Theology." In *Valuing the Earth: Economics, Ecology and Ethics,* edited by Herman Daly and Kenneth Townsend, 211-27. Cambridge MA: MIT Press, 1993.

———. "Protestant Theology and Deep Ecology." In *Deep Ecology and World Religions: New Essays on Sacred Grounds,* edited by David Barnhill and Roger Gottlieb, 213-27. New York: State University of New York Press, 2001.

———, and David Griffin. *Process Theology: An Introductory Exposition.* Louisville, KY: Westminster John Knox Press, 1996.

Cocco, Leyland. "How to Make a Carbon Tax Popular? Give the Proceeds to the People." *The Guardian,* December 4, 2018. https://www.theguardian.com/world/2018/dec/04/how-to-make-a-carbon-tax-popular-give-the-profits-to-the-people.

Cohen, Joel E. "Population Growth and the Earth's Carrying Capacity." *Science* 269 (1995): 341-6. https://doi.org/10.1126/science.7618100.

———. *How Many People Can the Earth Support?* Revised Edition. New York: W.W. Norton & Company, 1996.

Collomb, Jean-Daniel. "The Ideology of Climate Change Denial in the United States." *European Journal of American Studies* 9 (2014). https://doi.org/10.4000/ejas.10305.

Commoner, Barry. *The Closing Circle: Nature, Man and Technology.* New York: Bantam Books, 1972.

———. "Response," [to Paul Ehrlich and Paul Holdren, "Critique: One-dimensional Ecology," *Bulletin of the Atomic Scientists* 23 (May 1972), 16, 18-27]. *Bulletin of the Atomic Scientists* 23 (May 1972), 17, 42-56.

Confino, Jo. "Al Gore: Oil Companies 'Use Our Atmosphere as an Open Sewer,'" *The Guardian,* January 21, 2015, http://www.theguardian.com/sustainable-business/2015/jan/21/al-gore-lord-stern-oil-companies-fossil-fuels-climate-change.

Connif, Richard. "What's Wrong with Putting a Price on Nature?" *Yale Environment 360,* October 18, 2012. https://e360.yale.edu/features/ecosystem_services_whats_wrong_with_putting_a_price_on_nature.

Covey, Stephen R. *The Seven Habits of Highly Effective People Personal Workbook.* New York: Touchstone Press, 2004.

Crawford, Neta C. "Costs of War: United States Budgetary Costs of the Post 9-11 Wars Through FY2019:$5.9 Trillon Spent and Obligated." Watson Institute for International and Public Affairs, Brown University. November 14, 2018. https://watson.brown.edu/costsofwar/files/cow/imce/papers/2018/Crawford_Costs%20of%20War%20Estimates%20Through%20FY2019%20.pdf.

Cronk, Sandra. *Peace Be With You: The Spiritual Basis of the Friends Peace Testimony.* Philadelphia: Tract Association of Friends, 1984.

Crutzen, P.J."Albedo Enhancement by Stratospheric Sulfur Injections: A Contribution to Resolve a Policy Dilemma?" *Climatic Change* 77 (2006): 211-9. https://doi.org/10.1007/s10584-006-9101-y.

Cullather, Nick. *The Hungry World: America's Cold War Battle Against Poverty in Asia.* Cambridge, MA: Harvard University Press, 2010.

Dalin, Carol, Yoshihide Wada, Thomas Kastner, and Michael Puma. "Groundwater Depletion Embedded in International Food Trade." *Nature* 543 (2017):700-4. https://doi.org/10.1038/nature21403.

Dalton, Anne Marie, and Henry C. Simmons. *Ecotheology and the Practice of Hope.* Albany, NY: State University of New York, 2010.

Daly, Herman. "Sustainable Growth: An Impossibility Theorem." In: *Valuing the Earth: Economics, Ecology, Ethics,* edited by Herman Daly and Kenneth Townsend, 267-73. Cambridge, MA: MIT Press, 1993.

———. "The Steady-State Economy: Toward a Political Economy of Biophysical Equilibrium and Moral Growth." In *Valuing the Earth: Economics, Ecology, Ethics,* edited by Herman Daly and Kenneth Townsend, 325-63. Cambridge, MA: MIT Press, 1993.

———. *Beyond Growth: The Economics of Sustainable Development.* Boston: Beacon Press, 1996.

———, and John B. Cobb, Jr. *For the Common Good: Redirecting the Economy Toward Community, the Environment, and a Sustainable Future.* 2nd.Edition. Boston: Beacon Press, 1994.

———, and Kenneth Townsend, eds. *Valuing the Earth: Economics, Ecology, Ethics.* Cambridge, MA: MIT Press, 1993.

Dart, Martha. *Marjorie Sykes, Quaker Gandhian.* Syracuse, NY: Syracuse University Press, 1993.

Davis, John Emmeus, ed. *The Community Land Trust Reader.* Cambridge, MA: Lincoln Institute of Land Policy, 2010.

Dawkins, Richard. *The Selfish Gene.* Oxford, U.K.: Oxford University Press, 1976.

———.*The Blind Watchmaker: Why the Evidence of Evolution Reveals a Universe Without Design.* London: Penguin Books, 1986.

Declaration by Participants. Conference on Economic DeGrowth for Sustainability and Social Equity, Paris, April 18-19, 2008. http://events.it-sudpar-is.eu/degrowthconference/en/Declaration%20on%20Degrowth%20EN.pdf.

del Vasto, Lanza. *Gandhi to Vinoba: The New Pilgrimage.* London: Rider and Company, 1956.

———. *Return to the Source.* New York: Simon and Schuster, 1971.

———. *Warriors of Peace: Writings on the Technique of Nonviolence.* New York: Alfred A. Knopf, 1974.

Deranger, Erin. Interview with Amy Goodman on *Democracy Now!*, September 14, 2018. https://www.democracynow.org/2018/9/14/effective_tool_to_limit_greenhouse_emissions.

Devall, Bill. *Simple in Means, Rich in Ends: Practicing Deep Ecology.* Layton, UT: Gibbs Smith, Publisher, 1988.

———, and George Sessions. *Deep Ecology: Living as if Nature Mattered.* Layton, UT: Gibbs Smith Publishers, 1985.

———, and Warwick Fox. *Toward a Transpersonal Ecology: Developing New Foundations for Environmentalism.* New York: State University of New York Press, 1995.

Diamond, Richard. "Changing Trends: A Brief History of US Household Consumption of Energy, Water, Food, Beverages and Tobacco." *Proceedings of the 2004 American Council for an Energy-Efficient Economy Summer Study.* Pacific Grove, CA, 2004. https://eetd.lbl.gov/sites/all/files/publications/lbnl-55011.pdf.

Dominguez, Joe, and Vicki Robin. *Your Money or Your Life: Transforming Your Relationship with Money and Achieving Financial Independence.* New York: Penguin Books, 1993.

Doss, Cheryl. "The Role of Women in Agriculture." ESA Working Paper no. 11-02. Rome: United Nations Food and Agriculture Organization, March 2011. http://www.fao.org/docrep/013/am307e/am307e00.pdf.

Drengson, Alan, and Yuichi Inoue, eds. *The Deep Ecology Movement: An Introductory Anthology.* Berkeley, CA: North Atlantic Publishers, 1995.

Dyer, Gwynne. *Climate Wars: The Fight for Survival as the World Overheats.* London: Oneworld Publications, 2008, 2011.

Earth Charter Initiative. *The Earth Charter.* http://Earthcharter.org/discover/the-Earth-charter/.

Earth Policy Institute. http://www.Earth-policy.org/. (EPI is closed, but reports remain online.)

Earth Quaker Action Team. www.eqat.org.

Easlea, Brian. *Fathering the Unthinkable: Masculinity, Scientists and the Nuclear Arms Race.* London: Pluto Press, 1983.

Easwaran, Eknath. *A Man to Match His Mountains: Badshah Khan, Nonviolent Soldier of Islam.* Petaluma, CA: Nilgiri Press, 1984.

Eaton, Heather. "Ecological-Feminist Theology: Contributions and Challenges." In *Theology for Earth Community*, edited by Dieter Hessel, 77-92. Maryknoll, NY: Orbis Books, 1996.

Ecosystems Market Task Force. Realising *Nature's Value: The Final Report of the Ecosystems Market Task Force* [to the UK Department for Environmental and Rural Affairs]. March 2013. https://assets.publishing.service.gov.uk/government/uploads/system/uploads/attachment_data/file/316101/Ecosystem-Markets-Task-Force-Final-Report-.pdf.

Eddington, Arthur. "Science and the Unseen Worlds." Swarthmore Lecture 1929. London: George Allen and Unwin, Ltd., 1929.

Ehrlich, Paul. *The Population Bomb.* New York: Ballantine Books, 1968.

———, and Anne Ehrlich. *The Population Explosion.* New York: Simon and Schuster, 1990.

———, and Paul Holdren. "Critique: One-dimensional Ecology." *Bulletin of the Atomic Scientists* 23 (May 1972), 16, 18-27. [See also Barry Commoner, "Response." *Bulletin of the Atomic Scientists* 23 (May 1972), 17, 42-56.]

Einstein, Albert. Fundraising letter on behalf of the Emergency Committee of Atomic Scientists. Reported in "Atomic Education Urged by Einstein," *New York Times*, May 25, 1946.

Eisler, Riane. *The Chalice and the Blade*. New York, Harper and Row, 1988.

Ekta Parishad. "Mission." http://www.ektaparishad.com/en-us/about/mission.aspx.

Elon, Ari, Naomi Mara Hyman, and Arthur Waskow, eds. *Trees, Earth, and Torah: A Tu B'Shvat Anthology*. Philadelphia: The Jewish Publication Society, 2000.

Eshel, Gidon, Alon Shepon, Tamar Makov, and Ron Milo. "Land, Irrigation Water, Greenhouse Gas, and Reactive Nitrogen Burdens of Meat, Egg and Dairy Production in the United States." *Proceedings of the National Academy of Sciences of the United States of America* 111(2014):11996-2001. https://doi.org/10.1073/pnas.1402183111.

Evangelical Lutheran Church Environmental Task Force. *Caring for Creation: Vision, Hope, and Justice*. Minneapolis MN: Evangelical Lutheran Church in America, 1993.

Farmer Foodshare.org. http://www.farmerfoodshare.org/.

Farquhar, Brodie. "Wolf Reintroduction Changes Ecosystem," June 1, 2011. https://www.yellowstonepark.com/things-to-do/wolf-reintroduction-changes-ecosystem.

Feenstra, Ernest. "Christian Impact on Ecology." (Letter), *Science* 156 (1967): 737. http://dx.doi.org/10.1126/science.156.3776.737.

Femia, Francesco, and Caitlin Werrell. "Responsibility to Prepare: A Whole of Government Approach to Climate and Security in Three Steps." *United States Department of Defense Center for Climate and Security Briefer* No. 34, 31 March 2017. https://climateandsecurity.files.wordpress.com/2012/04/responsibility-to-prepare_a-whole-of-government-approach-to-climate-security-in-3-steps_briefer-341.pdf.

Ferraro, Augusto, Eleanor Highwood, and Andrew Charlton-Perez. "Weakened Tropical Circulation and Reduced Precipitation in Response to Geoengineering." *Environmental Science Letters* 9 (2014) 014001 (7 pp). http://doi:10.1088/1748-9326/9/1/014001.

Figueres, Christina. Quoted in Damian Carrington, "The Seven Trends That Could Beat Global Warming: 'There is Reason to Hope.'" *The Guardian*, Nov 8, 2017. https://www.theguardian.com/environment/2017/nov/08/seven-megatrends-that-could-beat-global-warming-climate-change.

Finch, Suzanne. *A Quaker Testimony to the Earth?* Bridport Prepatory Meeting for the Quaker Bookshop. London: Friends House, 2000.

Flinders, Carol. *Enduring Grace: Living Portraits of Seven Women Mystics*. New York: Harper Collins Publishers, 1993.

Food Tank. "Urban Farms and Gardens Are Feeding Cities Around the World." https://foodtank.com/news/2015/07/urban-farms-and-gardens-are-feeding-cities-around-the-world/.

Fortin, Ernest. "The Bible Made Me Do It." *The Review of Politics* 57 (1995): 197-223. https://doi.org/10.1017/S0034670500026875.

Foundation for Deep Ecology. http://www.deepecology.org/.

Fountain, Henry, Jugal K. Patel, and Nadja Popovich. "2017 Was One of the Hottest Years on Record: And That Was Without El Nino." *New York Times*, January 18, 2018. https://www.nytimes.com/interactive/2018/01/18/climate/hottest-year-2017.html.

Fox, Caroline. Diary. Quoted in *Quaker Faith and Practice,* Chapter 26.04. London: Britain Yearly Meeting, 5th Edition, 2013.

Fox, George. *The Journal of George Fox* (1643), edited by John L. Nickalls. Philadelphia: Religious Society of Friends, 1985.

———. *George Fox, Works,* Vols.1-8. Philadelphia: Marcus Gould and Isaac Hoppe, 1831. https://esr.earlham.edu/dqc/biblio.html.

———. Letter to Friends in the ministry, 1656. In *The Journal of George Fox* (1643), edited by John L. Nickalls, 262-3. Philadelphia: Religious Society of Friends, 1985.

———. "Epistle 128 (1656)." In *George Fox, Works, Vol. 7.* Philadelphia: Marcus Gould and Isaac Hoppe, 1831. http://esr.earlham.edu/qbi/gfe/e105-130.htm.

———. "To All Sorts of People In Christendom" (Doctrinals 274, 1667). In *George Fox, Works, Vol. 4.* Philadelphia: Marcus Gould and Isaac Hoppe, 1831. https://esr.earlham.edu/dqc/biblio.html.

———. "Epistle 292 (1672)." In *George Fox, Works, Vol. 8.* Philadelphia: Marcus Gould and Isaac Hoppe, 1831. http://esr.earlham.edu/qbi/gfe/e286-300.htm#e292.

———, Gerald Rogers, Henry Fell, Richard Hubblethorn, John Boulton, John Hindle, John Stubbs, et al. "A Declaration from the Harmless and Innocent People of God, called Quakers, Against All Plotters and Fighters in the World…Concerning Wars and Fighting." London: Wilson, 1660, F1786. http://www.qhpress.org/quakerpages/qwhp/dec1660.htm.

Fox, Matthew. *The Coming of the Cosmic Christ: The Healing of Mother Earth and the Birth of a Global Renaissance.* San Francisco: HarperSanFrancisco, 1988.

Francis (pope). "Laudato Si,': Care for Our Common Home." Encyclical letter given at Rome at St. Peter's Basilica, May 24, 2015. http://w2.vatican.va/content/francesco/en/encyclicals/documents/papa-francesco_20150524_enciclica-laudato-si.html.

Friedrich, Johannes, Mengpin Ge, and Andrew Pickens. "This Interactive Chart Explains World's Top 10 Emitters, and How They've Changed." April 11 2017, World Resources Institute. https://www.wri.org/blog/2017/04/interactive-chart-explains-worlds-top-10-emitters-and-how-theyve-changed.

Friendly Water for the World. https://watercharity.com/partner/friendly-water-world.

Friends Committee on National Legislation. "Environment & Energy: A Faithful and Moral Call to Conscience." https://www.fcnl.org/about/policy/issues/environment-energy.

Fukuoka, Masanobu. *The One-Straw Revolution: An Introduction to Natural Farming,* edited by Larry Korn. Translated by Chris Pearce, Tsune Kurosawa, and Larry Korn. Mapusa, Goa, India: Other India Press, 1992.

Galeano, Eduardo. *Open Veins of Latin America: Five Centuries of the Pillage of a Continent.* New York: Monthly Review Press, 1998.

Gandhi, M.K. "Hinduism." *Young India,* October 6, 1921. Quoted in Thomas Weber, *Gandhi as Disciple and Mentor.* Cambridge, UK: Cambridge University Press, 2004.

———. *The Collected Works of Mahatma Gandhi,* Volumes 1-98. New Delhi: Publications Division, Government of India, 1999. E-volumes at https://www.gandhiashramsevagram.org/gandhi-literature/collected-works-of-mahatma-gandhi-volume-1-to-98.php.

————."Our Brethren the Trees." *Young India*, December 5, 1921. Quoted in Thomas Weber, *Gandhi as Disciple and Mentor*. Cambridge, UK: Cambridge University Press, 2004.

————. "Not Even Half Mast," *Young India*, December 4, 1924. In *The Collected Works of Mahatma Gandhi*, Vol. 29, 404-10. https://www.gandhiashramsevagram.org/gandhi-literature/mahatma-gandhi-collected-works-volume-29.pdf.

————. Letter to Kirby Page. *The Hindu*, November 8, 1926. *In The Collected Works of Mahatma Gandhi*, Vol. 36, 45-7. https://www.gandhiashramsevagram.org/gandhi-literature/mahatma-gandhi-collected-works-volume-36.pdf.

————. "Harijans and Pigs," *Harijan* April 13, 1935. Quoted in Thomas Weber, *Gandhi as Disciple and Mentor*. Cambridge, UK: Cambridge University Press, 2004.

————. *Sarvodaya (The Welfare of All)*, edited by Bharatan Kumarappa. Ahmedabad, India: Navajivan Publishing House, 1954. Reprint 1958.

————, Mohandas K. *An Autobiography: The Story of My Experiments with Truth*. Translated by Mahadev Desai. Boston: Beacon Press, 1957. First published in 1927 and 1929.

Gatti, Roberto Cazzolla. "A Conceptual Model of New Hypothesis on the Evolution of Biodiversity." *Biologia* 71(2016): 343-51. http://doi.org/10.1515/biolog-2016-0032.

Gellman, Jerome (Yehudha). "Early Hasidism and the Natural World." In *Judaism and Ecology*, edited by Hava Tirosh-Samuelson, 369-85. Cambridge, MA: Harvard University Press, 2002.

General Synod of the Church of England. *Christians and the Environment: Report by the Board of Social Responsibility on Stewardship*. London: General Synod of the Church of England, July 1991.

Genuine Progress in the States. http://www.gpiinthestates.org/.

Gerber, P.J., H. Steinfeld, B. Henderson, B., Mottet, A., Opio, C., Dijkman, J., Falcucci, A., and Tempio, G. (2013). *Tackling Climate Change Through Livestock – A Global Assessment of Emissions and Mitigation Opportunities*. Rome: United Nations Food and Agriculture Organization. http://www.fao.org/docrep/018/i3437e/i3437e.pdf.

Ghose, Aurobindo. *The Integral Yoga: Sri Aurobindo's Teaching and Method of Practice*. Pondicherry, India: The Sri Aurobindo Ashram Press, 1993.

————. *The Life Divine*. Pondicherry: The Sri Aurobindo Ashram Press, 2010.

————, and The Mother. *The Destiny of Man*. Pondicherry, India: The Sri Aurobindo Ashram Press, 1969.

Gillett, Carl. *Reduction and Emergence in Science and Philosophy*. Cambridge, U.K.: Cambridge University Press, 2016.

Gilligan, Carol. *In a Different Voice: Psychological Theory and Women's Development*. Cambridge, MA: Harvard University Press, 1982.

Gimbutas, Marija. *Civilization of the Goddess: The World of Old Europe*. New York: Harper Collins, 1991.

Gleditsch, Nils."Armed Conflict and the Environment: A Critique of the Literature." *Journal of Peace Studies* 25 (1998): 381-400. https://doi.org/10.1177/0022343398035003007.

Global Burden of Disease 2017 Mortality Collaborators. "Global, Regional and National Age-Sex-Specific Mortality and Life Expectancy 1950-2017: A Systematic Analysis for the Global Burden of Disease Study 2017." *Lancet* 392 (2018): 1684-735. https://doi.org/10.1016/S0140-6736(18)31891-9.

Global Carbon Project. *Carbon Budget and Trends 2018*, December 5, 2018. www.globalcarbonproject.org/carbonbudget.

Global Footprint Network. http://www.footprintnetwork.org/.

Global Footprint Network. *Annual Report*, 2016. http://www.footprintnetwork.org/content/uploads/2017/07/GFN_AR_2016_final_lo.pdf

Gore, Al. *Earth in the Balance: Ecology and the Human Spirit*. New York: Rodale Press, 2006. First published in 1992.

Goswami, Amit. *The Self-Aware Universe: How Consciousness Creates the Material World*. New York: Jeremy P. Tarcher/Putnam Inc., 1995.

Goulet, Benjamin. "Forced to Move: Climate Change Already Displacing U.S. Communities." KCET Earth Focus blog, April 26, 2018. https://www.kcet.org/shows/earth-focus/forced-to-move-climate-change-already-displacing-us-communities.

Grameen Bank, Bank for the Poor. http://www.grameen.com/.

Granberg-Michaelson, Wesley. "An Ethics for Sustainability." *Ecumenical Review* 43 (1991): 120-30. https://doi.org/10.1111/j.1758-6623.1991.tb02682.x.

Granberg-Michaelson, Wesley. "Creation in Ecumenical Theology." In *Ecotheology: Voices from South and North,* edited by David Hallman, 96-106. Maryknoll, NY: World Council of Churches/Orbis Books, 1994.

Green Belt Movement. https://www.greenbeltmovement.org/.

Green Party of the U.S. "Summary of the Green New Deal." http://www.gp.org/green_new_deal.

Gregg, Richard B. *The Power of Nonviolence*. Philadelphia and London: J.B. Lippincott Co., 1935. (Revised Editions 1959, 1960). https://civilresistance.info/sites/default/files/thepowerofnonviolence0206.pdf.

————. *The Value of Voluntary Simplicity*. Pendle Hill Essays No.3. Wallingford, PA: Pendle Hill Publications, 1936.

————. *A Discipline for Non-Violence*. Pendle Hill Pamphlet No. 11. Wallingford, PA: Pendle Hill Publications, 1941.

Griffin, Susan. *Woman and Nature: The Roaring Inside Her*. London: The Women's Press, 1984. First published in 1978.

Gustavsson, Jenny, Christel Cederberg, Ulf Sonessen, Robert van Otterdijk, and Alexandre Meybek. *Global Food Losses and Food Waste: Extent, Causes and Prevention*. Rome: United Nations Food and Agriculture Organization, 2011. http://www.fao.org/docrep/014/mb060e/mb060e00.pdf.

Hale, Sarah E, John Jensen, Lena Jakobs, Patryk Oleszczuk, Thomas Hartnik, Thomas Hendrikssen, Gudny Okkenhaug, Vegard Martinsen, and Gerard Cornelissen. "Short-term Effect of the Soil Amendments Activated Carbon, Biochar, and Ferric Oxyhydroxide on Bacteria and Invertebrates." *Environmental Science and Technology* 47 (2013): 8674-83. http://www.doi.org/10.1021/es400917g.

Hallegatte, Stephanie, Mook Bangalore, Laura Bonzanigo, Marianne Fay, Tamaro Kane, Ulf Narloch, Julie Rozenberg, David Treguer, and Adrien Vogt-Schilb. *Shock Waves: Managing the Impacts of Climate Change on Poverty.* World Bank Climate Change and Development Series. Washington: World Bank, 2016. http://www.doi.org/10.1596/978-1-4648-0673-5.

Hallman, David, ed. *Ecotheology: Voices from South and North.* Maryknoll, NY: World Council of Churches/Orbis Books, 1994.

Hamburg, Margaret A. "Food Safety Modernization Act: Putting the Focus on Prevention." https://www.foodsafety.gov/news/fsma.html.

Hanh, Thich Nhat. *Interbeing: Fourteen Guidelines for Engaged Buddhism.* 3rd Edition. Berkeley, CA: Parallax Press, 1987.

Hansen, James. "Game Over for the Planet." *New York Times,* May 9, 2012. http://www.nytimes.com/2012/05/10/opinion/game-over-for-the-climate.html.

———."Get Out of Jail Free Card: Carbon Capture." June 12 2018, http://www.columbia.edu/~jeh1/mailings/2018/20180612_CarbonCapture.pdf.

———, Makiko Soto, Pusker Kharecha, Karina von Schuckmann, David J. Beerling, Junji Cao, Shaun Marcott, et al. "Young People's Burden: Requirement of Negative Carbon Emissions." *Earth System Dynamics* 8 (2016): 577-616. http://doi.org/10.5194/esd-8-577-2017.

Haraway, Donna. *Primate Visions: Gender, Race and Nature in the World of Modern Science.* New York: Routledge, 1989.

Harding, Garrett. "The Tragedy of the Commons." *Science* 162 (1968): 1243-8. https://doi.org/10.1126/science.162.3859.1243.

Harding, Sandra. *The Science Question in Feminism.* Ithaca, NY: Cornell University Press, 1986.

———, *Whose Science? Whose Knowledge? Thinking from Women's Lives.* Ithaca, NY: Cornell University Press, 1991.

Harris, Melanie L., ed. *Ecowomanism: African American Women and Earth-Honoring Faiths.* Maryknoll, NY: Orbis Books, 2017.

Hartung, William. *Trends in Major US Arms Sales in 2017: A Comparison of the Obama and Trump Administrations Trend Report.* Washington, DC: Center for International Policy, March 2018. https://securityassistance.org/sites/default/files/US%20Arms%20Sales%202017%20Report.pdf.

Harvey, Chelsea. "Hundreds of Scientists Slam Trump for Threatening to Abandon Paris Climate Accord." *Washington Post,* September 21, 2017. https://www.washingtonpost.com/news/energy-environment/wp/2016/09/21/375-u-s-scientists-slam-trump-for-threatening-to-abandon-paris-climate-accord/?utm_term=.4e66dd9d85a3.

Harvey, Fiona. "World's Climate Pledges Not Yet Enough to Avoid Dangerous Warming – UN." *The Guardian,* October 30, 2015. https://www.theguardian.com/environment/2015/oct/30/worlds-climate-pledges-likely-to-lead-to-less-than-3c-of-warming-un.

———. " 'Tipping Points' Could Exacerbate Climate Crisis, Scientists Fear." *The Guardian,* October 9, 2018. https://www.theguardian.com/environment/2018/oct/09/tipping-points-could-exacerbate-climate-crisis-scientists-fear.

———. "UN Climate Accord "Inadequate" and Lacks Urgency, Experts Warn," *The Guardian*, December 16 2018. https://www.theguardian.com/environment/2018/dec/16/un-climate-accord-inadequate-and-lacks-urgency-experts-warn.

Hawken, Paul, ed. *Drawdown: The Most Comprehensive Plan Ever Proposed to Reverse Global Warming.* New York: Penguin Books, 2017.

———, Amory Lovins, and Hunter Lovins. *Natural Capitalism: Creating the Next Industrial Revolution.* London: Earthscan, 1999.

Head, Tom. *Envisioning a Moral Economy.* Pendle Hill Pamphlet No. 410. Wallingford, PA: Pendle Hill Publications, 2010.

Henderson, Hazel. "The Coming Economic Transition." In *Alternatives to Growth-I*, edited by Dennis Meadows. Cambridge, MA: Bellinger Publishing Company, 1977.

Her Majesty's Treasury (U.K.) *The Economics of Climate Change: The Stern Review* (Chair, Nicholas Stern). London: Her Majesty's Treasury, 2006.

Herzfeld, Sally, and Alternatives to Violence Members. *This We Can Do: Quaker Faith in Action Through the Alternatives to Violence Project.* The James Backhouse Lecture. Australia Yearly Meeting of the Religious Society of Friends (Quakers), Inc., 2015. https://www.quakersaustralia.info/sites/aym-members/files/pages/files/FINAL_BL2015.pdf.

Hessel, Dieter. "Now That Animals Can be Genetically Engineered: Biotechnology in Theological-Ethical Perspective." In *Ecotheology: Voices from South and North*, edited by David Hallman, 284-99. Maryknoll NY: World Council of Churches/Orbis Books, 1994.

———, ed. *Theology for Earth Community: A Field Guide.* Maryknoll, NY: Orbis Books, 1996.

———. "Introduction: Why This Field Guide?" In *Theology for Earth Community: A Field Guide*, edited by Dieter Hessel, 1-20. Maryknoll, NY: Orbis Books, 1996.

———, and Rosemary Radford Ruether, eds. *Christianity and Ecology.* Harvard University Center for the Study of World Religions. Cambridge, MA: Harvard University Press, 2000.

Hochschild, Adam. *King Leopold's Ghost: A Story of Greed, Terror, and Heroism in Colonial Africa.* New York: Mariner Books, 1998.

Hodgson, Jacqi, and Rob Hopkins. *Transition in Action: Totnes and District 2030, An Energy Descent Plan.* Totnes, Devon, UK: Transition Town Totnes, 2010.

Holmgren, David. *Permaculture: Principles and Pathways Beyond Sustainability.* Revised Edition. Hepburn, Victoria, Australia: Holmgren Design Services, 2017. First published in 2002.

Holst, Johan Jorgen. "Security and the Environment: A Preliminary Exploration." *Bulletin of Peace Proposals* 20 (1989): 123-8. https://doi.org/10.1177/096701068902000202.

Hopkins, Rob. *The Transition Handbook: From Oil Dependency to Local Resilience.* Totnes, Devon, UK: Green Books, 2008.

———. *The Transition Companion: Making Your Community More Resilient in Uncertain Times.* Totnes, Devon, UK: Green Books, 2011.

———. *The Power of Just Doing Stuff: How Local Action Can Change the World.* Cambridge, UK: UIT/Green Books, 2013.

Horrell, David G. *The Bible and the Environment: Towards a Critical Ecological Biblical Theology*. London: Routledge, 2014.

Hunt, Cherryl. "Beyond Stewardship." Online syllabus. University of Exeter (UK) Department of Theology. https://humanities.exeter.ac.uk/theology/research/projects/beyondstewardship/.

Illich, Ivan. *Tools for Conviviality*. New York: Harper and Row, 1973.

Institute for Community Economics. *The Community Land Trust Handbook*. Emmaus, PA: Rodale Press, 1972.

Institute of Policy Studies. *The Souls of Poor Folk: Auditing America 50 Years After the Poor People's Campaign Challenged Racism, Poverty, the War Economy/Militarism and Our National Morality*, edited by Saurav Sarkar, Shailly Gupta Barnes, and Aaron Noffke. Washington: Institute of Policy Studies, April 2018. https://ips-dc.org/wp-content/uploads/2018/04/PPC-Audit-Full-410835a.pdf.

International Independence Institute. *The Community Land Trust: A Guide to a New Model of Land Tenure in America*. Cambridge, MA: Center for Community Economic Development, 1972.

International Union for Conservation of Nature. See their "Red Lists" of threatened species. (https://www.iucnredlist.org/

Jackson, Tim. *Prosperity Without Growth? The Transition to a Sustainable Economy*. UK Sustainability Commission, 2009. https://research-repository.st-andrews.ac.uk/bitstream/handle/10023/2163/sdc-2009-pwg.pdf?sequence=1.

Jain, Shobita. "Public Participation in Development." In *The Economics and Politics of Resettlement in India*, edited by Shobita Jain and Madhu Bala, 49-80. New Delhi: Dorling Kindersley (India) Pvt. Ltd., 2006.

———, and Madhu Bala, eds. *The Economics and Politics of Resettlement in India*. New Delhi: Dorling Kindersley (India) Pvt. Ltd., 2006.

Jaroslav, Tir, and Paul F. Diehl. "Demographic Pressure and Interstate Conflict: Linking Population Growth and Density to Militarized Disputes." *Journal of Peace Research 35* (1998): 319-339. https://doi.org/10.1177/0022343398035003004.

Jensen, Derrick. *Listening to the Land: Conversations About Nature, Culture, and Eros*. White River Junction, VT: Chelsea Green Publishing Company, 2004.

John Paul II (pope). "Redemptor Hominis." Encyclical letter given at Rome at St. Peter's Basilica, March 4, 1979. http://w2.vatican.va/content/john-paul-ii/en/encyclicals/documents/hf_jp-ii_enc_04031979_redemptor-hominis.html.

———. "Peace with God the Creator, Peace with All of Creation." Message for the Celebration of the World Day of Peace, January 1, 1990. http://w2.vatican.va/content/john-paul-ii/en/messages/peace/documents/hf_jp-ii_mes_19891208_xxiii-world-day-for-peace.html.

Johnson, Elizabeth. "Losing and Finding Creation in the Christian Tradition." In *Christianity and Ecology*, edited by Dieter T. Hessel and Rosemary Radford Ruether, 3-21. Cambridge, MA: Harvard University Press, 2000.

Johnson, George. *Fire in the Mind: Science, Faith, and the Search for Order*. New York: Vintage Books, 1996.

Johnson, Nathanael. "Do Industrial Agricultural Methods Actually Yield More Food Per Acre Than Organic Ones?" *Grist*. October 14, 2015. https://grist.org/food/do-industrial-agricultural-methods-actually-yield-more-food-per-acre-than-organic-ones/.

Joranson, P.N., and Ken Butigan. *Cry of the Environment.* Santa Fe NM: Bear and Company, 1984.

Jung, C.J. *The Undiscovered Self.* Boston: Little, Brown and Company, 1957.

———. Letter to Hélène Kieler, May 14, 1955. In *Letters of C. G. Jung,* Vol.2, 1951-1961, edited by Gerald Adler with Aniela Jaffe, translated by R.F.C. Hull, 254. London: Routledge and Kegan Paul, 1976.

Kay, C.E., and R.T. Simmons, eds. *Wilderness and Political Ecology: Aboriginal Influences and the Original State of Nature.* Salt Lake City: University of Utah Press, 2002.

Keller, Evelyn Fox. *Reflections on Gender and Science.* New Haven, CT: Yale University Press, 1985.

———. *A Feeling for the Organism: The Life and Work of Barbara McClintock.* New York, San Francisco: W.H. Freeman and Co., 1995.

———, and Helen Longino. *Feminism and Science.* New York: Oxford University Press, 1996.

Kelley, Donald Brooks. " 'A Tender Regard to the Whole Creation': Anthony Benezet and the Emergence of an Eighteenth Century Quaker Ecology," *Pennsylvania Magazine of History and Biography* 106 (1982): 69-88.

Kelly, Thomas. *Testament of Devotion.* New York: HarperCollins Publishers, Inc., 1992. First published in 1941.

Khalid, Fazlun M. "Islam and the Environment." In *The Encyclopedia of Global Environment Change, Vol. 5: Social and Economic Dimensions of Global Environmental Change,* edited by Peter Timmerman, 332-9. Chichester, UK: John Wiley and Sons, Ltd., 2002.

King, David. "Towards Decarbonising the Global Economy: The Direction of Travel After COP-21." Presentation to the International Energy Agency, Paris, January 29, 2016. http://www.gci.org.uk/Documents/King_IEA_29-Feb-2016.pdf

King, Martin Luther Jr. "Loving Your Enemies." In *Strength to Love,* 49-57. Philadelphia: Fortress Press, 1981. First published in 1963.

———. Speech delivered at the London City Temple, December 7, 1964. Transcript from *Democracy Now!* website, January 21, 2019. https://www.democracynow.org/2019/1/21/mlk_at_90_a_rediscovered_1965.

Klare, Michael. *Resource Wars: The New Landscape of Global Conflict.* New York: Metropolitan Books, 2001.

Klein, Naomi. *The Shock Doctrine: The Rise of Disaster Capitalism.* Toronto: Random House, 2007.

———. *This Changes Everything: Capitalism vs. the Climate.* New York: Simon and Schuster, 2014.

Koestler, Arthur. *The Ghost in the Machine.* New York: Penguin Books, 1990. First published in 1967.

———. "Beyond Atomism and Holism: The Concept of the Holon." In *Beyond Reductionism: New Perspectives in the Life Sciences,* edited by Arthur Koestler and J.R. Smythies, 192-216. Boston: Beacon Press, 1971.

———, and J.R. Smythies, eds. *Beyond Reductionism: New Perspectives in the Life Sciences.* Boston: Beacon Press, 1971.

Kohr, Leopold. "The Velocity of Populations." *Land Economics* 34 (1958): 178-81.

Kolbert, Elizabeth. *The Sixth Extinction: An Unnatural History.* New York, NY: Henry Holt and Company, 2014.

Korn, Larry. Introduction. In Masanobu Fukuoka, *The One-Straw Revolution: An Introduction to Natural Farming*, edited by Larry Korn. Translated by Chris Pearce, Tsune Kurosawa, and Larry Korn, xxi-xxxii. Mapusa, Goa, India: Other India Press, 1992.

Korten, David. *The Great Turning: From Empire to Earth Community*. Oakland, CA: Berrett-Koehler Publishers, 2007.

Kosiak, Steven. *Is the US Military Getting Smaller and Older, and How Much Should We Care?* Washington DC: Center for a New American Security Report. March 2017. https://www.cnas.org/publications/reports/is-the-u-s-military-getting-smaller-and-older.

Kosoy, Nicholas, and Esteve Corbera. "Payment for Ecosystem Services as Commodity Fetishism." *Ecological Economics* 69 (2010): 1228-36. https://doi.org/10.1016/j.ecolecon.2009.11.002.

Kramerae, Cheris, and Dale Spender. *Routledge International Encyclopedia of Women: Global Women's Issues and Knowledge*. New York, London: Routledge, 2000.

Krimsky, Sheldon. "Do Financial Conflicts of Interest Bias Research? An Inquiry into the 'Funding Effect' Hypothesis." *Science, Technology and Human Values* 38 (2012): 566-87. https://doi.org/10.1177/0162243912456271.

Kristensen, Hans, and Robert Norris. *Nuclear Notebook: Nuclear Arsenals of the World*. Chicago: Bulletin of Atomic Scientists. https://thebulletin.org/nuclear-notebook-multimedia.

Kuhn, Thomas. *The Structure of Scientific Revolutions: 50th Anniversary Edition*. Chicago: Chicago University Press, 2012. First published in 1962.

Kumarappa, J.C. *The Economics of Permanence: A Quest for a Social Order Based on Non-violence*. Wardha, India: Sarva Seva Sangh Prakashan, 1948. First published in 1945.

———. *The Non-Violent Economy and World Peace*. Sarva-Seva-Sangh, Wardha, India: A.W. Sahasrabuddhey, 1958.

LaDuke, Winona. *All Our Relations: Native Struggles for Land and Life*. Boston: South End Press, 1999.

Lakey, George. *Viking Economics: How the Scandinavians Got it Right and We Can Too*. Brooklyn, NY: Melville House Books, 2016.

Lakoff, George. *Moral Politics: How Liberals and Conservatives Think*. 3rd Edition. Chicago: University of Chicago Press, 2016. First published in 1997.

———, and Mark Johnson. *Metaphors to Live By*. Chicago: University of Chicago Press, 2003. First published in 1980.

Lancet Countdown on Health and Climate Change Project. http://www.lancetcountdown.org.

Land Institute, https://landinstitute.org/.

Layard, Richard. "Has Social Science a Clue?: What is Happiness? Are we Getting Happier?" Lionel Robbins Lecture Series, London, March 3-5, 2003. http://eprints.lse.ac.uk/47425/.

———. *Happiness: Lessons from a New Science*. London: Allen Lane, 2005.

Le Billon, Phillipe. "The Political Ecology of War: Natural Resources and Armed Conflict." *Political Geography* 20 (2001): 561-84. https://doi.org/10.1016/S0962-6298(01)00015-4.

Leopold, Aldo. *A Sand County Almanac, and Sketches Here and There*. New York: Oxford University Press, 1968. First published in 1949.

Lerner, Michael. *The Left Hand of God: Taking Back Our Country from the Religious Right.* New York: HarperCollins/HarperSanFrancisco, 2006.

Lifton, Robert Jay. *The Climate Swerve: Reflections on Mind, Habitat, and Survival.* New York and London: New Books, 2017.

———, and Greg Mitchell. *Hiroshima in America: A Half Century of Denial.* New York: Avon Books, 1996. First published in 1995.

Luther, Martin. "Lectures on Genesis," in *Works*, Vol. 1, ed. Jaroslav Pelikan (St. Louis, MO: Concordia, 1955), 47, quoted in Rex Amber, "Befriending the Earth: A Theological Challenge." *The Friends' Quarterly* 26 (1990): 8.

Macy, Joanna. *World as Lover, World as Self: Courage for Global Justice and Ecological Renewal.* Berkeley: Parallax Press, 2007.

Majot, Juliet, and Devlin Kuyek. "Big Meat and Big Dairy's Climate Emissions Put Exxon to Shame." *The Guardian*, November 7, 2017. https://www.theguardian.com/commentisfree/2017/nov/07/big-meat-big-dairy-carbon-emmissions-exxon-mobil.

Malthus, Thomas R. *An Essay on the Principle of Population.* Oxford: Oxford World's Classics, 1798.

McFague, Sally. "A Square in the Quilt." In *Spirit and Nature: Why the Environment is a Religious Issue*, edited by Steven Rockefeller and John Elder, 39-58. Boston, MA: Beacon Press, 1992.

———. *The Body of God: An Ecological Theology.* Minneapolis MN: Fortress Press, 1993.

McKibben, Bill. *Deep Economy: The Wealth of Communities and the Durable Future.* New York: Henry Holt and Co., 2007.

———. "What Exxon Knew About Climate Change." *New Yorker*, September 18, 2015. https://www.newyorker.com/news/daily-comment/what-exxon-knew-about-climate-change.

McRobie, George. *Small is Possible.* London: Abacus, 1982.

Meadows, Donella. "Dancing with Systems." The Donella Meadows Project, Academy for Systems Change, Donella Meadows Archives. http://donellameadows.org/archives/dancing-with-systems/.

———, Dennis L. Meadows, and Jorgen Randers. *Beyond the Limits.* Post Mills, VT: Chelsea Green Publishing Company, 1992.

———, Jorgen Randers, and Dennis Meadows. *Limits to Growth: The 30-Year Update.* White River Junction, VT: Chelsea Green Publishing Company, 2004.

———, Dennis L. Meadows, Jorgen Randers, and William W. Behrens III. *The Limits to Growth: A Report for the Club of Rome's Project on the Predicament of Mankind.* A Potomac Associates Book. New York: Universe Books, 1972.

Mehta, Subhash. "Bhoodan-Gramdan Movement—50 Years: A Review." http://www.mkgandhi-sarvodaya.org/bhoodan.htm.

Merchant, Carolyn. *The Death of Nature.* San Francisco: HarperSanFrancisco, 1982. First published in 1980.

Merton, Thomas. *Confessions of a Guilty Bystander.* New York: Doubleday, 1968.

Meyer, Aubrey. *Contraction and Convergence: The Global Solution to Climate Change.* Schumacher Briefings No. 5. Totnes, Devon, UK: Green Books, Ltd., 2000.

Millennium Ecosystem Assessment.. *Ecosystems and Human Well-being: Synthesis*. (Authors: Walter Reid, Walter, Harold A. Mooney, Angela Cropper, Doris Capistrano, Stephen R. Carpenter, Kanchan Chopra, Partha Dasgupta et al.) Washington, DC: Island Press, 2005.
https://www.millenniumassessment.org/documents/document.356.aspx.pdf.

Mishan, E.J. *Growth: The Price We Pay*. London: Staples Publishing, 1969.

Monbiot, George. "The Population Myth," September 9, 2009.
https://www.monbiot.com/2009/09/29/the-population-myth/.

————."Putting a Price on the Rivers and Rain Diminishes Us All." *The Guardian*, August 6, 2012.
https://www.theguardian.com/commentisfree/2012/aug/06/price-rivers-rain-greatest-privatisation.

————. "Disposable Planet." *The Guardian*, September 14, 2016.
http://www.monbiot.com/2016/09/15/disposable-planet/.

————."Farming Livestock for Food Threatens All Life on Earth, and "Free-Range" Steak is Worst of All." *The Guardian*, June 8 2018.
https://www.theguardian.com/commentisfree/2018/jun/08/save-planet-meat-dairy-livestock-food-free-range-steak.

Moran, Daniel, and Keiichiro Kanemoto. "Identifying Species Threat Hotspots from Global Supply Chain Data." *Nature Ecology and Evolution* 1 (2017): 23.
https://doi.org/10.1038/s41559-016-0023

Muhad, Munjed M. "Islamic Environmental Stewardship: Nature and Science in the Light of Islamic Philosophy." *Union Seminary Quarterly Review* 63 (2010): 145-63.

Muir, John. *A Thousand Mile Walk to the Gulf*, edited by William Frederic Badè. Boston and New York: Houghton Mifflin Company; Cambridge: The Riverside Press, 1916.

Murphy, Robert. "Amplifying Oren Cass's Critique of a Carbon Tax, Part 1." Institute for Energy Research, September 6, 2017.
https://www.instituteforenergyresearch.org/uncategorized/amplifying-oren-casss-critique-carbon-tax-part/.

Naess, Arne. *Gandhi and Group Conflict: An Exploration of Satyagraha. Theoretical Background*. Oslo: Universitietsforlaget, 1974. Quoted in David Rothenberg. *Is It Painful to Think? Conversations with Arne Naess*. Minneapolis: University of Minneapolis Press, 1993, xix.

————. "Self-realization: An Ecological Approach to Being in the World." *Trumpeter* 4 (3)(1987): 35-42.
http://trumpeter.athabascau.ca/index.php/trumpet/article/view/623.

————. *Ecology, Community, and Lifestyle: Outline of an Ecosophy*. Translated and revised by David Rothenberg. Cambridge, U.K.: Cambridge University Press, 1989.

————. "The Shallow and the Deep, Long-Range Ecology Movement: A Summary." In *The Deep Ecology Movement: An Introductory Anthology*, edited by Alan Drengson and Yuichi Inoue, 3-9. Berkeley, CA: North Atlantic Publishers, 1995.

————. *The Ecology of Wisdom: Writings by Arne Naess*, edited by Alan Drengson and Bill Devall. Berkeley, CA: Counterpoint Press, 2008.

————. "Lifestyle Trends Within the Deep Ecology Movement." In *The Ecology of Wisdom, Writings by Arne Naess*, edited by Alan Drengson and Bill Devall,140-1. Berkeley: Counterpoint Press, 2008.

Nagel, Thomas. "Reductionism and Antireductionism." In *The Limits of Reductionism in Biology*. Novartis Foundation Symposium #213. Chichester, U.K.: John Wiley and Sons, 1998. http://www.isnature.org/Events/2009/Summer/r/Nagel1998-Rednism%26AntiRednism.pdf.

———. *Mind and Cosmos: Why the Materialist Neo-Darwinian Conception of Nature is Almost Certainly False*. New York: Oxford University Press, 2012.

Nasr, Seyyed Hossein. *The Encounter of Man and Nature: The Spiritual Crisis of Modern Man*. London: Allen and Unwin, 1968.

———. *Religion and the Order of Nature*. New York: Oxford University Press, 1996.

———. "The Spiritual and Religious Dimensions of the Environmental Crisis." In *A Sacred Trust: Ecology and Spiritual Vision*, edited by David Cadman and John Carey, 118-48. Temenos Academy Papers No. 17. London: The Temenos Academy, 2002.

———. "Islam, The Contemporary Islamic World, and the Environmental Crisis." In *Earthcare: An Anthology of Environmental Ethics*, edited by David Clowney and Patricia Mosto, 82-90. Lanham, MD: Rowman and Littlefield Publishers, Inc., 2009.

———. Radio interview with Paul Kennedy, on "Ideas," August 15, 2015, Canadian Broadcasting Company. https://www.cbc.ca/radio/ideas/islam-and-the-environment-1.2914131.

National Academy of Sciences of the United States of America. *Himalayan Glaciers: Climate Change, Water Resources and Water Security*. Washington, DC: National Academies Press, 2014. Report in brief: https://www.nap.edu/resource/13449/Himalayan-Glaciers-Report-Brief-Final.pdf.

National Aeronautics and Space Administration. "Global Temperature." 2018. https://climate.nasa.gov/vital-signs/global-temperature/.

National Council of Churches (U.S.). Eco-justice Working Group. http://www.creationjustice.org/history.html.

National Opinion Research Center. General Social Survey, Final Report. *Trends in Psychological Wellbeing, 1972-2014*. Chicago: NORC, April 2015. http://www.norc.org/PDFs/GSS%20Reports/GSS_PsyWellBeing15_final_formatted.pdf.

National Priorities Project. "A Militarized Budget." April 30, 2017. https://www.nationalpriorities.org/analysis/2017/militarized-budget-2017/.

National Religious Partnership for the Environment (U.S.). http://www.nrpe.org/.

National Sustainable Agriculture Coalition. "2012 Census Drilldown: Organic and Local Food." May 16, 2014. http://sustainableagriculture.net/blog/2012-census-organic-local/.

Navdanya. http://www.navdanya.org/site/.

New Economics Foundation. "A Green New Deal: Joined-up Policies to Solve the Triple Crunch of the Credit Crisis, Climate Change and High Oil Prices." https://neweconomics.org/2008/07/green-new-deal.

Niles, D. Premain. "Justice, Peace and the Integrity of Creation." World Council of Churches. November 2003. http://www.wcc-coe.org/wcc/who/dictionary-article11.html.

Nonviolent Communication. http://www.nonviolentcommunication.com/.

North Carolina Waste Awareness and Reduction Network. "Clean Path 2025: Achieving an Economical Clean Energy Future for North Carolina." https://www.ncwarn.org/our-work/clean-path-2025/.

Nye, Joseph. *Nuclear Ethics*. New York: Free Press, 1986.

O'Connell, Mark. "Why Silicon Valley Billionaires Are Prepping for the Apocalypse in New Zealand." *The Guardian*, February 15, 2018. https://www.theguardian.com/news/2018/feb/15/why-silicon-valley-billionaires-are-prepping-for-the-apocalypse-in-new-zealand.

Organisation for Economic Co-operation and Development. *How's Life? 2017: Measuring Well-being*. Paris: OECD Publishing, 2017. https://doi.org/10.1787/how_life-2017-en.

Ostrom, Elinor. *Governing the Commons: The Evolution of Institutions for Collective Action*. Cambridge, UK: Cambridge University Press, 1990.

Pacific Institute. The World's Water: Information on the World's Freshwater Resources. Water Conflict Chronology. http://www.worldwater.org/conflict/list/.

Pareek, Shreya. "A Simple Technology that Can Solve India's Clean #Water Problem in Just Rs.3,000." *The Better India*, September 15, 2014. https://www.thebetterindia.com/13532/biosand-filters-providing-clean-drinking-water-remotest-areas-india/.

Parker, Janet, and Roberta Richards. "Christian Ethics and the Environmental Challenge." In *Theology for Earth Community*, edited by Dieter Hessel, 113-31. Maryknoll, NY: Orbis Books, 1996.

Paul, Eve Turow. "More Women Are Starting Companies From The Ground Up, Literally." *Forbes*, August 11, 2016. https://www.forbes.com/sites/eveturowpaul/2016/08/11/more-women-starting-companies-from-the-ground-up-literally/#3ceff1e56ee2.

Paul VI (pope). "Octogesima Adveniens." Apostolic letter to Cardinal Maurice Roy, Vatican, May 14, 1971. http://w2.vatican.va/content/paul-vi/en/apost_letters/documents/hf_p-vi_apl_19710514_octogesima-adveniens.html.

Penn, William. *No Cross, No Crown* (1669, 1682). 8th Edition, corrected. Leeds, UK: Printed by James Lister, 1743. https://archive.org/stream/nocrossnocrown00penn#page/.

———. *Some Fruits of Solitude* (1692). London and Ashford, Kent: Headley Brothers, 1905. https://archive.org/stream/somefruitssolit00penngoog#page/n0/mode/2up.

Pingali, Prabhu. "Green Revolution: Impacts, Limits, and the Path Ahead." *Proceedings of the National Academy of Sciences of the United States of America* 109 (2012): 12302-08. https://doi.org/10.1073/pnas.0912953109.

Plant, Judith, ed. *Healing the Wounds: The Promise of Ecofeminism*. Philadelphia: New Society Publishers, 1989.

Plant, Judith. Introduction to Part One: "Remembering Who We Are," in *Healing the Wounds: The Promise of Ecofeminism*, edited by Judith Plant, 5-6. Philadelphia: New Society Publishers, 1989.

———. "The Circle is Gathering." In *Healing the Wounds: The Promise of Ecofeminism*, edited by Judith Plant, 242-53. Philadelphia: New Society Publishers, 1989.

Plumwood, Val. *Feminism and the Mastery of Nature*. London: Routledge, 1992.

Polimeni, John, Koso Mayumi, Mario Giampietro, and Blake Alcott. *The Jevons Paradox and the Myth of Resource Efficiency Improvements.* London: Earthscan, 2008.

Pollan, Michael. *In Defense of Food: An Eater's Manifesto.* New York: Penguin Books, 2009.

Poor People's Campaign: A National Call for Moral Revival. https://www.poorpeoplescampaign.org/.

Porter, Michael, and Scott Stern with Michael Green. *Social Progress Index 2017.* Social Progress Imperative, 2017. http://www.socialprogressindex.com/assets/downloads/resources/en/English-2017-Social-Progress-Index-Findings-Report_embargo-d-until-June-21-2017.pdf.

Practical Action. https://practicalaction.org/.

Presbyterian Church (USA). *Restoring Creation for Ecology and Justice, A Report Adopted by the 202nd Assembly of the Presbyterian Church USA* (1990). Office of the General Assembly of the Presbyterian Church (USA), 1990, Louisville, KY. https://www.presbyterianmission.org/wp-content/uploads/restoring-creation-for-ecologyjustice.pdf

————. "On Lifting Up the Call to Restore the Creation." Statement approved by the 210th Presbyterian Church (USA) General Assembly, 2010. Office of the General Assembly of the Presbyterian Church (USA), Louisville, KY. https://presbyterian.typepad.com/files/call-to-restore-creation.pdf.

Presbyterian Eco-Justice Task Force. *Keeping and Healing the Creation.* Louisville KY: Presbyterian Church (USA), 1989.

Prevallet, Elaine. *Reflections on Simplicity.* Pendle Hill Pamphlet No. 244. Wallingford, PA: Pendle Hill Publications, 1982.

Primavesi, Anne. "A Tide in the Affairs of Women?" In *Ecotheology: Voices from South and North,* edited by David Hallman, 186-98. Maryknoll, NY: World Council of Churches/Orbis Books, 1994.

Pumphrey, Carolyn, ed. *Global Climate Change: National Security Implications.* Carlisle, PA: Strategic Studies Institute, May 2008. https://www.globalsecurity.org/military/library/report/2008/ssi_pumphrey.pdf.

Putinelu, Adela. "Are Carbon Markets an Effective Way to Address Climate Change?" *Climate Home News,* October 16, 2012. http://www.climatechangenews.com/2012/10/16/does-emissions-trading-really-work/.

Quaker Earthcare Witness. https://www.quakerearthcare.org/.

Quaker Institute for the Future. "Publications and Presentations of QIF and Associates," http://www.quakerinstitute.org/?page_id=5.

Quaker Peace and Social Witness, Britain Yearly Meeting. *Faithful Deeds: A Rough Guide to the Quaker Peace Testimony.* London: Quaker Books, 2002.

Quakers in the World. "Friends Rural Centre, Rasulia, India." http://www.quakersintheworld.org/quakers-in-action/361/Friends-Rural-Centre-Rasulia-India.

Queally, John. "Geoengineering Global Cooling: 'Insane, Utterly Mad and Delusional.'" *Common Dreams,* January 16, 2014. http://www.commondreams.org/headline/2014/01/16.

Rabhi, Pierre. *As in the Heart, So in the Earth: Reversing the Desertification of the Soul and the Soil.* Translated by Inner Traditions International. Rochester, VT: Park Street Press, 2006.

Rasmussen, Larry. "Theology of Life and Ecumenical Ethics." In *Ecotheology: Voices from South and North*, edited by David Hallman, 112-29. Maryknoll, NY: World Council of Churches/Orbis Books, 1994.

Ratcliffe, J.M. *Lead in Man and the Environment*. Chichester, UK: Ellis Horwood Ltd; New York: Halsted Press, 1981.

———, Jennie M. *Integrity, Ecology and Community: The Motion of Love*. Pendle Hill Pamphlet No. 403. Wallingford, PA: Pendle Hill Publications, 2009.

Raworth, Kate. *Doughnut Economics: Seven Ways to Think Like a 21st-Century Economist*. London: Penguin Random House, 2017.

Religious Action Center of Reform Judaism. "Position of the Reform Movement on the Environment." https://rac.org/position-reform-movement-environment.

Revesz, Rachel. "U.K To 'Scale Down' Climate Change and Illegal Wildlife Measures to Bring In Post-Brexit Trade, Secret Documents Reveal."*The Independent,* April 9, 2017. https://www.independent.co.uk/news/uk/politics/uk-government-to-scale-down-climate-change-and-illegal-wildlife-measure-a7674706.html

Right Sharing of World Resources. www.rswr.org.

Ripple, William, Christopher Wolf, Thomas M. Newsome, Mauro Galetti, Mohammed Alamgir Eileen Crist, Mahmoud I. Mahmoud, William F. Laurance, and 15,364 scientist signatories. "World Scientists Warning to Humanity: A Second Notice." *Bioscience* 67 (2017): 1026-8. https://doi.org/10.1093/biosci/bix125.

Ritchie, Hannah. "How Much of the World's Land Would We Need in Order to Feed the Global Population with the Average Diet of a Given Country?" Our World in Data, October 3 2017. https://ourworldindata.org/agricultural-land-by-global-diets.

———, and Max Roser."Meat and Seafood Production & Consumption," 2019. Our World in Data. https://ourworldindata.org/meat-and-seafood-production-consumption.

Roberts, David. "Sucking Carbon Directly Out of the Air Won't Solve the Climate Crisis." *Vox*, July 16 2018. https://www.vox.com/energy-and-environment/2018/6/14/17445622/direct-air-capture-air-to-fuels-carbon-dioxide-engineering.

Robinson, Marilynne. "What Are We Doing Here?" *New York Review of Books*, November 9 2017, 28 and 36.

Rocha, Juan C., Garry Peterson, Örjan Bodin, and Simon Levin. "Cascading Regime Shifts Within and Across Scales."*Science* 362 (2018): 1379-83. https://doi.org/10.1126/science.aat7850.

Rockström, Johan. Foreword, World Wildlife Fund, *Living Planet Report 2016: Risk and Resilience in a New Era*, 5-6. Gland, Switzerland, 2016. https://www.worldwildlife.org/pages/living-planet-report-2016.

Rojelj, Joeri, Michel den Elzen, Niklas Höhne, Taryn Fransen, Hanna Fekete, Harald Winkler, Roberto Schaeffer, Fu Sha, Keywan Riahi, and Malte Meinshausen. "Paris Agreement Climate Proposals Need a Boost to Keep Warming Well Below 2°C." *Nature* 534 (2016): 631–9. https://doi.org/10.1038/nature18307.

Rose, Steven. *Lifelines: Biology Beyond Determinism*. New York: Oxford University Press, 1998.

Rosenberg, Marshall. *Nonviolent Communication: A Language of Compassion*. Encinitas, CA: Puddledancer Press, 2001.

Roser, Max. "Fertility Rate," 2018. Our World In Data. https://ourworldindata.org/fertility-rate.

Roser, Max. "World Population Growth," 2018. Our World in Data. https://ourworldindata.org/wp-content/uploads/2013/05/updated-World-Population-Growth-1750-2100.png

Rothenberg, David. *Is It Painful to Think? Conversations with Arne Naess.* Minneapolis: University of Minneapolis Press, 1993.

Royal Society (London) and United States National Academy of Sciences. *Towards Sustainable Consumption: A Joint Statement by the Royal Society and the United States National Academy of Sciences.* London: The Royal Society, 1997. https://royalsociety.org/~/media/Royal_Society_Content/policy/publications/1997/10193.pdf.

Royle, Elizabeth. "One-third of Food Is Lost or Wasted: What Can Be Done." *National Geographic*, October 13, 2014. http://news.nationalgeographic.com/news/2014/10/141013-food-waste-national-security-environment-science-ngfood/.

Rubenstein, D., and J. Kealey. "Cooperation, Conflict, and the Evolution of Complex Animal Societies." *Nature Education Knowledge* 3 (2010): 78. https://www.nature.com/scitable/knowledge/library/cooperation-conflict-and-the-evolution-of-complex-13236526.

Ruether, Rosemary Radford. *Gaia and God: An Ecofeminist Theology of Earth Healing.* San Francisco: Harper, 1989.

———. "Ecofeminism and Theology." In *Ecotheology: Voices from South and North*, edited by David Hallman, 199-204. Maryknoll, NY: World Council of Churches/Orbis Books, 1994.

———. "Deep Ecology, Ecofeminism and the Bible." In *Deep Ecology and World Religions: New Essays on Sacred Ground*, edited by David Landis Barnhill and Roger S. Gottlieb, 229-42. New York: State University of New York Press, 2001.

———. *Integrating Ecofeminism, Globalization and World Religions.* Lanham, MD: Rowman and Littlefield Publishing Inc., 2005.

———. *Goddesses and the Divine Feminine: A Western Religious History.* Berkeley, CA: University of California Press, 2006.

Rupp, George. "Religion, Modern Secular Culture, and Ecology." *Daedelus* 130 (2001): 23-30, https://www.amacad.org/publication/religion-modern-secular-culture-and-ecology.

Sale, Kirkpatrick. *Human Scale Revisited: A New Look at the Classic Case for a Decentralist Future.* White River Junction, VT: Chelsea Green Publishing, 2007. (An update of the author's classic *Human Scale.* New York: Coward, McCann & Geoghegan, 1980.)

Sanford, A. Whitney. "Gandhi's Agrarian Legacy: Practicing Food, Justice and Sustainability in India." *Journal for the Study of Religion, Nature and Culture* 7 (2013): 65-87. http://dx.doi.org/10.1558/jsrnc.v7i1.65.

Santmire, Paul. *The Travail of Nature.* Philadelphia: Fortress Press, 1985.

Sarvodaya USA. http://www.sarvodayausa.org/.

Satterthwaite, David. "The Implications of Population Growth and Urbanization for Climate Change." *Environment and Urbanization* (2009): 545-67. https://doi.org/10.1177/0956247809344361.

Scarborough, Peter, Paul N. Appleby, Anja Mizrak, Adam D.M. Briggs, Ruth C.M. Travis, Kathryn E. Bradbury, and Timothy J. Key. "Dietary Greenhouse Gas Emissions of Meat-eaters, Fish-eaters, Vegetarians and Vegans in the UK." *Climatic Change* 125 (2014): 179-92. https://doi.org/10.1007/s10584-014-1169-1.

Schiller, Ben. "Europe's CO$_2$ Trading Scheme: Is It Time for a Major Overhaul?" *Yale Environment 360*, April 26, 2011. https://e360.yale.edu/features/europes_co2_trading_scheme_is_it_time_for_a_major_overhaul.

Schmandt, Jurgen, and C.H. Ward, eds. *Sustainable Development: The Challenge of Transition.* Cambridge, UK: Cambridge University Press, 2000.

Schumacher Center for New Economics. https://centerforneweconomics.org/.

Schumacher, E.F. *Small is Beautiful: Economics as if People Mattered.* New York: Harper and Row, 1975. First published in 1973.

———. "Nonviolence." Transcription of a lecture delivered in Berkeley, CA, 1976. http://www.centerforneweconomics.org/content/nonviolence.

———. *Good Work.* New York: Harper and Row, 1979.

Schurman, Virginia. "A Quaker Theology of the Stewardship of Creation." *Quaker Religious Thought* 24 (1992): 27-41.

Schwaegel, Christian. "Living in the Anthropocene: Toward a New Global Ethos." *Yale Environment 360*, January 24, 2011. http://e360.yale.edu/features/living_in_the_anthropocene_toward_a_new_global_ethos.

Schwarz, Barry. *The Paradox of Choice: Why More is Less.* New York: Harper Perennial, 2005.

Scott Bader Commonwealth. http://www.scottbader.com/about-us/.

Sessions, George, ed. *Deep Ecology for the 21st Century.* Boston, Shambhala Publications, Inc. 1995.

Sharp, Gene. *The Politics of Nonviolent Action* (3 volumes). Boston, MA: Porter Sargent Publishers, 1973.

Shiva, Vandana. *Staying Alive: Women, Ecology and Development.* London: Zed Books, 1989.

———. *The Violence of the Green Revolution: Agriculture, Ecology and Politics.* London: Zed Books, 1991.

———. *Biopiracy: The Plunder of Nature and Knowledge.* Boston: South End Press, 1997.

———. *Water Wars: Privatization, Pollution and Profit.* Brooklyn: South End Press, 2002. (Reprinted by North Atlantic Books, 2016).

———. *Earth Democracy: Justice, Sustainability, and Peace.* Brooklyn and Boston: South End Press, 2005.

———. *Who Really Feeds the World? The Failures of Agribusiness and the Promise of Agroecology.* Berkeley, CA: North Atlantic Books, 2016.

Slaughter, Thomas. *The Natures of John and William Bartram: The Pioneering Naturalists, Father and Son, in the Wilderness of Eighteenth Century America.* New York: Vintage Books, 1996.

Slow Food USA. https://www.slowfoodusa.org/.

Smith, Gerald Alonso. "The Purpose of Wealth: A Historical Perspective." In *Valuing the Earth: Economics, Ecology, Ethics,* edited by Herman Daly and Kenneth Townsend, 183-209. Cambridge, MA: MIT Press, 1993.

Smith, Tom W. "Happiness: Time Trends, Seasonal Variations, Intersurvey Differences and Other Mysteries." *Social Psychology Quarterly* 42(1) (1979):18-30. http://dx.doi.org/10.2307/3033870.

Sokol, Moshe. "What Are the Ethical Implications of Jewish Theological Conceptions of the Natural World?" In *Judaism and Ecology*, edited by Hava Tirosh Samuelson, 261-82. Cambridge, MA: Harvard University Press, 2002.

Solomon, Fred, and Robert Q. Marston, eds. *The Medical Implications of Nuclear War.* Washington: National Academies Press, 1986.

Spratt, T. *History of the Royal Society of London.* London, 1667. http://quod.lib.umich.edu/cgi/t/text/text-idx?c=eebo;idno=A61158.0001.001.

Springmann, Marco, Michael Clark, Daniel Mason-D'Croz, Keith Wiebe, Benjamin Leon Bodirsky, Luis Lassaletta, and Wim de Vries. "Options for Keeping the Food System Within Environmental Limits." *Nature* 562 (2018): 519-25. https://doi.org/10.1038/s41586-018-0594-0.

Staff of Mother Earth News®. *The Mother Earth News ®Handbook of Homemade Power.* New York: Bantam Books, 1974.

Steffen, Will, Johan Rockström, Katherine Richardson, Timothy M. Lenton, Carl Folke, Diana Liverman, Colin P. Summerhayes, et al. "Trajectories of the Earth System in the Anthropocene." *Proceedings of the National Academy of Sciences of the United States of America* 115 (2018): 8252-9. https://doi.org/10.1073/pnas.1810141115.

Stephan, Maria, and Erica Chenoweth. "Why Civil Resistance Works: The Strategic Logic of Nonviolence." *International Security* 33 no.1 (2008): 7-44. https://www.mitpressjournals.org/doi/pdf/10.1162/isec.2008.33.1.7.

Stockholm International Peace Research Institute. *Military Expenditure Database, 1949-2017.* https://www.sipri.org/databases/milex.

Stromberg, Joseph. "What Is the Anthropocene and Are We in It?" *Smithsonian Magazine*, January 2013. http://www.smithsonianmag.com/science-nature/what-is-the-anthropocene-and-are-we-in-it-164801414/.

Sunrise Movement Campaign for a Green New Deal. https://www.sunrisemovement.org/gnd.

Swimme, Brian, and Thomas Berry. *The Universe Story: From the Primordial Flaring Forth to the Ecozoic Era—A Celebration of the Unfolding of the Cosmos.* San Francisco: HarperSanFrancisco, 1992.

Taber, Bill. *The Prophetic Stream.* Pendle Hill Pamphlet No. 256. Wallingford, PA: Pendle Hill Publications, 1984.

Talberth, John, Clifford Cobb, and John Slattery. *The Genuine Progress Indicator: Executive Summary.* Redefining Progress, February 2007, http://rprogress.org/publications/2007/GPI2006_ExecSumm.pdf.

Taylor, Bron, ed. *Encyclopedia of Religion and Ecology.* New York: Bloomsbury Academic. 1st Edition, 2005.

Teilhard de Chardin, Pierre. *The Divine Milieu: An Essay on the Interior Life.* New York: Harper and Row, 2001. First published in 1957.

Thompson, Michael. "The Care of Our Planet." *The Friends' Quarterly* 26 (1990): 1-6.

Thoreau, Henry David. *Walden, or Living in the Woods.* New York: New American Library Edition, 1963. First published in 1854.

Tian, Nan, Aude Fleurant, Alexandra Kuimova, Pieter D. Wezeman and Siemon T. Wezeman. *Trends in World Military Expenditures 2017*. SIPRI Fact Sheet. Stockholm: Stockholm International Research Institute, May 2018. https://www.sipri.org/sites/default/files/2018-04/sipri_fs_1805_milex_2017.pdf.

Timberlake Earth Sanctuary. https://www.timberlakeearthsanctuary.com/.

Timmerman, Peter, ed. *The Encyclopedia of Global Environment Change, Vol. 5: Social and Economic Dimensions of Global Environmental Change*. Chichester, U.K.: John Wiley and Sons, Ltd., 2002.

Tirosh-Samuelson, Hava, ed. *Judaism and Ecology*. Cambridge, MA: Harvard University Press, 2002.

———. "Introduction. Judaism and the Natural World." In *Judaism and Ecology*, edited by Hava Tirosh-Samuelson, xxxiii-lxii. Cambridge MA: Harvard University Press, 2002.

Tobias, Michael. *Deep Ecology*. San Marcos, CA: Avant Books, 1988.

Triangle Land Conservancy. https://www.triangleland.org/.

Tuana, Nancy, ed. *Feminism and Science*. Bloomington, IN: Indiana University Press, 1989.

Tucker, Mary Evelyn. "The Role of Religions in Forming an Environmental Ethics." In *Theology for Earth Community*, edited by Dieter Hessel, 143-52. Maryknoll NY: Orbis Books, 1996.

———, and Christopher Key Chapple, eds. *Hinduism and Ecology*. Cambridge, MA: Harvard University Press, 2000.

———, and John Grim, eds. *Religions of the World and Ecology*. Series published Harvard University Center for the Study of World Religions and Harvard University Press, 1998 to 2011. (See individual volume entries in bibliography).

Union of Concerned Scientists. "Palm Oil." https://www.ucsusa.org/global-warming/stop-deforestation/drivers-of-deforestation-2016-palm-oil.

United Church of Canada. *One Earth Community: Ethical Principles for Environment and Development*. Toronto: United Church of Canada, 1992.

United Nations. Charter of the United Nations and Statute of the International Court of Justice, Chapter XXVII Environment, 7.d Paris Agreement. Paris, December 12, 2015. https://treaties.un.org/pages/ViewDetails.aspx?src=TREATY&mtdsg_no=XXVII-7-d&chapter=27&clang=_en.

United Nations. *United Nations Framework Convention on Climate Change*, 1992. FCCC/INFORMAL/84 GE.05-62220 (E) 200705. Geneva: United Nations. https://unfccc.int/resource/docs/convkp/conveng.pdf.

United Nations. *Report of the United Nations Conference in the Human Environment, Stockholm, June 2-16, 1972*. A/CONF.48/14/Rev.1. http://www.un-documents.net/aconf48-14r1.pdf.

United Nations Conference on Environment and Development (The Earth Summit), Chair Maurice Strong, Rio de Janeiro, June 3-14, 1992. http://www.un.org/geninfo/bp/enviro.html.

United Nations Conference on Environment and Development, Rio de Janeiro, June 3-14, 1992. *Agenda 21*. https://sustainabledevelopment.un.org/content/documents/Agenda21.pdf.

United Nations Convention to Combat Desertification. *Global Land Outlook*. Geneva: United Nations. 1st Edition, 2017. https://www.unccd.int/sites/default/files/documents/2017-09/GLO_Full_Report_low_res.pdf.

United Nations Department of Economic and Social Affairs. *Review of Implementation of Agenda 21 and the Rio Principles: Synthesis*. Prepared by the Stakeholder Forum for a Sustainable Future. January 2012. https://sustainabledevelopment.un.org/content/documents/641Synthesis_report_Web.pdf.

United Nations Department of Economic and Social Affairs, Population Division. *World Population Prospects: The 2017 Revision, Key Findings and Advance Tables*. Working Paper No. ESA/P/WP/248 New York: United Nations, 2017. https://population.un.org/wpp/Publications/Files/WPP2017_KeyFindings.pdf.

United Nations Department of Information. *Earth Summit: Agenda 21, The United Nations Program of Action from Rio*. UN Publication No. E93.111, December 1994, 9-10. https://www.dataplan.info/img_upload/7bdb1584e3b8a53d337518d988763f8d/agenda21-earth-summit-the-united-nations-programme-of-action-from-rio_1.pdf.

United Nations Development Program. *Sustainable Development Goals*. January 2016. http://www.undp.org/content/undp/en/home/sustainable-development-goals.html.

United Nations Division for Ocean Affairs and the Law of the Sea. *The United Nations Convention on the Law of the Sea of December 10, 1982*. (Full text). http://www.un.org/Depts/los/convention_agreements/texts/unclos/unclos_e.pdf.

United Nations Environment Programme. *Emissions Gap Report, Executive Summary*. Nairobi: UNEP, November 2018. https://wedocs.unep.org/bitstream/handle/20.500.11822/26879/EGR2018_ES_EN.pdf?sequence=10.

United Nations Environment Programme and GRID-Arendal. *Waste Crimes, Waste Risks: Gaps and Challenges in the Waste Sector*. Nairobi and Arendal, 2015. http://apps.unep.org/publications/index.php?option=com_pub&task=download&file=011703_en.

United Nations Food and Agriculture Organization. *Global Food Losses and Food Waste: Extent, Causes and Prevention* (Authors: J. Gustavsson, C. Cederberg, U. Sonessen, Robert van Otterdijk, and Alexandre Meybeck). Rome: United Nations Food and Agriculture Organization, 2011. http://www.fao.org/docrep/014/mb060e/mb060e00.pdf.

United Nations Food and Agriculture Organization. "SAVE FOOD: Global Initiative on Food Loss and Waste Reduction." http://www.fao.org/save-food/resources/keyfindings/en/.

United Nations Food and Agriculture Organization. "Urban Agriculture." http://www.fao.org/urban-agriculture/en/.

United Nations Food and Agriculture Organization. *World Livestock 2011: Livestock in Food Security*. Rome: United Nations Food and Agriculture Organization, 2011. http://www.fao.org/docrep/014/i2373e/i2373e.pdf.

United Nations Framework Convention on Climate Change. *Kyoto Protocol to the United Nations Framework Convention on Climate Change*. Kyoto, Japan, December 11, 1997. https://treaties.un.org/pages/ViewDetails.aspx?src=TREATY&mtdsg_no=XXVII-7-a&chapter=27&lang=en.

United Nations Framework Convention on Climate Change. "What Is the Paris Agreement?" https://unfccc.int/process-and-meetings/the-paris-agreement/what-is-the-paris-agreement.

United Nations Intergovernmental Panel on Climate Change. *Fifth Assessment Report (AR5) Synthesis. Summary for Policymakers.* (First to Fourth Assessment Reports also available at http://www.ipcc.ch/.) Geneva: November 2, 2014. http://www.ipcc.ch/pdf/assessment-report/ar5/syr/AR5_SYR_FINAL_SPM.pdf. https://ar5-syr.ipcc.ch/topic_summary.php.

United Nations Intergovernmental Panel on Climate Change. *Global Warming of 1.5C: Summary for Policymakers,* IPCC SR1.5, October 6, 2018. https://report.ipcc.ch/sr15/pdf/sr15_spm_final.pdf.

United Nations Office for Nuclear Disarmament Affairs. *Treaty on the Prohibition of Nuclear Weapons,* July 7, 2017.https://www.un.org/disarmament/wmd/nuclear/tpnw/

United Nations Sustainable Development Solutions Network. *World Happiness Report 2018,* edited by John H. Helliwell, Richard Layard, and Jeffrey D. Sachs. http://worldhappiness.report/ed/2018/.

United Nations University. "Solving the E-Waste Problem (StEP) Initiative." https://unu.edu/projects/solving-the-e-waste-problem-step-initiative.html#outline. 2007.

United Nations World Commission on Environment and Development (Chair, Gro Harlem Brundtland). *Our Common Future.* General Assembly Report A/42/427. Geneva: United Nations, 1987. http://www.un-documents.net/our-common-future.pdf.

United States Department of Agriculture Economic Research Service. "Organic Agriculture," https://www.ers.usda.gov/topics/natural-resources-environment/organic-agriculture/.

United States Department of Defense. *National Security Implications of Climate-Related Risks and a Changing Climate.* U.S. Department of Defense, 23 July 23, 2015. https://archive.defense.gov/pubs/150724-congressional-report-on-national-implications-of-climate-change.pdf?source=govdelivery.

United States Department of Defense Center for Climate and Security Working Group on Climate, Nuclear and Security Affairs. Christine Parthemore and Janne Nolan, eds. *A Framework for Understanding and Managing the Intersection of Climate Change, Nuclear and Security.* U.S. Department of Defense Center for Climate and Security, November 2017. https://climateandsecurity.files.wordpress.com/2017/11/working-group-on-climate-nuclear-and-security-affairs_report-one_2017_11_15.pdf.

United States Environmental Protection Agency. "EPA'S Budget and Spending." (FY 1990 to 2017). https://www.epa.gov/planandbudget/budget.

United States Environmental Protection Agency. "Sustainable Management of Electronics." https://www.epa.gov/smm-electronics.

United States Global Change Research Program. *Fourth National Climate Assessment Vol. II: Impacts, Risks, and Adaptation in the United States.* (Reidmiller, D.R., Alexa Jay, Christopher Avery, Daniel Barrie, Apurva Dave, Benjamin DeAngelo, Matthew Dzaugis et al., eds.) U.S. Global Change Research Program, Washington, DC, USA. https://nca2018.globalchange.gov/.

US Catholic Bishops. "Renewing the Earth: An Invitation to Reflection and Action on Environment in Light of Catholic Teaching." *Origins* 21 (1991): 425-32. http://www.usccb.org/issues-and-action/human-life-and-dignity/environment/renewing-the-earth.cfm.

van der Post, Laurens. Interview with Suzanne Wagner in the documentary *Matter of Heart*, directed by Mark Whitney. CG Jung Society of Los Angeles; Kino International Films, 1983.

van der Zee, Bibi. "James Hansen Rails Against Cap and Trade Plan in Open Letter." *The Guardian*, January 12 2010. https://www.theguardian.com/environment/2010/jan/12/james-hansen-carbon-emissions.

Vaughan, Adam. "Energy Sector's Carbon Emissions to Grow for the Second Year Running." Interview with Faith Birol, Director, International Energy Agency. *The Guardian*, October 8, 2018. https://www.theguardian.com/environment/2018/oct/08/energy-sector-carbon-emissions-grow-second-year-climate-change-coal.

Victor, David, and Charles Kennel. "Climate Policy: Ditch the 2°C Warming Goal."*Nature* 514 (2014): 30-1. https://www.nature.com/news/climate-policy-ditch-the-2-c-warming-goal-1.16018.

Victor, Peter. *Managing Without Growth: Slower by Design, Not Disaster.* Cheltenham, UK: Edward Elgar Publishing, 2008.

von Franz, Marie-Louise. Interview with Suzanne Wagner, in the documentary *Matter of Heart*, directed by Mark Whitney. C.G. Jung Society of Los Angeles; Kino International Films, 1983.

Wackernagel, Mathis, and William Rees. *Our Ecological Footprint.* Gabriola Island, BC: New Society Publishers, 1996.

Wainright, Hilary, and Dave Elliott. *The Lucas Plan: A New Trade Unionism in the Making?* London: Allison and Busby, 1982.

Waite, Richard, and Daniel Vennard. "Without Changing Diets, Agriculture Alone Could Produce Enough Emissions to Surpass 1.5C of Global Warming." World Resources Institute, October 17, 2018. https://www.wri.org/blog/2018/10/we-cant-limit-global-warming-15c-without-changing-diets.

Watts, Jonathan. "Concrete: The Most Destructive Material on Earth." *The Guardian*, February 25, 2019. https://www.theguardian.com/cities/2019/feb/25/concrete-the-most-destructive-material-on-earth.

Watts, Jonathan (and agencies). "Global CO_2 Levels Hit Record High." *The Guardian*, Oct 30, 2017. https://www.theguardian.com/environment/2017/oct/30/global-atmospheric-co2-levels-hit-record-high.

Watts, Nick, Markus Amann, Sonja Ayeb-Karlsson, Kristine Belesova, Timothy Bouley, Maxwell Boykoff, Peter Byass et al. "The Lancet Countdown on Health and Climate Change: From 25 Years of Inaction to a Global Transformation for Public Health." *Lancet* 391 (2017): 581-630. https://doi.org/10.1016/S0140-6736(17)32464-9.

Watts, Nick, Markus Amann, Nigel Arnell, Sonja Ayeb-Karlsson, Kristine Belesova, Helen Berry, Maxwell Boykoff, et al., "Lancet Countdown on Health and Climate Change: Shaping the Health of Nations for Centuries to Come," *Lancet* 392 (2018), 2479-514. http://dx.doi.org/10.1016/S0140-6736(18)32594-7.

Weaver, Jace, ed. *Defending Mother Earth: Native American Perspectives on Environmental Justice*. Maryknoll, NY: Orbis Books, 1996.

Weber, Thomas. *Gandhi as Disciple and Mentor*. Cambridge, UK: Cambridge University Press, 2004.

Werrell, Caitlin, and Franceso Femia. "A Responsibility to Prepare: Why the US National Security Community Takes Climate Risks Seriously." *United States Department of Defense Center for Climate and Security Briefer* No. 35, April 7 2017. https://climateandsecurity.files.wordpress.com/2012/04/a-responsibility-to-prepare_why-the-u-s-national-security-community-takes-climate-risks-seriously_briefer-35.pdf.

———, Francesco Femia, Sherri Goodman, and Shiloh Fetzek. "A Responsibility to Prepare: Governing in an Age of Unprecedented Risk and Unprecedented Foresight." *United States Department of Defense Center for Climate and Security Briefer* No. 38, August 2017. https://climateandsecurity.files.wordpress.com/2017/12/a-responsibility-to-prepare_governing-in-an-age-of-unprecedented-risk-and-unprecedented-foresight_briefer-38.pdf.

Westing, Arthur. (Stockholm International Peace Research Institute). *Ecological Consequences of the Second Indochina War*. London: Taylor and Francis, 1976.

———. (Stockholm International Peace Research Institute). *Weapons of Mass Destruction and the Environment*. London: Taylor and Francis, 1977.

———. (Stockholm International Peace Research Institute). *Warfare in a Fragile World: Military Impact on the Human Environment*. London: Taylor and Francis, 1980.

———. (Stockholm International Peace Research Institute). *Global Resources and International Conflict: Environmental Factors in Strategic Policy and Action*. Oxford, UK: Oxford University Press, 1986.

Wezeman, Pieter D, Aude Fleurant, Alexandra Kuimova, Nan Tian, and Siemon T. Wezeman. *Trends in International Arms Transfers 2017*. Stockholm: Stockholm International Peace Research Institute, March 2018. https://www.sipri.org/sites/default/files/2018-03/fssipri_at2017_0.pdf.

White, Lynn Jr. "The Historical Roots of Our Ecological Crisis." *Science* 155 (1967): 1203-7. https://doi.org/10.1126/science.155.3767.1203.

Whitman, Walt. "Song of Myself." In: *Whitman: Poems*. Selected by Peter Washington, 87-185. New York: Alfred A. Knopf, Inc., 1994. First published in Walt Whitman, *Leaves of Grass*, Brooklyn, NY, 1855.

Wikipedia. "Fossil Fuel Divestment." https://en.wikipedia.org/wiki/Fossil_fuel_divestment.

Wikipedia. "List of Community Currencies in the United States." June 2018. https://en.wikipedia.org/wiki/List_of_community_currencies_in_the_United_St ates.

Wikipedia."Native American Use of Fire in Ecosystems." https://en.m.wikipedia.org/wiki/Native_American_use_of_fire.

Wikipedia. "Three Sisters (agriculture)." https://en.wikipedia.org/wiki/Three_Sisters_(agriculture).

Wilber, Ken. *A Brief History of Everything*. Boston: Shambhala Publications, Inc., 1996.

————. *The Marriage of Sense and Soul: Integrating Science and Religion.* New York: Random House, 1998.

————. *Integral Spirituality: A Startling New Role for Religion in the Modern and Postmodern World.* Boston: Shambhala Publications, Inc., 2003.

Wilkinson, Richard, and Kate Pickett. *The Spirit Level: Why Greater Equality Makes Societies Stronger.* London: Bloomsbury Press, 2010.

Williams, Lynn, and Susan Epstein. *Overseas Contingency Operations Funding: Background and Status.* United States Congressional Research Service, February 7 2017. https://fas.org/sgp/crs/natsec/R44519.pdf.

Williams, W.G. "Aboriginal Use of Fire: Are There Any 'Natural' Plant Communities?" In *Wilderness and Political Ecology: Aboriginal Influences and the Original State of Nature,* edited by C.E. Kay and R.T. Simmons, 179-214. Salt Lake City: University of Utah Press, 2002.

Wohlleben, Peter. *The Hidden Life of Trees: What They Feel, How They Communicate.* Vancouver and Berkeley: Greystone Books, 2018.

Wolfson, Elliot R. "Mirror of Nature Reflected in the Symbolism of Medieval Kabbalah." In *Judaism and Ecology,* edited by Hava Tirosh-Samuelson, 305-31. Cambridge, MA: Harvard University Press, 2002.

Women's Earth Alliance. "Traditional Agriculture Solutions for Women Farmers in India." http://womensearthalliance.org/projects/2013-shakti-green-foundation-training/#.

Women's Organisation for Rural Development. "Our Services." http://mywordindia.org/services.php?p=environment_conserva.

Woolf, Dominic, James Amonette, F. Alayne Street-Perrott, Johannes Lehman, and Stephen Joseph. "Sustainable Biochar to Mitigate Global Climate Change." *Nature Communications* 1 (2010): 1-9. https://doi.org/10.1038/ncomms1053.

Woolman, John. *The Journal and Major Essays of John Woolman,* edited by Phillips P. Moulton. Richmond, IN: Friends United Press, 1989. First published in 1971.

————. "Considerations on Keeping Negroes (Part Second)." In *The Journal and Major Essays of John Woolman,* edited by Phillips P. Moulton, 198-237. Richmond, IN: Friends United Press, 1989. First published in 1971.

————. "A Plea for the Poor or A Word of Remembrance and a Caution to the Rich." In *The Journal and the Major Essays of John Woolman,* edited by Phillips P. Moulton, 238-72. Richmond, IN: Friends United Press, 1989. First published in 1971.

————. *Conversations on the True Harmony of Mankind and How it May Be Promoted* (1772), edited and introduced by Sterling Olmsted. Philadelphia: Wider Quaker Fellowship, 1987.

World Bank. World Development Indicators. *Global Air Travel Increase Between 1974 and 2014.* (graphic at http://www.bitsofscience.org/wordpress-3.0.1/wordpress/images/2016/02/global-air-travel-increase-graph.png).

World Commission on Protected Areas. *Economic Values of Protected Areas: Guidelines for Protected Area Managers,* edited by Adrian Phillips. Gland, Switzerland, and Cambridge, UK: International Union for the Conservation of Nature, 1998. https://www.iucn.org/downloads/pag_002.pdf.

World Commission on Protected Areas. *Indigenous and Traditional Peoples and Protected Areas: Principles, Guidelines and Case Studies*, edited by Javier Beltrán. Gland, Switzerland and Cambridge, UK: International Union for Conservation of Nature, 2000. https://www.portalces.org/sites/default/files/migrated/docs/879.pdf.

World Council of Churches. *The New Delhi Report of the Third Assembly of the World Council of Churches 1961*, edited by W.A. Visser t'Hooft. New York: Association Press, undated.

World Council of Churches. *Faith and Science In an Unjust World.* Report of the World Council of Churches' Conference on Faith, Science, and the Future. Massachusetts Institute of Technology, Cambridge, MA, July 12-24, 1979. Philadelphia: Fortress Press, 1980.

World Council of Churches. "No More Delays – Life on Earth is in Peril." Statement to the High-Level Ministerial Segment of the 16th Session of the UNFCCC Conference of Parties, Cancun, Mexico December 16, 2010. https://www.oikoumene.org/en/resources/documents/wcc-programmes/justice-diakonia-and-responsibility-for-creation/climate-change-water/statement-to-cop16-un-climate-conference-cancun.

World Economic Forum. *The Global Risks Report 2017*. 12th Edition. Geneva: World Economic Forum, 2017. http://wef.ch/risks2017.

WorldoMeters.Info. "World Population by Year," http://www.worldometers.info/world-population/world-population-by-year/.

Worldwatch Institute. Annual *State of the World* reports. Washington, DC: Worldwatch Institute. http://www.worldwatch.org/bookstore/state-of-the-world.

World Wildlife Fund. *Living Planet Report 2016: Risk and Resilience in a New Era.* Gland, Switzerland, 2016. https://www.worldwildlife.org/pages/living-planet-report-2016.

World Wildlife Fund. *Living Planet Report 2018: Aiming Higher.* Gland, Switzerland, 2018. https://www.worldwildlife.org/pages/living-planet-report-2018.

Yeomans, P.A. *The Keyline Plan.* Sydney: P.A. Yeomans, 1954. https://www.soilandhealth.org/wp-content/uploads/01aglibrary/010125yeomans/010125toc.html.

Zillman, John W. "A History of Climate Activities." *World Meteorological Organization Bulletin* 58 (2009): 141-50. https://public.wmo.int/en/bulletin/history-climate-activities.

Zohar, Danah. *The Quantum Self: Human Nature and Consciousness Defined by the New Physics.* New York: William Morrow Paperbacks, 1991.

Zumbrum, Josh. "IMF Raises Global Economic Outlook for This Year and 2018." *Wall Street Journal*, October 10, 2017. https://www.wsj.com/articles/imf-raises-global-economic-outlook-for-this-year-and-2018-1507640400.

Index

About the Author

Jennie M. Ratcliffe is an environmental research scientist, activist, and Quaker. Her lifelong concern has been to make connections between peace, justice and ecological sustainability as interdependent spheres of morality, spirituality and social responsibility; to integrate thinking and practice in science, religion, and ethics; and to join inward contemplation with outward action. After completing a Master's degree in pollution studies at Manchester University, a doctorate in environmental epidemiology and postdoctoral research in toxicology at the University of London in the U.K., she has worked in public health as an environmental research epidemiologist for almost 40 years, including at the US Centers for Disease Control and Prevention, the US National Institute of Environmental Health Sciences, and the Universities of London and North Carolina, and as an advisor for the World Health Organization, the European Union and other international bodies. She has also worked with Friends of the Earth, the British Society for Social Responsibility in Science, and Physicians for Social Responsibility, among other organizations, and helped found and participate in numerous local groups advocating for a more peaceable, equitable, and ecologically sustainable world.

A long-time member of Durham Friends Meeting in North Carolina, she has been active in peace, social and earthcare concerns within the Quaker community for many years, and was the Henry J. Cadbury Scholar in Quaker Studies at Pendle Hill in 2005-6. She has also traveled widely in the U.S., Europe, Africa, Asia and elsewhere to study the impacts of ecological destruction on human societies and the wider natural world, and to learn about ways we can preserve the commonwealth of life, grounding responses in spiritual and moral principles that can be translated into practice in diverse cultures and communities.

Milton Keynes UK
Ingram Content Group UK Ltd.
UKHW021011190424
441339UK00003B/18

9 781733 660006